PSYCHOACOUSTICS

Perception of Normal and Impaired Hearing
with Audiology Applications

Editor-in-Chief for Audiology
Brad A. Stach, PhD

PSYCHOACOUSTICS

Perception of Normal and Impaired Hearing with Audiology Applications

Jennifer J. Lentz, PhD

PLURAL
PUBLISHING
INC.

5521 Ruffin Road
San Diego, CA 92123

e-mail: information@pluralpublishing.com
Website: https://www.pluralpublishing.com

Typeset in 11/13 Adobe Garamond by Flanagan's Publishing Services, Inc.
Printed in the United States of America by McNaughton & Gunn, Inc.
23 22 21 20   2 3 4 5

Library of Congress Cataloging-in-Publication Data

Names: Lentz, Jennifer J., author.
Title: Psychoacoustics : perception of normal and impaired hearing with
   audiology applications / Jennifer J. Lentz.
Description: San Diego, CA : Plural Publishing, [2020] | Includes
   bibliographical references and index.
Identifiers: LCCN 2018028617| ISBN 9781597569897 (alk. paper) | ISBN
   1597569895 (alk. paper)
Subjects: | MESH: Auditory Perception—physiology | Psychoacoustics | Hearing
   Loss, Sensorineural
Classification: LCC QP461 | NLM WV 272 | DDC 612.8/5—dc23
LC record available at https://lccn.loc.gov/2018028617

Contents

Introduction	*ix*
Acknowledgments	*xii*
Reviewers	*xiii*

1 History — **1**
Learning Objectives — 1
Introduction — 1
Early Investigation of Perception — 1
The Origins of Psychoacoustics — 3
The Advent of the Telephone — 5
Auditory Assessment — 7
References — 11

2 Estimating Threshold in Quiet — **13**
Learning Objectives — 13
Introduction — 13
Acoustics: Pure Tones and the Decibel — 14
Physiological Representation of Sound — 20
Threshold of Human Hearing: MAP and MAF — 25
Measuring the Threshold — 31
Signal Detection Theory (SDT) — 38
Summary and Take-Home Points — 41
Exercises — 41
References — 43

3 Estimating Thresholds in Noise (Masking) — **45**
Learning Objectives — 45
Introduction — 45
Acoustics: Noise and Filters — 46
Physiological Factors — 50
Introduction to Masking — 52
The Critical Band and the Auditory Filter — 56
The Excitation Pattern — 61
Psychophysical Tuning Curves and Suppression — 65
Masking by Fluctuating Sounds — 67
Masking and Sensorineural Hearing Loss — 69
Clinical Implications of Masking — 72
Summary and Take-Home Points — 74
Exercises — 75
References — 76

4 Loudness and the Perception of Intensity — 79

Learning Objectives — 79
Introduction — 79
Acoustics: Intensity and the Decibel — 80
Physiological Representation of Stimulus Level — 81
Introduction to Measuring Loudness — 83
Loudness and Intensity — 84
Loudness and Frequency — 88
Calculating Loudness — 92
Reaction Time as a Measure of Loudness — 93
Intensity Discrimination — 96
Effects of Sensorineural Hearing Loss on Loudness — 101
Summary and Take-Home Points — 105
Exercises — 105
References — 107

5 Temporal Processing — 109

Learning Objectives — 109
Introduction — 109
Temporal Resolution: Gap Detection — 111
Temporal Resolution: Amplitude Modulation Detection — 120
Temporal Masking — 124
Comparison of Temporal Processing Measures — 126
Temporal Integration — 127
Effects of Hearing Loss on Temporal Processing — 131
Summary and Take-Home Points — 138
Exercises — 138
References — 140

6 Pitch Perception — 141

Learning Objectives — 141
Introduction — 141
Acoustics: Harmonic Complex Tones — 142
Theories of Pitch Perception — 145
Pitch of Pure Tones: Subjective Measures — 152
Pitch of Pure Tones: Frequency Discrimination — 156
Mechanisms for Coding the Pitch of Pure Tones — 158
Pitch of Complex Sounds — 160
Importance of Pitch Perception in Everyday Listening — 165
Pitch Perception in Listeners with SNHL — 167
Summary and Take-Home Points — 169
Exercises — 169
References — 171

7 **Hearing with Two Ears** **173**
Learning Objectives 173
Introduction 173
Binaural Advantages to Detection and Discrimination 174
Localization in the Horizontal Plane: Acoustics 175
Sound Localization in the Horizontal Plane: Physiological Basis 180
Sound Localization in the Horizontal Plane: Perception 182
Sound Localization in the Median Plane 185
Lateralization 185
Binaural Unmasking 190
Impact of Hearing Loss on Binaural Hearing 196
Summary and Take-Home Points 199
Exercises 200
References 201

8 **Clinical Implications** **203**
Learning Objectives 203
Introduction 203
Consequences of Impaired Perception 204
Effects of Amplification Strategies on Perception 207
Influence of Psychoacoustics on Diagnostic Audiology 212
Summary and Take-Home Points 218
Exercises 218
References 219

Glossary *221*
Index *227*

Introduction

NOTES ON THIS TEXT

I am writing this textbook after teaching psychological acoustics (commonly referred to as psychoacoustics) to clinical audiology students for over 15 years. Each year I have taught this course I have struggled to find a text appropriate for these students. No doubt, there are excellent texts available on the topic of psychoacoustics. However, all modern books on the topic cover only normal auditory perception and contain little to no review of perception by listeners with hearing loss. Yet, I argue that these students, and those studying auditory perception more generally, should have some exposure to the perceptual deficits imposed by sensorineural hearing loss. Not only will having this information help clinical audiologists to better care for their patients, but studies evaluating perception in listeners with sensorineural hearing loss also have contributed to our understanding of the mechanisms responsible for normal auditory perception. Consequently, this textbook provides a broad overview of auditory perception in normal-hearing listeners, and each chapter includes information on the effects that sensorineural hearing loss has on perceptual abilities.

When possible, this book will provide mechanistic explanations for the psychoacoustical findings in terms of physiology. We will ask "why?" and "how?" with a goal toward understanding what the auditory system is able to perceive and how the auditory system achieves perception. The main focus of this text is healthy auditory perception. However, as we work toward this goal, we will also evaluate the perceptual abilities of people with sensorineural hearing loss. The focus here is on listeners with sensorineural hearing loss of presumed cochlear origin, and the term *sensorineural hearing loss* will be used throughout the text as such.

The primary target audience is graduate students in audiology, who intend a clinical career and need an understanding of both normal and impaired auditory perception. Because the field of psychoacoustics has profoundly influenced clinical audiology, this book also discusses history of the two fields and clinical implications and applications of psychoacoustics. Students studying experimental psychology, audio engineering, engineering, and hearing science may also find that this book suits their needs. Notably, this text does not assume that students have a strong background in either acoustics or auditory physiology. However, because understanding both of these fields is important to fully understand psychoacoustics and the physiological mechanisms responsible for the perception of sound, this text provides an overview of the necessary elements of acoustics and physiology, on an "as-needed" basis.

The structure of the textbook differs from the other texts available on this topic. Traditionally, texts generally present a chapter on acoustics, one on auditory anatomy and physiology, and sometimes a chapter on methodology before delving into chapters on individual topics within the realm of psychoacoustics. In contrast, this text takes an approach similar to a problem-based approach in that each chapter presents self-contained information related to the acoustics, physiology, and methodologies as they apply to the specific topic being discussed. Naturally, certain chapters may refer back to previous chapters for a review of certain information, but the degree to which this occurs is fairly limited.

For the most part, each self-contained chapter presents the necessary information for understanding the specific topic. Essentially each chapter includes the following topics:

- Introduction to the topic and its importance
- Relevant acoustics
- Important physiological studies
- Perception by normal-hearing listeners
- Perception by listeners who have sensorineural hearing loss

In some chapters, clinical applications are discussed within the chapter, particularly those concepts that directly relate to primary audiology practice. However, the final chapter discusses the perceptual consequences of sensorineural hearing loss and more advanced clinical applications of psychoacoustics.

The self-contained organization allows students and faculty to select the areas of the most interest or relevance to the particular course or student, and students have the option of either reviewing the relevant acoustics and physiology pertinent to the topic at hand, or not. This way, students do not need to review a full chapter on acoustics or anatomy and physiology in order to obtain the necessary background for the specific topic. It also allows students a better opportunity to integrate material across the various fields and to quickly determine which acoustic or physiological principles are most relevant for the subject being discussed. Because psychoacoustics is intimately integrated into clinical audiology, the first and final chapters illustrate the deep connection between the two fields.

This text also emphasizes applied learning, as actively engaging with course material is both more effective and more efficient for learning that material. As such, ancillary materials, available online, are included for the use of both instructors and students. These materials include in-class and laboratory exercises to facilitate student engagement with course topics. At the end of each chapter, there is a set of exercises designed to develop critical thinking about psychoacoustics and to assist students in learning to apply psychoacoustic information to the more general fields of audiology and auditory perception. Together, these materials should allow students to develop a deeper understanding of psychoacoustic topics and how those topics relate to hearing loss and audiological practice.

Finally, this textbook is not intended to provide a comprehensive overview of the large variety of psychoacoustic studies or experiments. Rather, it is intended to give students sufficient information to understand how the ear achieves auditory perception, what the capabilities of the ear are, and how hearing loss influences that perception. It also provides students with a foundation for further study in the area to apply psychoacoustic principles to diagnostic audiology and audiological rehabilitation.

EVERY AUDIOLOGIST IS, AT SOME LEVEL, A PSYCHOACOUSTICIAN

The fields of audiology and psychoacoustics are intertwined. Audiometric testing originated directly from the field of psychoacoustics, and early audiologists and otologists worked closely with the early psychoacousticians in developing tools for audiological assessment. In some sense we can consider every audiologist to be a psychoacoustician. Perhaps the most obvious example of this is evident in the audiogram—a behavioral assessment of auditory abilities. The audiogram, which relates the ability to detect a sound to the frequency of that sound, forms the core of audiological assessment. Any audiologist who collects an audiogram is relying on over 100 years of psychoacoustic knowledge and methodological development. In fact, the audiogram remains the most reliable and accurate method to assess auditory sensitivity today, as physiological tests have not advanced enough to adequately replace the audiogram. In fact, this may never happen: Physiological assessment does not measure *hearing*, but rather measures the *representation* of sound within the auditory system. As a result, we continue to rely on patients' reports of their perceptions to make both scientific advancements and clinical decisions.

Although many audiologists routinely collect psychophysical data, the audiologist makes a very limited set of measurements on perceptual abilities. Primary and common assessments include the audiogram, a measurement of the speech recognition threshold (SRT), and word recognition scores. However, these measurements do not characterize the wide range of perceptual abilities that underlie the ability to communicate in everyday environments. Successful communication requires representation of sound intensity, frequency, temporal characteristics, and information from the two ears. Deficits in any one of these representations can lead to deficits in the ability to communicate in the variety of environments encountered by humans. Consequently, we can easily argue that audiologists should more thoroughly assess various auditory perceptions. A century of research tells us that the audiogram and associated speech tests (typically conducted in quiet) do not describe how well a patient perceives the acoustic characteristics of sound that are important to differentiate between sounds or extract it from background noise.

The audiogram is an historical assessment tool, developed in the early 1900s, originally used because we had limited knowledge of the ear, and we did not have access to technology that could easily generate and manipulate complex sounds in real time for audiological assessment. The recent century has repeatedly demonstrated that the audiogram does not reflect our multiple auditory perceptual abilities. The audiogram is critically important for addressing site of lesion (whether a hearing loss is conductive, in the outer or middle ear, or sensorineural) and is also widely used to guide hearing aid fitting. However, this text will illustrate that the variability in perceptual deficits experienced by listeners with sensorineural hearing loss is quite high and that the audiogram does not provide a measurement of any other level of auditory perception besides detection. As such, measurement of perceptual abilities in conjunction with the audiogram may ultimately provide crucial and important information to an audiologist, who can then recommend the most appropriate hearing aid algorithms for a specific patient.

Acknowledgments

I would like to thank all of the students at Indiana University who took my course on psychoacoustics and taught me as much as I taught them (I hope). Some of those years were harder than others, but there is no doubt that working with them over the years showed me how to better communicate psychoacoustics material. I would also like to thank my clinical colleagues for their years of discussion on the connection between psychoacoustics and audiology. Those conversations have allowed me to better apply the principles of psychoacoustics to clinical practice. I can only begin to thank my PhD mentor, Virginia Richards, for taking a chance 25 years ago on an engineering student who knew nothing about experimental psychology and for giving me the foundation for the content of this text. The contributions of my postdoctoral advisor, Marjorie Leek, who taught me the value of scholarship and the impact of hearing loss on auditory perception, are also evident throughout this book. Last, but most definitely not least, I would like to thank my family and loved ones for their tireless support and patience.

Reviewers

Plural Publishing, Inc. and the author would like to thank the following reviewers for taking the time to provide their valuable feedback during the development process:

Inyong Choi, PhD
Assistant Professor
Department of Communication Sciences
    and Disorders
University of Iowa
Iowa City, Iowa

Erin M. Ingvalson, PhD
Assistant Professor
School of Communication Science and
    Disorders
Florida State University
Tallahassee, Florida

Bomjun J. Kwon, PhD
Associate Professor
Department of Hearing, Speech and Language
Gallaudet University
Washington, District of Columbia

Alyssa R. Needleman, PhD
Clinical Director and Associate Professor
Department of Audiology
Dr. Pallavi Patel College of Health Care
    Sciences
Nova Southeastern University
Fort Lauderdale, Florida

Lauren A. Shaffer, PhD, CCC-A
Associate Professor, AuD Program Director
Department of Speech Pathology and
    Audiology
Ball State University
Muncie, Indiana

1

History

LEARNING OBJECTIVES

Upon completing this chapter, students will be able to:

- List the main pioneers in psychoacoustics
- Describe how the history of psychoacoustics has influenced the field of audiology
- Explain the history of audiometric threshold measurement

INTRODUCTION

Knowledge of the association between sound and its perception has been around for many centuries. However, the primary roots of psychoacoustics date back to the early 1700s, when the philosophers of the time began to lay the foundation for the field of experimental psychology, which studied human behavior. This chapter provides an historical perspective of psychoacoustics by first presenting a history of experimental psychology and then discussing how those developments led to the fields of psychoacoustics and audiology, which were, in some ways, developed together. For this chapter, I have particularly relied on the publications by Boring (1961) on the history of experimental psychology, Schick's (2004) and Yost's (2015) articles on the history of psychoacoustics, and Jerger's (2009) book on the history of audiology.

This chapter reviews the origins of modern psychoacoustics by covering:

- The roots of psychophysical measurement
- The development of psychoacoustics
- The role of Bell labs
- Connecting psychoacoustics, Bell labs, and audiology
- The history of the audiogram

EARLY INVESTIGATION OF PERCEPTION

The idea that one could evaluate perception using physical stimuli has been around for centuries. However, it wasn't until the early 1800s when experimental science was sufficiently advanced to produce reliable and systematic assessment of perception and its relationship to the physical world. Hence, the field of *psychophysics* was born. At this time, scientists were interested in the sense of hearing, but they also evaluated the senses of touch and vision. Many of the techniques used to study auditory perception were originally developed for the purposes of evaluating other sensory modalities. Some techniques, particularly the scientific instruments but also the measurement methods, were designed specifically for the assessment of hearing. In a reciprocal relationship, those other disciplines adopted and modified the tools that were originally created for the hearing sciences. The purpose of this chapter is to give the reader a brief overview of principles of psychoacoustics from an historic view and to illustrate how these discoveries have impacted modern audiology.

As we travel back in time to the early 1800s, we observe the development of the field of *psychophysics* and more specifically, *psychoacoustics*, which involved the evaluation of the perception of sound. These early investigators asked questions such as "under what parameters can humans:

- *detect* stimuli?" Measurements in this vein usually involve manipulating various stimulus parameters (like frequency and amplitude) and measuring the *absolute threshold*, the lowest stimulus level that evokes a sensation.
- *differentiate* between two stimuli?" These experiments measure the *just noticeable difference* (**JND**), also known as the *difference limen*, defined as the amount a stimulus must be changed on a particular dimension before the change is detectable.
- *describe* the magnitude of the stimulus or the difference between stimuli?" In these experiments, the loudness, the pitch, or the quality of sounds is measured.
- *recognize* sounds?" Here, experiments adopt meaningful stimuli, and we measure the ability to identify musical instruments, words in speech, and even environmental sounds.

Our discussion of the origin of psychological measurement should begin with Ernst Heinrich Weber (pronounced Vay-burr; 1795–1878), although he was not the first to connect observation of perception with a physical stimulus. Weber, however, was the first to develop a systematic method of inquiry evaluating the relationship between the magnitude of physical stimuli and their associated sensation or perception. Although his work was conducted primarily in the areas of touch and vision, in 1834 he discovered what is now known as **Weber's law** (see Chapter 4). He noticed that, for pressure on the skin, the JND in weight was about 1/30th of the weight. Further evaluation has demonstrated that this principle has evidence from many other sensory modalities, including hearing and vision.

One of Weber's students, Gustav Fechner (1801–1887), formalized Weber's work with mathematics. He noted, in particular, that there was a way to *measure* the magnitude of sensation. Fechner's work was revolutionary: his claim was that the conscious perception of a stimulus is related to size of the stimulus in the physical world and that perception and physical stimuli are, in some sense, interchangeable. This idea formed the foundation for all modern psychophysics and opened the door to the measurement of perception. Fechner coined the term "psychophysics" and published his experiments on sensory measurements in his 1860 book *Elements of Psychophysics*, where he described psychophysical methods and psychophysical relationships. His book marked the beginning of experimental psychology because it brought sensation and perception, otherwise thought to be unmeasurable, under the requirements of measurement. His three methods of measuring absolute thresholds and differential thresholds are still fundamental in modern psychoacoustic measurement. He developed the **method of limits** (which, in modified form, is the method used to measure an audiogram), the **method of adjustment**, and the *method of constant stimuli*, techniques that are discussed in Chapter 2. In some cases, modifications to these methods have yielded efficient measurements of perception. We use variants of all of these procedural methodologies in psychoacoustic measurement today. His view that perception and physics are connected is a foundation of our current practice: In the fields of psychoacoustics and audiology, we manipulate sound and measure the perceptual consequences. Without his seminal contributions to the study of perception, diagnostic audiology and psychoacoustics would be very different fields.

THE ORIGINS OF PSYCHOACOUSTICS

Despite the impact that Fechner and Weber have had on the field, neither conducted experiments in hearing. Rather, Hermann von Helmholtz (1821–1894), made some of the first psychoacoustic observations in the auditory modality. His book, *Sensations of Tone*, published in 1863, served as the foundational text on auditory perception for decades. This book, along with Fechner's, allowed the evaluation of hearing to be more than scientific observation. Rather, experimentation allowed auditory perception to be quantified under systematic evaluation. We could now connect physical acoustics with the perception of the physical dimensions.

One important aspect of Helmholtz's view of sensory systems was the idea that physiology was the basis of perception. His views have greatly influenced modern psychoacoustics, which commonly strives to determine the limits of auditory perception as well as to discern the physiological mechanisms responsible for auditory perception. Helmholtz's view laid the groundwork for physiological models, some of which were proposed in the mid-1800s. For example, Helmholtz's theory of pitch was based on the "acoustic law" developed by

Georg Ohm (1789–1854), which applied the principles of *Fourier analysis* developed by Fourier (1768–1830). This theory stated that the ear conducts a form of Fourier analysis, which allows complex sounds to be divided into sinusoidal components. In order to test this spectral theory of pitch, Helmholtz developed the innovative *Helmholtz resonator* (shown in Figure 1–1). By varying the size of the neck opening and the volume of the cavity, the Helmholtz resonator could produce sounds of different frequencies.

Yet, August Seebeck (1805–1849) devised a clever experiment using a rotary siren (one of which is illustrated in Figure 1–2) that demonstrated inconsistencies in Helmholtz's

FIGURE 1–1. A Helmholtz resonator. From Helmholtz (1863).

FIGURE 1–2. One of Seebeck's sirens. From Koenig (1889).

spectral theory of pitch. Seebeck's results posed substantial problems for Helmholtz's theories and were bitterly disputed at the time (Turner, 1977). Unfortunately for Seebeck, he passed away almost a century before his experimental results were reconsidered and formalized into a theory by J. F. Schouten (1940). Schouten's *residue theory* suggested pitch perception could also be based on a temporal representation (in contrast to the spectral representation proposed by Helmholtz) of sound. Variants of Helmholtz's and Schouten's theories are still discussed today and both form the foundation of modern models of pitch perception (see Chapter 6).

Lord Rayleigh (James William Strutt, 1843–1919) was strongly influenced by the work of Helmholtz. His book *The Theory of Sound* also discussed acoustic problems using mathematics. This work laid the groundwork for future study linking acoustics with perception. Rayleigh was also keenly interested in the ability to localize sounds in space. He proposed that two acoustic cues are used for sound localization: intensity differences and time differences across the ears. The intensity differences were produced by the presence of the head in the sound field, which can effectively block sound transmission. The time differences were produced by the differential travel times of sound across the ears. This theory, called the **Duplex Theory of Sound Localization**, has been validated numerous times (see Chapter 7).

Although the investigations presented above are not exhaustive, these representative studies illustrate that the earliest psychoacoustic work was conducted on the perception of pitch and space. Little evaluation of loudness and its relationship to intensity was conducted. If we pause to consider the environment that these pioneers were working in, we can gain a better understanding of why the early work was conducted in these primary areas. Technology such as sound level meters

and earphones had not been developed at that time. While Fechner developed some techniques to measure perception in the mid-1800s, the devices to manipulate and measure sound levels were not built until the 1920s. Controlling and characterizing the intensity of a sound was even more difficult than manipulating frequency or spatial location. For example, changing the length of strings, altering the properties of materials, or changing size of a tuning fork could manipulate frequency. A Helmholtz resonator or a siren, similar to that developed by Seebeck, could also be used to generate sounds with specific frequencies. On the other hand, techniques at that time did not allow manipulation of intensity without varying the frequency of a sound.

Measurements of the auditory perception of intensity were therefore somewhat restricted and were extremely imprecise. Otologists quantified hearing loss by using tuning forks and made measurements of how long a patient could hear a sound or how far away an examiner could be before a patient could not hear a sound. Due to the limitations in achieving both accurate and precise intensity levels, early scientists focused their endeavors more on pitch and sound localization than other acoustic quantities.

Yet, one of Helmholtz's students, Wilhelm Wundt (1832–1920), did not let these limitations stymie his interest in sound perception and, in particular, the perception of sound intensity. Notably, Wundt developed many instruments that allowed him to measure the perception of sound in a controlled way. His sound pendulum and falling phonometer allowed him to alter sound intensity without changing the frequency characteristics of a sound (Schick, 2004). Examples of these devices are shown in Figures 1–3 and 1–4. Both of these devices functioned by dropping an object that struck a panel. The height of the object would determine the intensity of the sound generated when it hit the panel.

FIGURE 1–3. A sound pendulum used by Wundt. From Spindler and Hoyer (1908).

FIGURE 1–4. A falling phonometer used by Wundt. From Zimmerman (1903).

He also developed a sound hammer and a sound interrupter, which allowed the quantification of intensity and time, among a variety of other devices.

Wundt performed some of the earliest quantitative experiments evaluating why we are able to hear tones of different levels and why some combinations of musical notes are appealing to the ear and some are not. His work, published in his writings *Principles of Physiological Psychology* (1873–1874) came to be one of the more important texts in psychology, and he founded the first formal laboratory for psychological research in 1879 at the University of Leipzig. Wundt is considered the "father of experimental psychology," as he treated psychology as separate from biology or philosophy, and was the first to call himself a psychologist. His influence was far reaching and has had an impact on all areas of experimental psychology.

THE ADVENT OF THE TELEPHONE

Although Wundt was able to control the sound intensity in his experiments, the introduction of telephone receivers and sound level meters made measurements of the perception of sound intensity more feasible. Alexander Graham Bell's invention formed the basis of the technology that allows us to precisely and accurately control and manipulate sound today. Along with Western Electric, its precursor company, Bell Telephone Labs (commonly called Bell Labs), focused on the research and development of telephone-associated equipment. The contributions of Bell Labs after its formation in 1925, in particular, have been integral to the fields of psychoacoustics and audiology. Much of their work involved the development of technologies that are now used to assess and to characterize hearing.

During this time frame, we also saw the development of the decibel as a unit to describe sound level. The unit, of course, was named to honor A. G. Bell, who passed away in 1922. Development of the decibel has had a profound impact on our ability to characterize hearing, including the use of suffixes such as dB SPL (sound pressure level), dB A (A weighted), and dB HL (hearing level), all of which are used to describe the level of sound in various ways.

Some of the most seminal work in the field of psychoacoustics originated at Bell Labs. Examples include:

- Wegel and Lane (1924), who made the first quantitative measurements on masking, the process by which one sound influences the ability to detect another sound (see Chapter 3)
- Sivian and White (1933) measured some of the first calibrated auditory detection thresholds and compared measurements made over headphones with those obtained in the free field (see Chapter 2)
- Fletcher and Munson (1933), who, along with Steinberg, made the earliest measurements of equal loudness contours (see Chapter 4)
- Steinberg, Montgomery, and Gardner (1940) conducted large-scale measurements of auditory detection abilities across a representative group of people living in the United States.
- Fletcher (1940) formalized theories masking (see Chapter 3).

The investigations mentioned here do not provide a comprehensive list of the work conducted at Bell Labs, but they represent some of the more important studies conducted at the time. Their work was innovative, inventive, and impactful. Their investigations have proven to be foundational on the topics of threshold, loudness, and masking. Note in particular, however, that the investigations at that time did not involve other auditory percepts, such as pitch and spatial hearing. Such experiments were not as relevant to the development of the telephone, where engineers were evaluating the limits of hearing to establish the constraints necessary for telephone receivers and associated equipment.

Although all of the investigators listed above deserve credit and recognition, it is worth pointing out the contributions of Har-

vey Fletcher, a research engineer at Western Electric and later Bell Labs from 1916 to 1949. Fletcher made some of the greatest contributions to both psychoacoustics and audiology during his tenure there and was also a founding member of the Acoustical Society of America, one of the premier organizations in support of acoustics. His contributions to the field were widespread and influential.

Remarkably, he, along with R. L. Wegel, developed the first commercial audiometer, the Western Electric Model 1-A audiometer (Fletcher, 1992), which was the size of a large cabinet and therefore was not practical. Yet, none of the other audiometers in use at the time were practical either. For example, Cordia Bunch, a psychologist at the University of Iowa, built the first audiometer developed in the United States, but he and his colleagues were the only ones to use it. Fletcher and Wegel's audiometer, on the other hand, was a commercial audiometer and sold for roughly $1500, which would be about $25,000 in modern currency. Because of the steep price tag and the inability of portability, Fletcher and Wegel developed the first commercial and portable audiometer, the Western Electric Model 2-A, soon afterward.

Yet, developing the audiometer was only one of Fletcher's many achievements. As Allen (1996) describes, Fletcher was the first to accurately measure auditory threshold, the first to measure the relationship between loudness and intensity and loudness and frequency. Further, he developed the model of masking in application still today. His experiments led to the modern-day audiogram and contributed to our knowledge of loudness (discussed in Chapter 4). His two books *Speech and Hearing*, published in 1929, and *Speech and Hearing in Communication*, published in 1953, were considered authoritative at the time and, in many cases, remain so today. Fletcher also coined the term "audiogram" and developed the unit of dB hearing level, the decibel metric in use today to describe hearing abilities (Jerger, 1990). If that were not enough, he also made substantial contributions to our knowledge of speech perception and developed a tool (originally called the Articulation Index, now revised to the Speech Intelligibility Index [SII]) that allows one to calculate the amount of speech information available in different frequency bands. The SII is able to robustly predict intelligibility scores for certain speech materials and acoustic environments (ANSI-3.5, 2017) and is now used in industrial applications and to assess the impact of hearing loss on speech perception.

AUDITORY ASSESSMENT

During the early-mid 1900s, we saw a revolution in the way that hearing was tested. Fletcher, along with his colleague Wegel, collaborated with an otologist, Edmund Prince Fowler (1872–1966), and began their work in measuring hearing thresholds. With regard to assessing hearing, these scientists evaluated absolute threshold (the lowest detectable sound level) and quantified the highest level of hearing in terms of the *threshold of feeling*, which they called *maximum audibility*. Along the way, they also developed the tools and units with which to quantify the threshold and developed the graphical depictions we use today.

Thus, Fowler and Wegel developed what we now call the audiogram. At the time, it was standard to quantify frequency in cycles per second (note: the unit hertz was not established until 1930), and at the time, Wegel had already been plotting frequency in octaves, rather than using a linear scale. However, there was no standard for depicting the level (*y*) axis, and this was a topic hot for discussion. Two issues were of interest: the units to be used and the scale on which the thresholds should be plotted. At the time, auditory thresholds (as well as other auditory measurements, such

as the *maximum audibility*) were plotted in sound pressure units, such as dynes/cm². It was fairly straightforward to use a logarithmic axis at the time, based on the works of Weber and Fechner, and was consistent with engineering tradition. Although the decibel was not in use yet, plotting auditory thresholds on a logarithmic scale was very similar to the modern practice of plotting thresholds in decibels.

An illustration of Wegel's representation is shown in Figure 1–5, which plots both auditory threshold (*minimum audibility*) and the threshold of feeling (*maximum audibility*), measured in more than 40 people. Wegel defined the range between the minimum audibility and maximum audibility curves as the *sensation area*. Wegel's sensation area had an elliptical shape because both the minimum and maximum audibility curves were frequency dependent. Today, we would call the sensation area the **dynamic range of hearing**. From Wegel's data, we see that the dynamic range of hearing was frequency dependent and was the largest in the mid-frequency range (e.g., about 500–6000 Hz).

At that time, Wegel and Fowler also were conducting measurements of hearing in listeners with hearing loss. The auditory thresholds of a listener with hearing loss, reported by Wegel (1922), are also plotted in Figure 1–5. We observe that this patient's thresholds were higher than the minimum audibility curve and fell in the middle of the sensation range. Using data such as these, Wegel and Fowler considered that there might be an easier way to depict the amount of hearing loss in which the dynamic range of hearing was taken into account. Wegel and Fowler observed that hearing thresholds could be quantified as a percentage of the dynamic range at each frequency. They counted the number of logarithmic steps between the minimum and maximum audibility curves and then counted the number of steps between minimum audibility and the patient's threshold. Dividing these two values

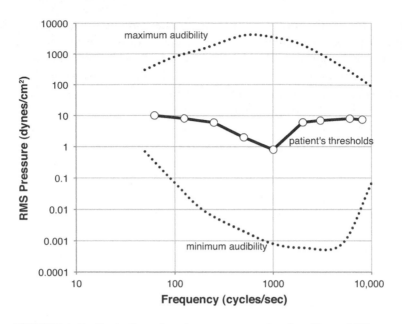

FIGURE 1–5. Illustration of early measurements of auditory abilities. Maximum audibility represents the threshold of feeling, and minimum audibility represents auditory threshold in normal-hearing listeners. Thresholds obtained from a patient with hearing loss are also shown. Adapted from Wegel (1922).

and subtracting from 100% provided a *percent of normal hearing*. To illustrate this method, Figure 1–6 shows data from the same patient in Figure 1–5. Wegel and Fowler felt that plotting the data in this way better quantified how much dynamic range was left for a listener with impaired hearing.

Fletcher, however, did not agree with the percent of hearing loss approach, and strongly argued against it. He renamed the *y*-axis to sensation units and changed the line at the top of the graph to 0 sensation loss. Essentially, Fletcher's rearrangement put zero at the top, rather than at the bottom, of the figure and did not represent hearing loss in terms of the range of hearing, but rather the amount of sensation loss with respect to the minimum audibility curve. Over the years, as the dB became more widely used, it became common to plot the *y*-axis of an audiogram using dB hearing level, rather than hearing or sensation loss. The line

at the top, however, remained at 0 dB HL, the value used in audiograms today.

> Fowler conducted numerous studies on measuring absolute thresholds in listeners with hearing loss. He was the first to report that listeners with sensorineural hearing loss experience a smaller dynamic range but a similar range of loudness as listeners with normal hearing. He called this phenomenon *loudness recruitment* (Fowler, 1928), a term we still adopt today.

As the audiogram and audiometers became more widespread in their use, measurements of hearing abilities in listeners with good and poor hearing were conducted on both large and small scales. Such work was

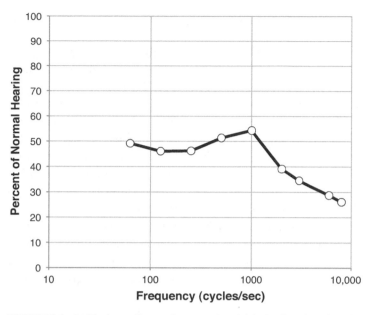

FIGURE 1–6. Early audiometric report in which the hearing threshold is converted into a percentage of normal hearing. Based on the patient's threshold from Figure 1–5.

necessary in order to quantify hearing loss and to establish normative data in the healthy population. Due to the necessity of normative measures, Willis Beasley carried out a large survey to establish the thresholds of healthy listeners as part of a U.S. Public Health Service general health survey in 1935 and 1936. Beasley's study was designed to obtain the audiometric thresholds for people who had good hearing (about 4,500 people), and people with presumed or suspected hearing loss were specifically excluded from data analysis. Using the Western Electric 2-A audiometer, the survey provided the first large-scale estimates of normal hearing in the frequency range from 64 to 8192 Hz reported in dB SPL (Glorig, 1966). In 1951, results from the "Beasley survey" were adopted as the basis for calibration of audiometers in the United States and determined the relationship between dB SPL, which uses a physical reference, and dB HL, which uses the perceptual reference, in the ASA-1951 standard.

Beasley's survey results were problematic, however. In 1952, Dadson and King conducted a similar survey in England and found thresholds to be approximately 10 dB better than those reported in the United States. Studies were then conducted in a number of other countries, all of which conformed to the English measurements, and not those made in the United States. In an effort to determine the source of this discrepancy, Aram Glorig conducted another survey at the Wisconsin State Fair in 1954, in which the exact procedures used by Beasley were adopted. These data essentially replicated the results of Beasley, leading Glorig to return to the Wisconsin State Fair in 1955 and use a different method to estimate threshold, which adopted an ascending and descending method of limits. Using this procedure, Glorig found measurements to be in agreement with those obtained in the United Kingdom and Japan. Glorig was able to conclude that by using better threshold estimation techniques than those adopted by

Beasley, lower threshold estimates were achievable. His work illustrated that both the auditory sensitivity of the listener <u>and</u> the method used to estimate that sensitivity influenced the measurement.

In 1964, a new standard was issued (ISO-64). Although minor updates to the standard have been made throughout the past 50 years, the audiometric standard remains largely unchanged. To illustrate this, the ASA-51 standard, the ISO-64 standard, and the modern ANSI 3.6-2010 standard are listed in Table 1–1. Table 1–1 illustrates a roughly 10 dB difference between the ASA-51 and the later ISO-64 and ANSI-2010 standards. Note the drastic similarity between the ISO-64 standard and the ANSI-2010 standard, particularly below 6 kHz.

In addition to collecting data on people with good hearing, investigators were interested in the prevalence of hearing loss and the effects of age on hearing. Bell Labs conducted another survey of hearing designed to sample the range of auditory thresholds in the population. These measurements at the San Francisco and New York world fairs in 1939, therefore, did not exclude listeners with suspected auditory problems. Steinberg, Montgomery, and Gardner (1940) reported their data on the hearing abilities of over 15,000 people with ages ranging from 10 to 59 years. Although these measurements were not made with robust threshold estimation procedures, the measurements largely characterized the hearing of the population of average Americans. They noted in particular that hearing was best for their participants between the ages of 10 and 19, and slowly worsened with age. They also documented that these declines predominantly occurred in the high frequencies and

TABLE 1–1. Reference threshold levels in dB SPL (RETSPL) for standards ASA-51 (first column), ISO-64 (second column), and ANSI-2010 (third column)* Values from Glorig (1966).

Frequency (Hz)	Reference Threshold Levels in dB SPL		
	1951 ASA	1964 ISO	2010 ANSI
125	54.5	45.5	45
250	39.5	24.5	25.5
500	25	11	11.5
1000	16.5	6.5	7
1500	16.5	6.5	6.5
2000	17	8.5	9
3000	16	7.5	10
4000	15	9	9.5
6000	17.5	8	15.5
8000	21	9.5	13

*ASA-51 and ISO-64 use a Western Electric 705-A earphone, and ANSI-2010 uses a TDH-39 supra-aural earphone.

that thresholds were better for women than for men, even in the same age group.

We cannot understate the contributions of these investigators to the fields of psychoacoustics and audiology. However, we should consider how the work conducted over 100 years ago has impacted these fields. As we have seen, work in the area of auditory perception prior to the 1900s predominantly focused on pitch and spatial perception, whereas the work between 1920 and 1940 focused on threshold testing, loudness, and masking. The work conducted by Bell Labs, of course, was directed toward developing technologies for the telephone and focused, in particular, on knowledge that was important for advancing that technology. Consequently, the study of auditory perception was strongly influenced by the goals of the day. Now, modern psychoacoustics evaluates a variety of auditory perceptual abilities and also considers physiological mechanisms responsible for those abilities. Since the time of Bell labs, we have greatly advanced our knowledge of hearing loss beyond that provided by the audiogram.

The audiogram, as a representation of hearing abilities, has a great deal of historical impact, and it has essentially been used in the same form for almost a century now. We should recognize, however, that the audiogram is grossly limited in its ability to characterize how well a particular patient might understand speech in a noisy or complex situation. Because it can only characterize perceptual abilities at the detection threshold level, it is not a terribly useful tool for assessing perception at other levels. I would suggest that a focus of the next century could be the development of better tools and metrics that identify the specific deficits experienced by listeners, with thought toward using that information to determine which rehabilitation options may be the most beneficial to individual patients.

REFERENCES

Allen, J. B. (1996). Harvey Fletcher's role in the creation of communication acoustics. *Journal of the Acoustical Society of America, 99*(4), 1825–1839.

ANSI/ASA S3.5-1997. (R2017). *American National Standard methods for calculation of the speech intelligibility index.* New York, NY: American National Standards Institute.

ANSI/ASA S3.6-2010. *American National Standard specification for audiometers.* New York. NY: American National Standards Institute.

Boring, E. G. (1961). The beginning and growth of measurement in psychology. *Isis, 52*(2), 238–257.

Dadson, R. S., & King, J. H. (1952). A determination of the normal threshold of hearing and its relation to the standardization of audiometers. *Journal of Laryngology and Otology, 66*(8), 366–378.

Fechner, G. (1966). *Elements of psychophysics* (Vol. 1). New York, NY: Holt, Rinehart and Winston.

Fletcher, H. (1929). *Speech and hearing.* New York, NY: Van Nostrand.

Fletcher, H. (1940). Auditory patterns. *Reviews of Modern Physics, 12*(1), 47.

Fletcher, H. (1953). *Speech and hearing in communication.* Huntington, NY: Krieger.

Fletcher, H., & Munson, W. A. (1933). Loudness, its definition, measurement and calculation. *Bell Labs Technical Journal, 12*(4), 377–430.

Fletcher, H. (1992). *Harvey Fletcher 1884–1981.* NAS Online. National Academy of Sciences. Retrieved from https://www.nap.edu/read/2037/chapter/10#180

Fowler, E. P. (1928). Marked deafened areas in normal ears. *Archives of Otolaryngology, 8*(2), 151–155.

Glorig, A. (1966). Audiometric reference levels. *Laryngoscope, 76*(5), 842–849.

Helmholtz, H. (1863/1954). *On the sensation of tone.* English translation published in 1954 by Dover Publications, New York. (First German edition, *On the sensation of tone as a physiological basis for the theory of music,* published in 1863.)

Jerger, J. (2009). *Audiology in the USA.* San Diego, CA: Plural.

Koenig, R. (1889). *Catalogue des Appareils d'Acoustique construits par Rudolph Koenig.* Paris, France: s.n.

Rayleigh (Strutt, J.W.; 1877). *The theory of sound, vol I.* London, UK: Macmillan.

Schick, A. (2004). History of psychoacoustics. In *Proceedings of 18th International Congress on Acoustics (ICA)* (Vol. 5, pp. 3759–3762), Kyoto Acoustical Science and Technology for Quality of Life.

Schouten, J. F. (1940). The residue and the mechanism of hearing. In *Proceedings Koninklijke Nederlandse Akademie Van Wetenschappen, 43,* 991–999.

Seebeck, A. (1843). Ueber die Sirene. *Annals of Physics and Chemistry, 60,* 449–481.

Sivian, L. J., & White, S. D. (1933). On minimum audible sound fields. *The Journal of the Acoustical Society of America, 4*(4), 288–321.

Spindler and Hoyer (1908). *Apparate für psychologische Untersuchungen.* Preisliste XXI. Göttingen.

Steinberg, J. C., & Gardner, M. B. (1937). The dependence of hearing impairment on sound intensity. *Journal of the Acoustical Society of America, 9*(1), 11–23.

Steinberg, J. C., Montgomery, H. C., & Gardner, M. B. (1940). Results of the World's Fair hearing tests. *Bell Labs Technical Journal, 19*(4), 533–562.

Strutt, J. W. (Lord Rayleigh; 1877). *The theory of sound vol I.* London, UK: Macmillan.

Turner, R. S. (1977). The Ohm–Seebeck dispute, Hermann von Helmholtz, and the origins of physiological acoustics. *The British Journal for the History of Science, 10*(1), 1–24.

Wegel, R. (1922). Physical examination of hearing and binaural aids for the deaf. *Proceedings of the National Academy of Sciences, 8,* 155–160.

Wegel, R., & Lane, C. E. (1924). The auditory masking of one pure tone by another and its probable relation to the dynamics of the inner ear. *Physical Review, 23*(2), 266–285.

Wundt, M. (1902). *Principles of physiological psychology* (5th ed., English translation published in 1904). New York, NY: Swan Sonnenschein and Co.

Yost, W. A. (2015). Psychoacoustics: A brief historical overview. *Acoustics Today, 11,* 46–53.

Zimmermann, E. (1903). *XVIII. Preis-Liste über psychologische und physiologische Apparate* (p. 29). Leipzig, Germany: Eduard Zimmermann.

2

Estimating Threshold in Quiet

LEARNING OBJECTIVES

Upon completing this chapter, students will be able to:

- Describe pure tones using appropriate acoustic terminology
- Relate tone detection to physiological representations
- Discuss the difference between MAP and MAF functions
- Use knowledge of auditory pathologies to predict changes to MAP functions
- Analyze strengths and weaknesses of different psychophysical measurement techniques
- Discuss the importance of reducing response bias from psychophysical and audiological measurement

---

INTRODUCTION

One of the core psychoacoustic and audiological assessments is the measurement of *absolute threshold*, the minimum detectable level of a sound in the absence of external noise. The absolute threshold is a reflection of *auditory sensitivity* at the detection level, and provides a measure of the lower limit hearing. From a psychoacoustic standpoint, measurements of absolute threshold have greatly influenced the development of technologies (such as the telephone, stereo systems, and hearing aids) but also have contributed to our understanding of the relationship between sound and its perception. In clinical audiology, measuring absolute threshold forms the foundation of the audiogram, which is useful both in its ability to characterize the hearing loss of a particular patient and in guiding hearing aid fitting. In order to obtain a full understanding of this important measurement, one must also possess an understanding of a variety of concepts underlying sound detection, including acoustics, measurement techniques, and psychophysical principles.

Although this chapter primarily focuses on the ability of the ear to detect sounds, we should also recognize that detection is an important precursor to the comprehension of complex sounds such as speech, music, and environmental sounds. Detection is often considered the lowest level of auditory behavior in the hierarchy of auditory skills, as described by Erber (1982). In this hierarchy, there are four levels of auditory perception:

- *Detection:* Detection of sound simply implies that one is able to perceive the presence of a sound stimulus. Detection is often quantified in terms of the lowest sound level necessary for a stimulus to be detected.
- *Discrimination:* Discrimination is the ability to hear that two sounds are different from each other. A variety of different acoustic dimensions can be evaluated using discrimination tasks (such as frequency, intensity, or timing).
- *Recognition:* Recognition occurs when a sound is attached to an object, or a label. It is also sometimes referred to as *identification*, a term also used throughout this book.
- *Comprehension:* Comprehension is the process by which sounds are assigned meaning.

Psychoacoustics primarily focuses on the detection and discrimination levels, although some experiments also address identification abilities. Both detection and discrimination abilities are necessary precursors to recognize and comprehend complex sounds. Deficits in low-level abilities preclude good performance in higher-level abilities, although a listener could have a deficit in a higher-level ability and not a lower-level one. For example, problems with detecting sounds can have a large impact on the ability to recognize and comprehend speech. In contrast, a listener may have difficulty comprehending speech in the absence of deficits at the detection level.

This chapter specifically focuses on interpreting *absolute threshold* measured using *detection*. Other chapters will cover a variety of auditory abilities at the discrimination level, with some discussion of identification. This chapter, which is focused on the ability to detect pure tones, covers the following topics:

- Acoustics of pure tones
- Physiological representation of pure tones
- Absolute threshold measured in free field and over headphones
- Quantifying the effects of hearing loss on threshold
- Measuring threshold: clinical and research methods
- Signal detection theory

ACOUSTICS: PURE TONES AND THE DECIBEL

The pure tone is one of the most basic forms of sound and, importantly, is the foundation of a typical audiometric assessment in the form of the *audiogram*, a report of the ability to detect pure tones as a function of frequency. Pure tones are preferred for audiometric testing over other sounds (such as noises or modulated sounds) as they contain a single frequency and therefore are the most *frequency-specific* sounds. A single parameter is sufficient to fully characterize the amplitude or sound pressure of the tone. Of all potential stimuli, the pure tone is acoustically very simple, and produces a relatively simple response in the auditory system.

Representations: Waveforms and Spectra

Pure tones follow a pattern of vibration that is sinusoidal, characterized by the following equation that describes the *waveform*, which is a plot of instantaneous amplitude (y) versus time (t):

$$y = a\sin(2\pi ft + \theta) \qquad \text{Eq. 2–1}$$

where a = amplitude, f = frequency, and θ = phase. The frequency of a stimulus is quantified in cycles per second (Hz), and the phase is quantified in degrees or radians. The amplitude of sound is a general way to describe its size, or the amount of vibration. When referring to actual physical stimuli and their representation in the environment, we describe the amplitude of sound in terms of its sound pressure in *pascals*, a metric unit named after Blaise Pascal, which is defined as a force per unit area (1 newton per square meter).

To fully represent a pure tone, then, one need specify the amplitude, frequency, and the phase. For the purposes of this chapter, we consider the phase of the pure tone to be zero degrees, as the ear cannot sense the phase of a single pure tone. However, the ear can sense phase differences between tones and across the two ears, and so we should not always neglect the phase of pure tones.

The waveform is used to represent temporal properties of sound, or how sound varies over time. The waveform of a pure tone follows a simple sinusoidal pattern in which the maximum amplitude is equal to the minimum amplitude but with the opposite sign. The time (in seconds) to complete a single cycle (one complete transition of the sinusoidal function) is the period (denoted T). The waveform of a 1000-Hz tone is illustrated in Figure 2–1, which shows that one cycle is completed in 0.001 seconds, or 1 ms. The period can be converted into frequency (units of hertz) by the formula $f = 1/T$.

The waveform is related to the *spectrum*, a plot of amplitude versus frequency through a process called Fourier analysis, which allows any stimulus waveform to be represented by a series of pure tones. A line at a single frequency illustrates the spectrum of a pure-tone stimulus, as observed in Figure 2–2 for the 1000-Hz

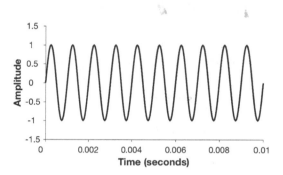

FIGURE 2–1. A waveform of a 1000-Hz tone with an amplitude of 1 and 0° starting phase.

FIGURE 2–2. A spectrum of the 1000-Hz tone illustrated in Figure 2–1.

tone plotted in Figure 2–1. A complex stimulus, on the other hand, can be represented as a series of lines, with each line representing the amplitude and frequency of a constituent tone. This representation of the spectrum can be referred to as a *line spectrum*.

Due to the periodic (repeating) nature of a sinusoid and its simple characterization, a pure tone always reaches the same maximum and minimum amplitude each cycle. Consequently, the pure tone can be described with a single amplitude value. The *a* in Eq. 2–1 is the *peak amplitude*, the maximum amplitude value achieved by any sound wave. Figure 2–1 illustrates this stimulus with a peak amplitude of 1. Because sound is a pressure wave, the peak amplitude is a term often interchanged with the term *peak pressure*, or the maximum pressure achieved by the sound stimulus.

A pure tone also contains only a single frequency, illustrated in Eq. 2–1 where *f* is a single value. Figure 2–2, which plots the spectrum in terms of amplitude vs. frequency, illustrates that the pure tone contains only a single frequency, making it quite straightforward to

determine that the frequency of this particular pure tone is 1000 Hz. Notably, the spectrum does not represent the temporal characteristics of sound like the waveform, and the waveform does not represent the frequency characteristics like the spectrum. Both representations have their advantages, and students should be comfortable with both representations in order to fully understand the range of auditory abilities covered in psychoacoustics.

Duration Effects

Acoustic Considerations

The spectrum illustrated in Figure 2–2 represents a pure tone of infinite duration. However, it is physically impossible to generate a sound of infinite duration. Therefore, we must also consider the effect that the duration of a sound stimulus has on the representation of that sound. The longer the duration of a pure tone, the more frequency specific that pure tone will be. The *time-frequency tradeoff* governs this relationship in the following way: a short-duration sound must have a broad bandwidth spectrum. The only way to achieve a narrow bandwidth spectrum is to provide a long duration. However, long-duration sounds can, and often do, have broad spectra, such as white noise. More detail will be provided about noise stimuli in Chapter 3.

In sum, a long-duration tone has only one frequency: it is frequency specific. A short-duration tone can never be frequency specific. The duration of a tone has a drastic influence on the frequencies present in the stimulus, and has a primary effect of broadening the spectral peak of the stimulus. The increase in the frequencies present in the stimulus is called *spectral splatter*, which is characterized by the *bandwidth*, or the range of frequencies contained within the stimulus. Figure 2–3, which shows the spectrum of a short-duration pure

A common question is when to use a waveform to represent sound and when to use a spectrum to represent sound. For some types of sounds, either representation is equally effective. A pure tone is a good example of this—the frequency and amplitude of the sound can be determined from both the waveform and the spectrum. On the other hand, the waveform is most useful if one is interested in evaluating the temporal characteristics of a stimulus, such as how the amplitude of speech changes over time. The spectrum is more valuable when one wants to evaluate the frequency content of sounds, such as the formants in a vowel stimulus.

FIGURE 2–3. Spectrum of a short-duration pure tone. The frequency of the pure tone is indicated by f_c, which is the center frequency of the spectral representation. Nulls are shown to occur at $f_c \pm n/$duration (d), where n is the nth null.

tone, illustrates this effect and shows a stimulus with a much broader bandwidth than the infinitely long pure tone illustrated in Figure 2–2. The duration of the pure tone determines the frequencies of the *nulls*, which are frequencies at which there is no energy. We can calculate the high-frequency and low-frequency nulls of the primary spectral peak for a tone with center frequency, f_c, as

$$hf_{n1}=f_c+1/d, \text{ and}$$
$$lf_{n1}=f_c-1/d, \qquad \text{Eq. 2–2}$$

where d = the duration of the stimulus; hf_{n1} is the high-frequency null of the primary lobe, and lf_{n1} is the low-frequency null of the primary lobe. Additional nulls, both higher and lower than the frequency of the pure tone, will occur and can also be calculated from the duration of the stimulus. As we observe in Fig-

ure 2–3, the spectrum is no longer a straight line at a single frequency at f_c, the frequency of the tone. Rather, additional frequencies are now present in the spectrum, which shows a broadening of the spectral peak and a small number of *side lobes*, small "bumps" in the spectrum at frequencies higher and lower than the center frequency. The duration of the stimulus determines the bandwidth (BW) of the primary lobe and the bandwidth of these side lobes. Because the location of the nulls can be calculated directly from the duration, reducing the duration of the tone increases the breadth of the spectral peak and increases the distance between the side lobes.

From Eq. 2–2 we can calculate the amount of spectral splatter generated by decreasing the duration. The bandwidth of the spectral peak is given by $hf_{n1} - lf_{n1} = 2/d$. For example, a tone with a 2-sec duration has a bandwidth of the main lobe of 1 Hz. On the other hand, a tone with a 2-ms duration has a bandwidth of the main lobe of 1000 Hz. Consequently, a very brief tone is not frequency specific and may contain unwanted frequencies. Extremely short tones, like those that are 10 μs or 1 μs in duration, are considered broadband within the scope of audiology and psychoacoustics.

This section has demonstrated the importance of considering the duration and its relationship to the frequency content of sounds. We must always be cognizant of the consequences of stimulus manipulations when determining the sounds and their durations for psychoacoustic and audiologic considerations.

Tone Duration in Assessment of Auditory Threshold

With respect to measuring absolute threshold, we should ensure that we are using frequency-specific stimuli. For audiometric measurements, the American Speech-Language-Hearing Association (ASHA) has developed a set of specific recommendations for the durations of the pure tones used in audiometric testing. These recommendations are specific to audiometry, and different stimulus durations may be used for psychoacoustic testing. Here, we will evaluate the relationship between the ASHA recommended pure-tone durations and the frequency specificity of the stimuli used in audiometric testing. When measuring the audiogram, ASHA recommends using a pure-tone duration of 1 to 2 seconds for testing with steady tones and three, 200-ms presentations when testing with pulsed tones (ASHA, 2005). Because audiometric testing is most commonly conducted at the octave and inter-octave frequencies ranging 250 to 8000 Hz, we will evaluate the time-frequency tradeoff for the frequencies across this range.

Consider two of the durations within ASHA's recommendations: 2 seconds for a steady tone and 200 ms for a pulsed tone.

According to our previous analysis of spectral splatter, the 2-second tone has a spectral peak bandwidth of 1 Hz, whereas the spectral peak bandwidth of the 200-ms tone is 10 Hz. For both of these durations, the majority of stimulus energy is contained within a fairly narrow bandwidth around the signal frequency. Thus, ASHA's recommendations for the durations of pure tones yield very little spectral splatter. No matter the audiometric frequency tested (e.g., 250 Hz or 500 Hz), these durations will yield pure tones that have no frequencies in common with other frequencies tested in the audiogram. We can then treat each frequency tested in the audiogram as being independent from the other frequencies from an acoustic standpoint.

In fact, from an acoustic standpoint, ASHA's guidelines are extremely conservative. Even 20-ms pure tone would have a spectral peak bandwidth of 100 Hz, and thus the spectral spread of a 20-ms, 250-Hz tone used in audiometry would still provide a frequency representation independent from a 500-Hz tone. We can conclude, then, that ASHA's recommendations of pure-tone durations are not primarily driven by acoustic principles. Rather, as we will see in Chapter 5 of this text, the pure-tone duration requirements are driven by perceptual principles.

There are times, however, when testing requires the use of brief tones. One must consider the implications for brief sounds in these cases. Consider the impact of using a 2-ms tone. A 2-ms, 500-Hz tone will contain frequencies from 0 to 1000 Hz, and a 2-ms, 1000-Hz tone will contain frequencies from 500 to 1500 Hz. In this case, both tones have frequencies between 500 and 1000 Hz in common. From an acoustics perspective alone, these two tones are not independent, and this duration would be a poor choice for audiometric testing particularly for low audiometric frequencies. An audiological application of the use of short-duration stimuli is tone-burst auditory brainstem response (ABR), which is sometimes used as a physiological alternative to an audiogram. This tool uses durations between 2 and 10 ms. As a result, the technique yields less frequency-specific results than audiometry.

Decibels

We have seen previously that the peak amplitude is sufficient to characterize a pure tone. However, there is a drawback to using peak amplitude when describing sounds other than pure tones. Although the peak amplitude provides an unambiguous descriptor of the size of the sine wave, it is rarely appropriate for complex sounds because many of these sounds experience large amplitude changes with time. To demonstrate this point, the waveform of a harmonic sound is shown in Figure 2–4. In this stimulus, the peak (maximum) amplitude does not provide a strong depiction of the overall amplitude characteristics of that sound. The majority of amplitude in this sound is low relative to the peak amplitude. Consequently, it is common to represent the amplitude of a sound using metrics other than the peak amplitude.

A common way to represent the overall amplitude, or pressure, of the sound shown in Figure 2–4 with a single number is to use the integrated term, *rms (root mean squared) pressure*. For a pure tone, there is a fixed relationship between peak pressure and rms pressure, given by Eq. 2–3.

$$P_{rms} = 0.707 * p_{peak},$$ Eq. 2–3

where P_{rms} = rms pressure and p_{peak} = peak pressure. Note that the units, pascals (Pa; N/m^2), for rms pressure and peak pressure are the same.

Rather than being a simple average, which would be zero for any sine wave, rms pressure is calculated by

$$\sqrt{\sum \frac{(p_i)^2}{N}}.$$

In this equation, the pressure (p) at time i is calculated at each of N points that sample a single period. Essentially the rms calculation squares the wave, takes the mean of those squared values across one period, and then takes the square root.

Although the rms calculation allows characterization of complex sounds by a single number, it is very uncommon to describe the level of sounds detectable by humans in terms of pressure. The smallest detectable pressure by the human ear is roughly 20 µPa (or 20 × 10^{-6} Pa) and the largest sound represented (before damage occurs) is about 2 Pa. Because the range of pressures represented by the ear is so large, we rarely use pascals in acoustics, psychoacoustics, or audiology. Rather, the decibel is almost ubiquitously utilized.

The decibel is also an integrated term, and is based on the long-term rms pressure, rather than the peak pressure. A common decibel metric used to describe sound is dB SPL, or decibels in *sound pressure level*. The dB SPL reference is an approximation of the threshold for human hearing and is 20 µPa.

FIGURE 2–4. Waveform of a complex sound with large amplitude variation.

Decibel SPL can be calculated by the following equation:

$$\text{dB SPL} = 20 \log(P_1/P_{ref}), \qquad \text{Eq. 2–4}$$

where P_1 is the rms pressure of the measured sound and P_{ref} is the reference pressure of 20 µPa.

To illustrate the relationship between pascals and dB, we can use the stimuli in Figure 2–1 to determine the rms amplitude and dB SPL level. First, we assume that the peak amplitude in the waveform of Figure 2–1 is represented in pascals, and is 1 Pa. From Eq. 2–3, we can calculate the rms pressure as 0.707 Pa. Using this value in Eq. 2–4, we see that the dB SPL value of this tone is 91 dB SPL [$20\log(0.707/20 \times 10^{-6})$ = 91 dB SPL]. Note that we often use the term *sound pressure level* when referring to the sound pressure in dB SPL.

Summary

Because psychoacoustics is concerned with measuring the limits of auditory perception on various acoustic dimensions, understanding the waveform and spectral representation of sound is important. The waveform, which plots amplitude versus time, contrasts with the spectrum, which plots amplitude versus frequency. The waveform can only be represented using instantaneous amplitude, but the spectrum typically uses a decibel metric. However, the two representations are two sides of the same coin, so shortening the duration of the stimulus will concomitantly lead to a broadening of the bandwidth of the stimulus.

PHYSIOLOGICAL REPRESENTATION OF SOUND

We consider the auditory system to consist of four components: the outer, middle, and inner ear, in conjunction with the central auditory system. Each of these components has a distinct role to play in the ability to hear, and changes to each of these systems can drastically affect perception. Consequently, a brief review of each component of the auditory system is provided here. A schematic of the main anatomical structures of the ear is shown in Figure 2–5.

Outer and Middle Ear

The outer ear primarily consists of the pinna and ear canal. The components of the pinna and ear canal, together, amplify incoming sound, predominantly for frequencies ranging between 2000 and 3500 Hz (Shaw, 1974). The tympanic membrane lies at the end of the ear canal and vibrates in response to the incoming (and now amplified) sound. The middle ear transmits the vibrations of the tympanic membrane to the cochlea, via the ossicular chain, which consists of the malleus, incus, and stapes and serves to provide an impedance match between the air-filled communication medium and the fluid-filled cochlea. The ossicular chain provides a second source of amplification, with an emphasis on frequencies between 600 and 1800 Hz (Kurokawa & Goode, 1995). The frequency-gain functions, also referred to as **transfer functions**, for the outer and middle ears are shown in Figure 2–6.

The transfer function of the outer ear shows only a small amount of gain below 1000 Hz, and the amount of gain increases with increasing frequency until it peaks at approximately 2500 Hz. The middle ear shows a broader response, with the most gain around 800 Hz. The heavy, solid line illustrates the combined response of the outer and middle ears. The combined transfer function demonstrates that the outer and middle ear, together, provide amplification over a wide

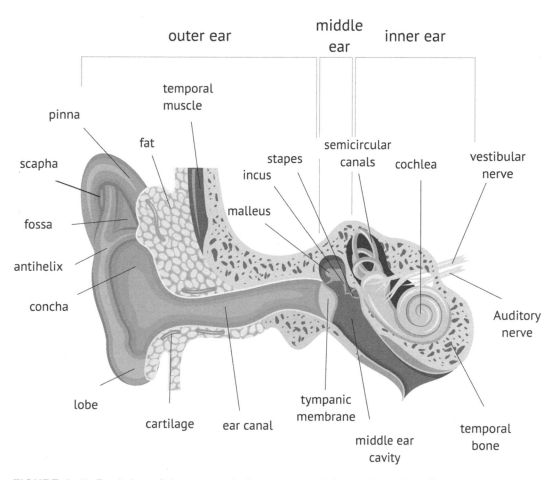

FIGURE 2–5. Depiction of the anatomical structures of the peripheral auditory system. Image adapted from stockshoppe/Shutterstock.com.

range of frequencies, between roughly 600 and 4000 Hz.

Changes to the outer and middle ear structures can have a direct influence on their transmission properties. In particular, middle ear disorders such as otosclerosis and otitis media affect the stiffness of the ossicular chain in the early stages and then the mass in the later stages. Increasing the stiffness of the middle ear system primarily reduces the gain provided in the low frequencies, whereas increasing the mass mostly reduces the gain provided in the high frequencies.

Inner Ear

The auditory portion of the inner ear is responsible for transducing sound energy into neural signals that are interpretable by the central auditory system and higher brain centers. The inner ear consists of a vestibular portion and an auditory portion (the cochlea); only the auditory portion is reviewed here.

The form of the inner ear is that of a snail-shaped coil embedded in the dense temporal bone of the skull. Two membranes divide the cochlea into three chambers along

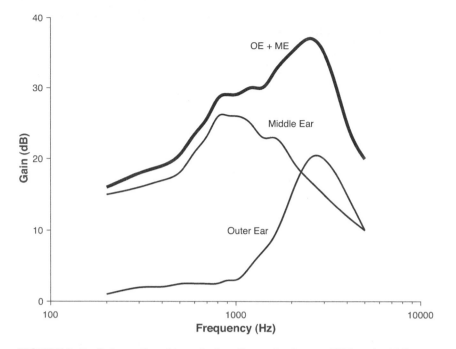

FIGURE 2–6. Schematics of transfer functions of outer ear (OE) and middle ear (ME), along with the total gain provided by the combined outer and middle ear. The combined function reflects amplification between 2000 to 3500 Hz from the outer ear and 600 to1800 Hz from the middle ear.

its length, the basilar and Reissner's membrane. The footplate of the stapes interfaces directly with the membranous oval window of the cochlea. Its vibratory motion stimulates the fluids of the cochlea to vibrate. Vibration of these cochlear fluids causes a vibration in the basilar membrane (BM), which is the primary membrane for coding sound in the ear.

The basilar membrane has mechanical properties that vary along its length. The base (the portion closest to the stapes footplate) of the basilar membrane is relatively narrow and stiff, whereas the apex (at the center of the coil) is relatively wide and less stiff. Changes in the properties along the length of the BM lead to a mass and stiffness gradient that results in different resonant properties down its length. These changes cause different areas of the BM to vibrate in response to different frequencies,

a process that we now refer to as ***tonotopic organization***.

Helmholtz (1857) developed the first sophisticated theory of tonotopic organization, and von Békésy's (1960) Nobel prize–winning experimental work directly supported this theory. From von Békésy's work, we now know the following:

- *Tonotopic organization occurs at the basilar membrane.* High-frequency sounds vibrate near the base of the basilar membrane while low frequencies peak near the apex of the basilar membrane. These results provided clear support for a frequency analysis mechanism being present in the ear.
- *Vibration occurs in the form of a traveling wave.* The ***traveling wave*** is a wave of basilar membrane vibration that trav-

els through the basilar membrane until it reaches its place of maximum vibration. This movement is illustrated in Figure 2–7, which shows various time points of a wave as it moves down the length of the cochlea. We also observe that the traveling wave builds slowly as it travels down to the apical region of the basilar membrane, and drops quickly after reaching its point of maximum vibration.

Von Békésy's studies used cadaver cochlea and high-level stimuli. As a result, he measured passive responses, reflecting purely mechanical properties of the BM. His measurements demonstrated broad tuning: a large portion of the BM was activated by a single sound. Modern in vivo measurements illustrate a much more narrowly tuned traveling wave, in that a pure tone vibrates many fewer basilar membrane locations (Narayan, Temchin, Recio, & Ruggero, 1998; Rhode, 1971; Sellick, Patuzzi, & Johnstone, 1982). Thus, in vivo, the cochlea provides a more frequency-specific representation than originally thought. Although von Békésy was unable to measure BM responses to a variety of stimulus levels, measurements down to levels of 10 dB SPL indicate that cochlear tuning is much sharper at low versus high levels (Robles, Ruggero, & Rich, 1986).

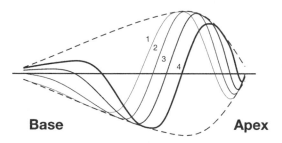

FIGURE 2–7. Traveling wave of a pure tone. The different time points (1–4) illustrate the progression of the wave traveling down the length of the basilar membrane from base to apex. Adapted from von Békésy (1966).

Three rows of outer hair cells and one row of inner hair cells line the length of the cochlea. The outer hair cells are responsible for enhancing the vibration on the basilar membrane, particularly at low levels, sharpening the tuning of the vibration on the basilar membrane, and compressing the range of vibration represented by the basilar membrane. These hair cells lead to the mammalian ability to hear very low level sounds, and loss of these hair cells can cause a reduction in hearing sensitivity up to about 60 dB (Sellick et al., 1982). The inner hair cells transduce the vibratory signal into neural activity and synapse with the auditory nerve. Most afferent neurons (the neurons that send signals to higher auditory centers) synapse with the inner hair cells, and the tonotopic organization of the BM is maintained. Loss of either inner hair cells, their synaptic connections to the auditory nerve, or auditory nerve fibers has the potential to cause complete deafness. The amount of hearing loss and the frequencies affected will depend on the severity and location of the damage.

Auditory Nerve: Amplitude Coding

The auditory nerve plays a critical component in transducing the amount of vibration on the basilar membrane. Ninety-five percent of auditory nerve fibers are considered to be type I fibers, which are the fibers that synapse with the inner hair cells and provide afferent connections to higher levels in the auditory system. These fibers are responsible for providing a neural representation, or code, of basilar membrane vibration. These fibers carry the information from the cochlea to the central auditory system in the form of action potentials, also known as spikes (Sachs & Abbas, 1974). Type I neurons code the amplitude of basilar membrane vibration via firing rate, defined as the number of action potentials per second. Increasing stimulus level increases the firing rate of the fiber. Note that the size of an action potential does not vary with the frequency or amplitude of the stimulating sound stimulus (via the amount of BM vibration).

Individual type I fibers typically have a spontaneous firing rate (SR), in which they generate action potentials even in the absence of stimulation. Three different types of type I fibers are present in the auditory nerve fiber bundle, classified based on their spontaneous firing rates: high SRs (about 18–250 spikes/second), medium SRs (about 0.5–18 spikes/second), and low SRs (<0.5 spikes/second).

As the amplitude of a stimulus is increased, the measured spike rate of a single auditory nerve fiber also tends to increase. To illustrate this, auditory nerve fiber behavior is often plotted using a ***rate-level function***, which plots the neuron's output firing rate as a function of the input stimulus level. Figure 2–8 illustrates typical rate-level func-

tions for auditory nerve fibers with different spontaneous rates, based on data collected by Winter, Robertson, and Yates (1990). We observe a strong relationship between the firing rate of a neuron and the stimulus level. Using Figure 2–8, we also note that *the threshold and SR of a neural fiber are related.* The threshold of a neuron is defined as the lowest sound level that leads to a measureable increase in the driven spike rate. High spontaneous rate fibers have low thresholds, whereas low spontaneous fibers have high thresholds. Figure 2–8 shows that the high spontaneous rate fiber begins firing above its spontaneous rate at a very low input stimulus level (<5 dB SPL). On the other hand, the low spontaneous rate fiber does not fire above its spontaneous rate until an input level of roughly 25 dB SPL is achieved.

Neurons demonstrate saturation, which occurs when increases in stimulus level no longer lead to increases in firing rate. For example, note the very low level at which saturation

FIGURE 2–8. Auditory nerve rate-level functions for the three different Type I auditory nerve fibers, classified by their spontaneous firing rate (SR). Based on data from Winter, Robertson, and Yates (1990).

occurs for the high SR/low threshold fiber in Figure 2–8, which begins at a level of about 30 dB SPL.

The characteristics of the three different fiber types are as follows:

- *high SR/low threshold fibers.* These fibers respond at low levels, have high spontaneous rates, and small dynamic ranges. They saturate at about 25 to 30 dB SPL. Roughly 60% of fibers fall into this category.
- *medium SR/medium threshold fibers.* These fibers code for moderate stimulus levels and have moderate spontaneous rates. Their dynamic range is still small but is larger than that of the low-threshold fibers. Roughly 25% of fibers fall into this category.
- *low SR/high threshold fibers.* These fibers code for high stimulus levels and have low spontaneous rates. Their dynamic range is the largest of all fibers but rarely exceeds 60 dB (Palmer & Evans, 1979). Roughly 15% of fibers fall into this category.

Due to the saturation and limited dynamic ranges of individual fibers, an individual neuron cannot code the entire range of sound levels that are perceived by the human ear. The dynamic range (the range of levels between threshold and saturation) of an individual neuron is on the order of 20 to 40 dB and rarely exceeds 60 dB. Note that the dynamic range of human hearing is considered to be approximately 100 to 120 dB, suggesting that all three fiber types must be used to represent the entire dynamic range of hearing. Consider then that the high SR/low threshold fibers would be most involved in representing low-level stimuli, such as when auditory threshold is measured. On the other hand, high threshold/low SR fibers are most involved in auditory detection when a background noise is present.

Our ability to hear sounds, then, is a consequence of outer and middle ear amplification, basilar membrane representation and auditory nerve firing. As we will see in other sections and chapters of this book, disorders of any of these physiological structures will lead to disruptions in psychophysical ability. The locus of that disruption, of course, influences the nature of the perceptual deficits. Perhaps the most obvious is the effect that auditory disorders have on the absolute threshold, discussed in subsequent sections of this chapter.

THRESHOLD OF HUMAN HEARING: MAP AND MAF

By the 1930s, a number of scientists had made measurements of auditory thresholds at various frequencies. The data shown in Figure 2–9 are a compilation of these measurements adapted from Sivian and White (1933). These measurements illustrate the minimum detectable sound pressure level in dB SPL of young human listeners as a function of frequency when measured in the free field and over headphones. For the ***minimum audible field (MAF)*** measurements, sounds were presented over a loudspeaker (i.e., in the free field) and calibrated at a location 1 m away from the speaker. Note that for these free-field measures, the listeners were able to use both ears. For the ***minimum audible pressure (MAP)*** measurements, sounds were presented monaurally (i.e., to a single ear) over headphones, and measurements were based on a calibration reference level at the tympanic membrane.

The MAP/MAF curves in Figure 2–9 illustrate two primary findings:

- *Frequency effects.* The minimum detectable sound pressure level varied as a function of frequency. Notably, the frequency of a pure tone had a large impact on the ability to hear that sound. A higher sound pressure level was needed for detection at both the very low frequencies and the very high frequencies, with frequencies between

FIGURE 2–9. Absolute threshold curves for minimum audible field (MAF; filled symbols) and minimum audible pressure (MAP); unfilled symbols) plotted in dB SPL. Adapted from Sivian and White (1933).

1000 and 6000 Hz being the easiest to detect. From this result, we see that healthy humans can detect the mid-frequency sounds at lower sound pressure levels than high- or low-frequency sounds. The minimum just detectable sound level in dB SPL can vary by more than 40 dB, depending on the frequency tested.

- *Measurement differences.* The free-field measurement (MAF) yielded much lower thresholds than the MAP, with differences in the range of 10 to 15 dB, but often greater. Three primary factors contribute to this result (Sivian & White, 1933):
  - *Listening with two ears versus one.* Generally, listening with two ears yields a lower threshold than listening with one, but the effect is only about 2 dB (Robinson & Dadson, 1957).
  - *Reflections of sound from the body.* The body interacts with the sound field,

and reflections from the head and torso increase sound level at the tympanic membrane.
  - *Amplification provided by the pinna and meatus.* Headphones eliminate certain resonant properties of the external ear that contribute to sound amplification.

These measurements have strong implications for our auditory perception. First, consider the implications for superior audibility in mid frequencies versus low and high frequencies. Sounds in this frequency range are more easily detected than other sounds, and therefore are used in sirens and alarms. These frequencies, notably, also contribute substantially to speech understanding, and therefore are the most important to amplify for listeners with sensorineural hearing loss. Second, consider the benefits provided by free-field over headphone listening. We are afforded a number of advantages provided by our external ear and our body, as well as having two ears. Such results have important consequences for the development of technologies, which can capitalize on the natural effects of auditory perception.

Connecting Physiology to the MAP/MAF

The outer and the middle ear have a large influence on the shape of the MAP and MAF. The valley in the MAP/MAF is generally thought to reflect the sound transfer characteristics of the outer and middle ears. Recall that the combined outer and middle ear transfer function has a peak between 600 and 6000 Hz, corresponding to the range of best absolute thresholds. Both structures have frequency transmission characteristics that vary as a function of frequency, as illustrated in in Figure 2–6. On the other hand, the cochlea is thought to transmit sound roughly equally at all frequencies (Rosowski, 1991). Of course, the cochlea is critically involved in the ability to detect sounds, but it has little effect on the *shape* of the MAP/MAF due to its flat frequency-transmission characteristics. Not surprisingly, then, there is a strong correlation between the MAP/MAF and the transfer characteristics of the outer and middle ears. That peak in the combined outer- and middle-ear transfer function has a direct correspondence to the valley in the MAP/MAF curves in Figure 2–9, which is where humans have the best auditory sensitivity.

The auditory nerve also has a role in the detection of sounds, as it codes the information on the basilar membrane. For threshold-level stimuli, the only fibers available to code the vibration are the high-SR/low-threshold fibers. These are the only fibers that respond to sound levels below 20 dB SPL, and therefore are the only fibers active during threshold testing. These fibers increase their firing rate in response to very low-level sounds, ultimately leading to auditory detection of the tone.

Recent studies in animals have suggested that the low-SR/high-threshold auditory nerve fibers and their associated synaptic connections may be more easily damaged than the high SR/low threshold auditory nerve fibers when exposed to high levels of sound (Kujawa & Liberman, 2009). Auditory threshold testing may not reveal damage to the high-threshold fibers, due to the low stimulus levels associated with threshold. Consequently, it seems possible that supra-threshold tests would be necessary to identify loss of or damage to the high-threshold fibers. Scientists have speculated that loss of these fibers might contribute to speech perception difficulties in noise, even in the absence of elevated auditory thresholds.

Effects of Hearing Loss

The MAP and MAF functions were measured using earphones or speakers as transducers. Both of these transducers activate the air conduction pathway of the ear and involve the entire auditory system. Consequently, conductive (damage in the outer or middle ear) and sensorineural (damage at the level of the cochlea or auditory nerve) hearing loss can have a drastic effect on the MAP and MAF curves. As mentioned earlier, we consider the MAP and MAF curves to be a consequence of the frequency transfer characteristics of the outer, middle, and inner ear. Therefore, it is rather straightforward to make predictions about the effects of hearing losses that alter the transmission characteristics of the components of the ear on the MAP/MAF.

Disordered changes to the function or structure of each component of the ear can yield frequency-specific effects. Changes to the resonant properties of the external ear (such as via growths or malformations) or occlusion (such as via wax or objects) will directly affect hearing in a frequency-specific manner. Changes to the mass or stiffness of the middle ear will also alter the frequency-transmission characteristics of the system and yield frequency-specific effects. Damage to outer or inner hair cells often is frequency specific as well, as certain locations along the length of the cochlea are often impacted more by disease and noise exposure. Each of these disorders will then influence specific portions of the MAP/MAF curves. In many cases, the degree of damage and the location of the damage can be associated with a predictable change in hearing.

Clinical Example: Otosclerosis

All disorders that affect hearing thresholds will influence the MAP and MAF, and here we discuss otosclerosis as an example. Otosclerosis is a condition in which the ossicular bones are resorbed and replaced by a spongy, vascularized bone. In the later stages of the disease, the bony growths lead to fixation of the stapes footplate to the oval window. In the early stages, the disease is considered to be stiffness based from an acoustics standpoint. That is, the disease increases the stiffness of the middle ear system, which leads to a decreased ability to transmit low-frequency sound. Because the low-frequency gain of the middle-ear frequency-transfer function is diminished, a low-frequency hearing loss will result. Any change in frequency transmission of the ear will map into a matched elevation in threshold of the MAP/MAF function. For example, a decrease in sound transmission of 10 dB from 250 to

1000 Hz due to otosclerosis will elevate MAP/MAF thresholds between 250 and 1000 Hz by a corresponding 10 dB. This change is illustrated by the unfilled symbols in Figure 2–10, which demonstrates the low-frequency elevated MAP thresholds in the presence of early-stage otosclerosis.

As the disease progresses, however, the bony growths add mass to the ossicular chain. Because the increase in mass diminishes sound transmission at high frequencies, a high-frequency hearing loss (in addition to the already present low-frequency hearing loss) occurs. The presence of advanced disease will then elevate thresholds in the MAP/MAF functions on the high-frequency side. The effects of later-stage otosclerosis are shown as the filled symbols on the MAP function of Figure 2–10, which demonstrates that the MAP thresholds at all frequencies are elevated.

It is clear from Figure 2–10 that auditory pathology can change the shape of the MAP and produce an upward shift in the MAP. However, because the MAP function is not constant across frequencies, we would need to subtract the shifted MAP values from the normative MAP values to determine the threshold change imposed by the auditory pathology. Although this calculation is fairly straightforward and is easily visible in Figure 2–10 when the normative MAP values are plotted along with the measured threshold values, measurements are not conducted in dB SPL in clinical applications, as we discuss in the next section.

Using dB HL

In clinical situations, we are often interested in knowing how an individual's hearing differs with respect to normative data, or typical auditory behavior. Although the MAP/MAF curves illustrate typical auditory thresholds, they are measured with reference to a fixed

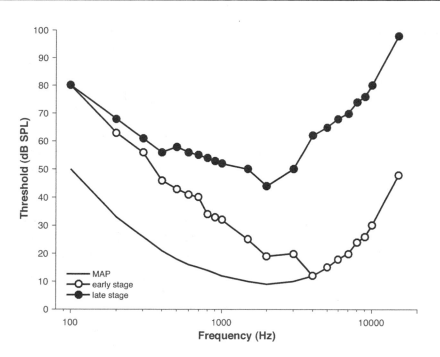

FIGURE 2–10. MAP curve for a patient with early-stage and late-stage otosclerosis. The normal MAP curve is shown as the solid line. Early- and late-stage otosclerosis curves are shown using unfilled and filled symbols, respectively.

acoustic quantity that does not vary with frequency (i.e., the 20 µPa reference for dB SPL). Because the MAP/MAF curves are frequency dependent, using dB SPL as the normative reference can lead to difficulty in observing changes in the curve that might be caused by hearing loss. In audiology, then, the more commonly used dB reference is dB HL, or dB hearing level. dB HL is based on a measure of normal auditory sensitivity based on young, normal-hearing listeners, and uses the MAP curve as the reference. Thus, any value on the MAP curve becomes 0 dB on the dB HL scale. The following equation applies:

dB HL = measured threshold in dB SPL– reference threshold in dB SPL (RETSPL).

Conversions of dB SPL to dB HL for audiometer Telephonics (TDH-39) headphones are listed in Table 2–1. Note that

TABLE 2–1. Reference Threshold Values in dB SPL for TDH-39 Earphones

Frequency (Hz)	Reference Threshold in dB SPL	dB HL
125	45.5	0
250	25.5	0
500	11.5	0
1000	7	0
2000	9	0
4000	9.5	0
8000	13	0

Source: RETSPL values are from ANSI (2010).

dB HL typically refers to the sound level at threshold and describes the amount of hearing loss. In cases when we want to reference the level of a sound to a listener's hearing loss, we can use dB sensation level (dB SL), defined as:

$$dB\ SL = dB\ SPL\ of\ the\ sound$$
$$-\ RETSPL - dB\ HL\ of\ the\ patient.$$

For example, a 1000-Hz tone presented at 80 dB SPL to a listener with a hearing loss of 40 dB HL, would have a sensation level of 33 dB SL.

Using the dB HL reference allows much easier observation of deviations in hearing with respect to what is considered typical. Plotting data in this way is referred to as the ***audiogram***. By normalizing the data, it is more straightforward to visualize the amount of hearing loss. Another major difference between the audiogram and the MAP/MAF curves is that better thresholds are illustrated at the top of the audiogram, and poorer thresholds are indicated at the bottom. To illustrate these two factors, the data from Figure 2–10 are plotted in dB HL in Figure 2–11. When

thresholds are plotted in this way, we observe that this early-stage otosclerosis is associated with hearing loss only in the low frequencies and no loss above 2 kHz. On the other hand, late-state otosclerosis is associated with a similar amount of hearing loss in dB across the frequency range. Particularly for the late-stage otosclerosis case, the audiogram should allow easier visualization of how much hearing levels change across the audiometric frequencies.

> The interested reader is referred to the short section in Chapter 1 that discusses the historical reasons for plotting the audiogram "upside down" and for using dB HL. Jerger (1990) notes that plotting the audiogram in this way is rather unfortunate because it breaks with scientific convention, where values on *y*-axes are plotted in an ascending manner.

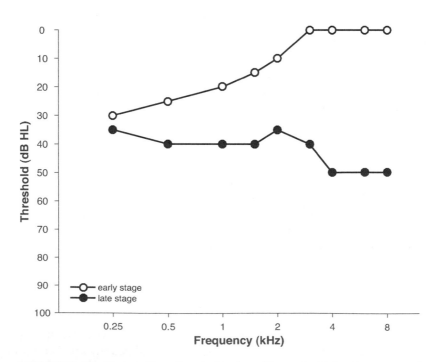

FIGURE 2–11. The auditory thresholds from Figure 2–10 (early-stage and late-stage otosclerosis) are re-plotted in audiogram format in dB HL.

A common way to quantify the degree (or severity) of hearing loss is to categorize absolute thresholds based on ranges of dB HL, a practice first proposed by Goodman (1965) with more modern criteria provided by Clark (1981) and shown in Table 2–2. These terms are appropriate for use in describing thresholds among clinicians, but they have been demonstrated to provide little value, and can even be detrimental, in conveying the severity of communication difficulties to both patients and their families. In many cases, particularly in reference to children, these terms lead patients to underestimate the severity of their hearing loss (Haggard & Primus, 1999). Using these categories, however, can provide a general guide for the expected speech understanding difficulties experienced by listeners with sensorineural hearing loss.

MEASURING THE THRESHOLD

The Psychometric Function

Measuring the ability of the ear to detect sounds is a core of both audiology and psychoacoustics. In many cases, we are interested in the absolute (or detection) threshold, as we have just observed in our description of MAP/MAF measurements. It is easy, but a mistake, to assume that stimulus levels above the threshold always yield detection and stimulus levels below the threshold are undetectable (or inaudible). Rather, the term "threshold" usually refers to a sound level associated with a somewhat arbitrarily chosen percentage of detections, like 50% or 75%. For any psychoacoustic task, there is a range of stimulus parameters for which performance is between 0% and 100%. For example, a range of stimulus levels (e.g., 0–25 dB SPL) might be associated with detection abilities ranging from 0 to 100%, as shown in Figure 2–12.

Figure 2–12 illustrates a ***psychometric function***, which plots the percentage of sound detections as a function of signal level in dB SPL. In the example illustrated here, the method used to determine the response to a given stimulus was a ***yes/no*** task. In a *yes/no* task, a listener is given an observation interval in which the stimulus is either present or not. The listener then responds either "yes, I heard a signal" or "no, I did not hear a signal." An experimental ***trial***, defined as the observation interval plus the response interval, for a yes/no experiment is illustrated in Figure 2–13.

TABLE 2–2. Terms Used to Describe Hearing Loss Based on Hearing Levels

Hearing Threshold Level in dB HL	Hearing Loss Label
–10 to 15	Within Normal Limits
16–25	Slight Hearing Loss
26–40	Mild Hearing Loss
41–55	Moderate Hearing Loss
56–70	Moderately Severe Hearing Loss
71–90	Severe Hearing Loss
91+	Profound Hearing Loss

Source: From Clark (1981).

FIGURE 2–12. An example of a psychometric function for detecting a pure tone in quiet, which illustrates that performance increases with increasing signal level.

Yes/No

FIGURE 2–13. Illustration of a single trial of a yes/no paradigm. This is a signal-present trial.

Measuring the psychometric function typically employs **the method of constant stimuli**, one of the three classical psychophysical procedures used to measure perceptual abilities. Implementation of this method requires some *a priori* knowledge of the stimulus levels to be tested, often acquired during pilot experimentation or from other published studies. In order to implement this method, then, the experimenter determines the set of stimulus levels to be tested that will span the range of performance. In the example of the psychometric function illustrated in Figure 2–12, the stimulus levels might be 7, 11, 15, 19, and 23 dB SPL. Stimuli are then presented to the listener in random order multiple times in order to obtain a reliable percent detection measure. Because this method requires presenting stimuli many times at many different stimulus levels in order to get a measurement of performance at each of those stimulus levels, it can be fairly time consuming.

Figure 2–12 shows that increasing the sound level increases the percentage of stimulus detections. The threshold is then defined as some arbitrary level of performance, which is typically 50% or higher. If the threshold were defined as 50% detections, the threshold for this listener would be about 15 dB SPL. If only the threshold is of interest, measuring a psychometric function is rather inefficient, as only stimulus levels in the region of the threshold are useful for measuring it.

In contrast to the method of constant stimuli, which can be time consuming and requires *a priori* knowledge of the stimulus levels to be selected, the other two classical methods, the **method of adjustment** and the **method of limits**, offer more flexibility and efficiency. The *method of adjustment* is unique in that it allows the listener to adjust the stimulus and find the threshold. While this method is appealing and can yield a threshold in a matter of seconds, it has no fixed response percentage associated with threshold, and thresholds depend greatly on how individual listeners define their threshold. Because of the weaknesses associated with the method of adjustment, it is not commonly used to estimate threshold. However, various experiments assessing subjective percepts (like loudness or pitch) still adopt this method, and its implementation has greatly influenced our understanding of these perceptions.

Regarding threshold estimation, however, a more commonly adopted classical method is the method of limits. In the ascending method of limits, the stimulus is first presented at an inaudible level, and the experimenter gradually increases the stimulus level until the listener is able to perceive it. On the other hand, the descending method of limits starts at an audible stimulus level and the experimenter decreases the stimulus level until it is not detectable. Averaging these two levels, then, yields the listener's threshold. Experimentally, it has been found that listeners can anticipate stimulus presentations or become accustomed to hearing a stimulus

(habituation). These concerns led to the development of adaptive procedures that are now commonly used in modern psychoacoustic applications. The procedure now adopted for clinical threshold measurement is a modified version of the method of limits and has similar characteristics to the adaptive procedures discussed next.

Adaptive Procedures

Adaptive procedures allow an experimenter or clinician to home in on the threshold level rather quickly. An adaptive procedure samples multiple points on the psychometric function, in an attempt to find a single point, such as the threshold. As long as the psychometric function governing the specific auditory behavior follows an increasing pattern like that shown in Figure 2–12, adaptive procedures can be used to estimate the threshold. In these cases, the percent detection associated with the threshold is commonly defined by the adaptive procedure used. Note also that the parameters of the adaptive procedures used must be carefully considered in the context of the psychometric function. The adaptive procedure must sufficiently sample the psychometric function by testing stimulus levels that fall within the sloped portion of the psychometric function. Because an adaptive procedure should obtain most of its measurements at signal levels within the sloped region of the psychometric function, it can be efficient by not presenting too many trials associated with 0% and 100% detections.

The Modified Hughson–Westlake Procedure

Although not a true adaptive procedure, the modified Hughson–Westlake method used to estimate auditory thresholds in the clinic (ASHA, 2005) is very similar in nature to adaptive procedures. The modified Hughson–Westlake procedure provides an efficient measurement of the detection threshold and is the result of considerations of the following principles:

- limited effects of the patient anticipating a signal presentation
- familiarization
- sufficient sampling of the psychometric function, and
- efficient threshold estimation.

In this procedure, the tester (often the audiologist) presents a stimulus and waits briefly for a patient response (a "yes" or a "no"). This paradigm uses an *undefined obser-vation interval*, that is, the patient (or listener) does not know when the stimulus will be pre-sented. In this way, the method *prevents a patient from anticipating* when a stimulus is presented, ensuring that the method will not yield a threshold lower than the true threshold.

The procedure begins testing with a stimulus presented at a level high enough to familiarize the patient with the test stim-uli (usually 20–30 dB above the estimated threshold). *Familiarization* is needed so that a patient understands task requirements and what he is listening for. Familiarization is achieved when the tester finds a stimulus level at which a patient responds reliably; this value is always above the patient's threshold.

After familiarization, the adaptive proce-dure begins. Upon a detection ("yes") response, the stimulus level is decreased by 10 dB. This change in level is the *step size* of the procedure. The sets of trials in which the stimulus level is decreasing are referred to as the *descending runs*, which continue until a listener does not detect the presence of the signal. At this point, the stimulus level is increased by 5 dB; these are the *ascending runs*, which will continue until the listener detects the signal. At that point, a descending run is again initiated. This

procedure, commonly called the *10-dB down, 5-dB up* procedure or the *10-down, 5-up* pro-cedure, is continued until the patient responds to at least two out of three stimulus presen-tations at the same level on the ascending runs. The final value is taken as the threshold, leading to a very *efficient* means of estimating threshold. This procedure yields a threshold that corresponds to 50% or higher detections. Marshall and Jesteadt (1986) estimated that the clinical procedure converges at about 85 to 95% detections. An example of this procedure is illustrated in Figure 2–14, which illustrates a threshold estimate of 50 dB HL and a pro-cedure that started at 30 dB HL. Note that familiarization occurred at the presentation level of 70 dB HL.

The span of the psychometric function in dB drives the selection of the parameters of the modified Hughson–Westlake proce-dure. Without knowing the shape of the psy-chometric function, we could not determine the appropriate parameters for implementa-tion of the procedure. As a result, the modi-fied Hughson–Westlake procedure *sufficiently samples the psychometric function* to obtain a threshold. To see the reasons for this, we first look back to Figure 2–12, where we observe that the psychometric function for detecting a tone in quiet has a range of approximately 12 dB (the dB values that encompass about 5%–95% detections). Although this psycho-metric function represents that of a normal-hearing listener detecting a pure tone in quiet, the range of a psychometric function for detection does not change in the presence of hearing loss (Marshall & Jesteadt, 1986).

Any adaptive procedure that samples the psychometric function for detection should use a step size smaller than the range encompassed by the psychometric function. This is the only way that a tester can ensure that an adaptive procedure will sample some of the stimulus levels that fall within the psychometric func-tion. If the adaptive procedure selected pre-

FIGURE 2–14. An example of the modified Hughson-Westlake procedure, estimating a threshold of 50 dB HL. The stimulus level in dB HL is plotted versus the trial number. A "+" sign indicates a positive ("yes") response and a "–" sign indicates a negative ("no") response.

sentation levels associated with 0% or 100% detections, the procedure could easily misestimate the threshold of the listener. Thus, an adaptive procedure must use a step size that, at some point, will test a presentation level that falls within the range of the psychometric function. By finding a signal level associated with a no response and then using ascending runs with a 5-dB step size, the audiologist ensures that a presentation level will fall in the range of the psychometric function.

The 10-dB down, 5-dB up step size also allows for an *efficient* and relatively rapid assessment of threshold. Further enhancing the efficiency is the practice of stopping the threshold estimation procedure after at least two responses out of three stimulus presentations on the ascending runs. This allows an adept audiologist to collect a full audiogram in about 15 minutes, allowing time to conduct additional diagnostic assessments.

Note that using a smaller step size can be appropriate for audiometric testing, as the ascending runs will sample the psychometric function using the smaller step size. Of course, this procedure will take longer to implement and may result in different test-retest reliability. Such modifications are usually only implemented in the clinic under uncommon circumstances, such as when a listener is suspected of feigning hearing loss, either intentionally or unintentionally.

The Adaptive Staircase Procedure

The modified Hughson–Westlake procedure has a test-retest reliability of about ±5 dB, which can be sometimes too poor for psychoacoustic testing. Furthermore, the modified

Hughson–Westlake is only appropriate for estimating the absolute threshold, and not other auditory abilities that involve discrimination or identification. Consequently, other forms of adaptive procedures are adopted for research purposes, as they can allow for better test-retest reliability, although they typically are more time consuming than the modified Hughson–Westlake procedure. A common adaptive procedure used in psychophysical testing is the ***adaptive staircase method***, an adaptive method in which the signal levels are determined by a listener's previous responses (e.g., Levitt, 1971). As with the clinical method, the staircase procedure makes the task easier (e.g., increases the stimulus level) when listeners make errors of detection or discrimination and makes the task more difficult (e.g., decreases the stimulus level) when listeners make correct detections or discriminations.

The staircase procedure is commonly paired with a ***forced-choice*** paradigm, illustrated in Figure 2–15. In a forced-choice paradigm, at least two, but sometimes more, observation intervals are presented. Only one randomly chosen interval contains the signal (the signal-present interval); all other intervals do not (the signal-absent intervals). Listeners select which interval contains the signal, and they will be either correct or incorrect.

Figure 2–15 illustrates what a single trial of a forced-choice task might look like. Two-interval, two-alternative forced choice indicates that there are two observation inter-

vals and two choices. The 2I–2AFC is a very common forced-choice paradigm, along with 3I–3AFC, three intervals and three choices, adopted in psychoacoustics.

Implementing the staircase method requires selection of a large number of parameters that are already predetermined for the clinical method: the starting signal level, the step size, and the criterion for stopping the staircase. In many cases, researchers estimate auditory abilities for a variety of tasks, such as the discrimination tasks that are discussed in subsequent chapters in this book. No matter the task, however, some of the same procedural principles that apply for the clinical method are the same, including familiarization and sufficient sampling of the psychometric function. The researcher, however, is not always interested in using a highly efficient method and may sacrifice efficiency for better test-retest reliability.

Experiments commonly use either a "2-down 1-up" or a "3-down 1-up" staircase procedure to estimate threshold. In the 2-down 1-up procedure, a listener must make a correct decision on two consecutive trials before the stimulus level is decreased. A single missed detection causes an increase in signal level. In contrast, three consecutive stimulus detections are required for a decrease in signal level in the 3-down 1-up procedure. In these procedures, threshold is determined by averaging the signal levels at the reversals, or the stimulus levels at which listeners' responses

2I-2AFC

FIGURE 2–15. Illustration of a single trial of a 2-Interval/2–Alternative Forced-Choice (2I–2AFC) paradigm. The signal is present in the first interval.

switched direction. When other parameters of the staircase procedure are selected appropriately, in theory, the 2-down 1-up procedure estimates 71% correct detections and 3-down 1-up estimates correct 79% detections. In practice, however, the staircase procedure generally estimates points that are higher than the theoretical target on the psychometric function (Kollmeier, Gilkey, & Sieben, 1988). As with the clinical procedure, the *starting signal level* should be higher than the final threshold estimate in order to familiarize the listener. In Figure 2–16, the starting signal level is 65 dB SPL, well above the final threshold of 43 dB SPL. The *step size*, which is 5 dB in Figure 2–16, also must yield presentation levels that sample the psychometric function. Finally, the experimenter needs to determine *when to end* the threshold estimation procedure. Usually research experiments end the procedure after a certain number of trials or after a certain

number of reversals. Stopping after a fixed number of trials ensures that every threshold estimate will take roughly the same amount of time, but ending after a fixed number of reversals ensures that the psychometric function has been sampled a specific number of times. Figure 2–16 shows a threshold estimate that ended after 40 trials.

Note also that whereas efficiency is a requirement for the clinician, it is not always the highest priority of the researcher. In this case, the researcher can sacrifice efficiency to achieve better test-retest reliability than may be possible, or even warranted, in the clinic. Thus, a staircase procedure, when implemented in the research lab, may include many more trials or reversals than would be used in a clinical application. One additional feature of the implementation of psychoacoustic procedures in the laboratory is that thresholds are always measured more than once; each

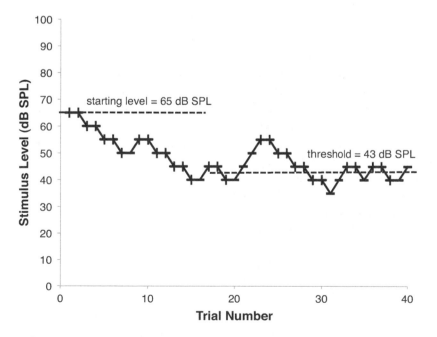

FIGURE 2–16. Illustration of a 2-down, 1-up adaptive staircase procedure estimating a threshold of 43 dB SPL. The stimulus level in dB SPL is plotted versus the trial number. A "+" sign indicates a correct response and a "–" sign indicates an incorrect response.

threshold measurement is repeated, generally at least three times. The repeated measurements allow experimenters to assess the reliability and validity of the threshold estimate.

SIGNAL DETECTION THEORY (SDT)

General Description

In many areas of psychoacoustics, and particularly in clinical assessment, we are interested in the *auditory sensitivity* of the listener, essentially what the ear can do. However, we must also consider the *response proclivity* of the listener, or how the listener responds to the stimuli. We also refer to response proclivity as *response bias*, more explicitly defined as the listener's tendency to say, "Yes I heard something." Listeners may come to the laboratory or the clinic with different motivations for participation, and these factors must be considered in any psychoacoustic or audiological assessment.

In order to illustrate the impact of response bias, let us consider more closely a *yes/no* detection experiment: a listener is presented with two types of trials: signal-absent trials and signal-present trials. After any given observation interval, the listener must determine whether his internal response (the neural representation of the stimulus) resulted from a signal being present or not. Because there are many variables involved in coding a sound (including environmental and physiological factors), no signal is associated with a deterministic internal response.

Green and Swets (1966) developed a robust framework within which to characterize this problem and termed it *signal detection theory*. In this framework, we can consider the internal response generated by a signal (or the absence of one) to be represented by two probability distributions. Figure 2–17 illustrates this concept and shows one probability distribution associated with the absence of the signal (plotted to the left on the axis) and the one associated with the presence of the signal (plotted to the right). Because signal detection theory applies to measurements near threshold, performance is not at 100%, and these distributions overlap to some degree. The greater the overlap (or the smaller the signal level), the more difficult the task will be for the listener and the poorer the auditory sensitivity.

The listener has to determine, based on the internal response alone, whether the signal was presented. Here, the listener only has access to the internal response, but we assume that familiarization and learning over multiple trials allow the listener to learn the patterns of activity associated with the signal-absent and signal-present distributions. The theory assumes that the listener establishes a *criterion*, or an amount of *internal response* above which he will answer, "Yes I heard a signal" and below which he will answer, "No I did not hear a signal." The criterion reflects the *response bias* of the listener, the tendency to say, "Yes I heard a signal." Once the criterion is established, we illustrate it on Figure 2–17 as a vertical line. Although the criterion can be placed anywhere along the *x*-axis, the location of the criterion falls into three distinct categories:

- *Neutral.* This criterion is centered exactly between the two distributions. In this case, the listener has no bias, or proclivity, to say "yes" more frequently than "no."
- *Conservative.* This criterion is placed anywhere to the right of the neutral criterion, and is illustrated in Figure 2–17. In this case, a listener has a stronger tendency to say "no" than to say "yes."
- *Liberal.* This criterion is placed to the left of the neutral criterion. Here, a listener is more likely to say "yes" than to say "no."

The criterion separates the two original distributions into four different regions. These

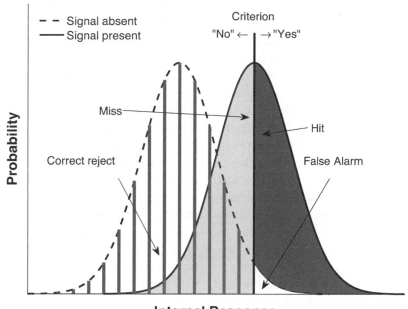

FIGURE 2–17. Illustration of the probability distributions underlying signal detection theory. The distribution on the left (*dashed line*) shows the signal-absent distribution, whereas the distribution on the right (*solid line*) shows the signal-present distribution. The different shaded areas represent four potential signal/response categories. Dark gray = hits (signal present, "yes" response); Light gray = misses (signal present, "no" response); white = false alarms (signal absent, "yes" response); and striped = correct rejections (signal absent, "no" response).

regions are determined by whether the signal is absent or present (left vs. right distribution) and whether the listener answers "no" or "yes" (internal response falls to the left or right of the criterion). These regions are all labeled on Figure 2–17, and are defined as:

- *True Positive (or Hit).* Listener says "yes" when a signal is present—illustrated by the dark region.
- *False Positive (or False Alarm).* Listener says "yes" when a signal is not there—illustrated by the white region.
- *False Negative (or Miss).* Listener says "no" when a signal is present—illustrated by the light gray region.
- *True Negative (or Correct Rejection).* Listen-

ers says "no" when a signal is not there—illustrated by the striped region.

Under the neutral criterion, a listener will have the highest number of correct detections. Note, however, that this listener will have some false positives due to the overlapping distributions. A listener adopting a conservative criterion will have fewer false positives (and possibly none) but also fewer true positives. The listener with a liberal criterion will have many false positives as well as a high proportion of true positives. In this way, both liberal and conservative criteria will lead to a lower percent correct, and therefore both types of criteria can cause an experimenter to misestimate the threshold.

Signal detection theory has numerous applications in the medical field, and is frequently adopted during development of medical tests. In clinical audiology, newborn hearing screening provides a great example of signal detection theory at work. Newborn hearing screenings are based on a physiological test of cochlear function: the otoacoustic emission. Babies who have an otoacoustic emission above a certain level "pass" the newborn hearing screening, and babies whose emission falls below that level or cannot be recorded are "referred" for follow-up testing. The otoacoustic emission varies in size along a continuum, and so the field must decide how big the emission must be to be associated with a pass. Any baby with an emission bigger than that criterion level will pass the test, and any baby with a smaller emission will be referred. The field has determined that identifying hearing loss as early as possible is the primary goal and that missing a baby with hearing loss is far more detrimental than referring babies with good hearing. Thus, newborn hearing screenings adopt a liberal criterion—there are many false positives and many babies are referred who do not have hearing loss. The hope is that by sending many babies for follow-up testing, the babies who really have hearing loss (the true positives) will not be overlooked (a false negative).

Application of Signal Detection Theory

It is uncommon to use a yes/no paradigm and a signal detection theory framework when an estimate of threshold is desired. Consequently, a number of strategies can be taken by an experimenter to ensure that listeners adopt neutral criteria. In the research realm, the forced-choice paradigm is extremely popular, as the criterion will be applied to both observation intervals and is effectively canceled out.

The clinical procedure also adopts particular strategies in order to encourage a patient to adopt a neutral criterion. Listeners can adopt both conservative and liberal criteria during an audiometric evaluation, and an audiologist or experimenter should be aware of the consequences of adopting these nonneutral criteria on the threshold estimate. In one extreme case, listeners exaggerating their hearing loss are overly conservative in their responses. The listener with a conservative bias has a decreased tendency to say,

"Yes I heard something," and only responds to signals presented at relatively high sensory levels. We can see from Figure 2–17 that this listener will produce very few false positives compared with the misses, as the white area under the curves is much smaller than the light gray area. Consequently, a lack of false positives is a potential indicator that a listener has adopted an overly conservative criterion.

On the other hand, an extremely liberal responder produces the opposite result: many false positives. Both types of patients can lead to inaccurate audiograms unless audiologists are able to encourage their patients to adopt a neutral criterion. Patients with conservative criteria can produce audiograms with hearing thresholds that are higher (worse) than their true hearing abilities, and the reverse can be true for those adopting liberal criteria. A high false positive rate can make it difficult for an audiologist to determine whether a patient response was a hit or a false positive. Many facets of the clinical procedure encourage patients to adopt neutral, or even moderately liberal, criteria such as:

- *Instructions.* "Respond even if you think you hear a sound, or it sounds faint and far away." These instructions invite listeners to guess, allowing them comfort in producing a false positive. Audiologists should be encouraged by patients who produce some false positives—a false positive is an indicator that the patient has not adopted an excessively conservative criterion.
- *Retesting 1000 Hz.* This is a check to determine the criterion has not changed. If thresholds are lower (better) upon retest, it is possible that the patient initially adopted a conservative criterion and during testing has adopted a more neutral one.
- *Familiarization.* By starting at a level above the patient's estimated threshold (e.g., 30 dB HL for a normal-hearing patient), the patient has time to learn the task and adopt a reasonable criterion. If a patient struggles to hear the sound at the beginning of the threshold search, he could adopt a criterion that is either too conservative or too liberal throughout the entire threshold search.
- *Randomizing the temporal interval between sounds.* An audiologist can control the time between stimulus presentations, and this manipulation can be very helpful to estimate threshold for patients adopting a liberal criterion. This practice might encourage listeners to adopt a neutral criterion, but if they continue to adopt a liberal criterion, a long temporal separation between stimulus presentations will allow the tester to associate the signal presentation with the response and disambiguate hits from false positives.

SUMMARY AND TAKE-HOME POINTS

The measurement of threshold has formed the foundation of the fields of psychoacoustics and audiology. Measurement techniques have illustrated that threshold varies depending on the frequency being tested, the mode of testing (i.e., free-field vs. headphones), and the specific measurement technique used. In all cases, the experimenter must be aware that perceptual measurements are a consequence of auditory abilities and a listener's response bias. Care and consideration must be taken to reduce or eliminate the effects of a listener bias, or the thresholds being reported may not be valid.

The following are key take-home points of this chapter:

- Absolute thresholds vary depending on the frequency tested, with mid-frequency sounds associated with the lowest absolute thresholds.
- Absolute thresholds collected from free-field measures can be more than 15 dB better than testing over headphones. Acoustic interactions between the sound and the body, amplification by anatomical structures, and binaural effects contribute to these differences.
- All adaptive procedures are based on knowing the psychometric function, which characterizes the perception as a function of changing the strength of the signal being presented. Knowledge of the psychometric function is critical to establish the variables necessary for using adaptive procedures.
- Response bias always has the potential to influence psychophysical measurement, and techniques should be employed to reduce or eliminate the effects of bias on the estimate of threshold..

EXERCISES

1. Calculate whether a 100-ms pure tone will be sufficiently frequency specific to produce representations independent from one another at the audiometric frequencies of 250, 500, and 1000 Hz. In

your answer, consider whether there is overlap of frequencies between the various tones. From an acoustics standpoint alone, would this duration be sufficiently short for testing hearing thresholds?

2. Calculate the dB SPL level for an rms pressure of .0002 Pa. Next calculate the dB SPL level for an rms pressure of 0.002 Pa. How many times bigger is the increase in pressure? How many dB bigger is the more intense sound? Do this calculation for 0.02 Pa to establish the relationship between changes in pressure and dB. Discuss this relationship.

3. For the sounds in Exercise 2, what are the dB HL values if the sound was 500 Hz? How about 4000 Hz? Discuss why frequency does not impact dB SPL but does impact dB HL values.

4. An increase in middle ear mass (e.g., placement of pressure-equalizing [PE] tubes in the tympanic membrane) will alter the transfer function of the middle ear in the high frequencies by decreasing the amount of amplification provided. Sketch new transfer function of the middle ear under this situation. Discuss the changes you have sketched and how absolute thresholds are expected to change.

5. The auditory nerve (AN) is responsible for transmitting signals represented in the cochlea to higher auditory centers. As mentioned previously, there are three types of AN nerve fibers: low-, middle-, and high-threshold fibers. Consider the impact on the audiogram for a complete loss of low-threshold fibers. Sketch. Consider the impact on the loss of high-threshold fibers. Sketch. Discuss how well the audiogram reflects the function of the entire auditory nerve.

6. In the early onset of otitis media, the buildup of fluid in the middle ear leads to an increase in the stiffness of the middle ear system. With that information, con-

sider the impact of otitis media on the MAP function. Sketch.

7. Presbycusis, also known as age-related hearing loss, begins in the high frequencies and slowly progresses to lower and lower frequencies. Consider the impact of early-stage presbycusis on the MAP function and later-stage presbycusis on the MAP by providing sketches. Discuss how these effects are different from those provided by otitis media.

8. Consider the same case presented in Exercise 2–7, but now consider why plotting audiometric thresholds in dB HL rather than dB SPL allows a better illustration of the frequencies affected most by the scenario. Discuss the advantages of using dB HL over dB SPL for this particular clinical application.

9. Patient X has a unilateral hearing loss in which the left ear is completely deaf, and the right has normal hearing. Patient Z has two ears with normal hearing. Sketch predicted MAF functions for these two listeners. Sketch predicted MAP functions for the left ear for both patients.

10. a. List one advantage and one disadvantage of each of the laboratory adaptive staircase procedure and the modified Hughson–Westlake clinical procedure to estimate threshold.
    b. Provide a circumstance when each procedure would be preferred with explanation.

11. Consider the impact of the following decisions as they apply to the staircase procedure for estimating threshold. Discuss whether these decisions may affect the threshold or other test-related factors.
    a. Step size too big
    b. Step size too small
    c. Starting level too high
    d. Starting level too low

12. Consider the following situations that can occur in audiometry and discuss how

the situation might impact the patient's criterion and the subsequent effect on the threshold measured.

a. Adopting a pattern of stimulus presentations during audiometric testing
b. Testing a patient with tinnitus
c. Providing a visual cue to a patient during testing

REFERENCES

American Speech-Language-Hearing Association. (2005). *Guidelines for manual pure-tone threshold audiometry* [Guidelines]. Retrieved from http://www.asha.org/policy

Clark, J. G. (1981). Uses and abuses of hearing loss classification. *ASHA, 23*(7), 493–500.

Erber, N. P. (1982). Glenondale auditory screening procedure. In *Auditory training* (pp. 47–71). Washington, DC: Alexander Graham Bell Association.

Green, D. M., & Swets, J. A. (1966). *Signal detection theory and psychophysics*. New York, NY: Wiley.

Haggard, R. S., & Primus, M. A. (1999). Parental perceptions of hearing loss classification in children. *American Journal of Audiology, 8*, 83–92.

Jerger, J. (2009). *Audiology in the USA*. San Diego: Plural Publishing.

Kollmeier, B., Gilkey, R. H., & Sieben, U. K. (1988). Adaptive staircase techniques in psychoacoustics: A comparison of human data and a mathematical model. *Journal of the Acoustical Society of America, 83*(5), 1852–1862.

Kujawa, S. G., & Liberman, M. C. (2009). Adding insult to injury: Cochlear nerve degeneration after "temporary" noise-induced hearing loss. *Journal of Neuroscience, 29*(45), 14077–14085.

Kurokawa, H., & Goode, R. L. (1995). Sound pressure gain produced by the human middle ear. *Otolaryngology–Head and Neck Surgery, 113*(4), 349–355.

Leek, M. R. (2001). Adaptive procedures in psychophysical research. *Perception and Psychophysics, 63*(8), 1279–1292

Levitt, H. (1971). Transformed up-down methods in psychoacoustics. *Journal of the Acoustical Society of America, 49*(2B), 467–477.

Marshall, L., & Jesteadt, W. (1986). Comparison of pure-tone audibility thresholds obtained with audiological and two-interval forced-choice procedures. *Journal of Speech and Hearing Research, 29*(1), 82–91.

Narayan, S. S., Temchin, A. N., Recio, A., & Ruggero, M. A. (1998). Frequency tuning of basilar membrane and auditory nerve fibers in the same cochleae. *Science, 282*(5395), 1882–1884.

Palmer, A.R. and Evans, E.F. (1979). On the peripheral coding of the level of individual frequency components of complex sounds at high sound levels. In Creutzfelt, Scheich, & Schreiner (Eds.), *Hearing Mechanisms and Speech*, 19–26. Berlin: Springer-Verlag.

Rhode, W. S. (1971). Observations of the vibration of the basilar membrane in squirrel monkeys using the Mössbauer technique. *Journal of the Acoustical Society of America, 49*(4B), 1218–1231.

Robinson, D. W., & Dadson, R. S. (1957). Threshold of hearing and equal-loudness relations for pure tones, and the loudness function. *Journal of the Acoustical Society of America, 29*(12), 1284–1288.

Robles, L., Ruggero, M. A., & Rich, N. C. (1981). Basilar membrane mechanics at the base of the chinchilla cochlea. I. Input-output functions, tuning curves, and response phases. *Journal of the Acoustical Society of America, 80*(5), 1364–1374.

Rosowski, J. J. (1991). The effects of external- and middle-ear filtering on auditory threshold and noise induced hearing loss. *Journal of the Acoustical Society of America, 90*(1), 124–135.

Sachs, M. B., & Abbas, P. J. (1974). Rate versus level functions for auditory nerve fibers in cats: Tone burst stimuli. *Journal of the Acoustical Society of America, 56*(6), 1835–1847.

Sellick P. M., Patuzzi R., & Johnstone B. M. (1982). Measurement of basilar membrane motion in the guinea pig using the Mössbauer technique. *Journal of the Acoustical Society of America, 72*(1), 131–141.

Shaw, E. A. G. (1974). Transformation of sound pressure level from the free field to the eardrum in the horizontal plane. *Journal of the Acoustical Society of America, 56*(6), 1848–1861.

Sivian, L. J., & White, S. D. (1933). On minimum audible sound fields. *Journal of the Acoustical Society of America, 4*(4), 288–321.

von Békésy, G. (1960). *Experiments in hearing*. E. G. Wever (Ed.). New York, NY: McGraw-Hill.

Winter, I. M., Robertson, D., & Yates, G. K. (1990) Diversity of characteristic frequency rate-intensity functions in guinea pig auditory nerve fibres. *Hearing Research, 45*(3), 191–202.

3

Estimating Thresholds
in Noise (Masking)

LEARNING OBJECTIVES

At the end of this chapter, students will be able to:

- Describe the acoustic characteristics of noise
- Discuss the impact of noise on detection of pure tones
- Compare the psychoacoustical techniques used to measure masking
- Explain how masking is used to measure frequency selectivity
- Integrate knowledge of impaired auditory physiology with psychoacoustical masking results in listeners with SNHL

INTRODUCTION

The previous chapter covered the psycho-acoustic principles underlying the detection of sounds in quiet. However, we rarely spend time in quiet environments and are surrounded by noise of all types, from white noise to speech babble. In almost all cases, the presence of noise leads to difficulties in perceiving the sounds of interest. We call this effect *masking*, broadly defined as the process by which the presence of one sound interferes with the perception of another. In this chapter, we are concerned with the effect masking has on detection ability. However, masking can also be applied to discrimination, recognition, and comprehension.

Two major types of masking are relevant to the perception of sound: *energetic masking*, which occurs when the energy in a masker competes directly with the energy in a signal, and *informational masking*, which occurs when the masker perceptually competes with the signal. Informational masking can be caused from many sources: temporal variations in a stimulus, uncertainty about a stimulus, or even linguistic content. The mechanisms responsible for both types of masking are very different, with energetic masking being traced to a primarily peripheral representation and informational masking typically mediated by central processes. This chapter focuses on the mechanisms responsible for energetic masking.

A number of factors dictate whether one sound will mask another, including the power of the masker compared with the signal, the frequency characteristics of the masker compared with the signal, and the temporal structure of the masker relative to the signal. These characteristics will be discussed with a focus on the following aspects of masking:

- *Masking by noise and pure tones.* This section reviews how intensity and frequency content influence the effectiveness of a masker.
- *Frequency selectivity and the auditory filter.* Masking experiments have been critical to our understanding of the frequency selectivity of the ear, or the ability of the auditory system to represent one frequency as independent of another. These studies have led to a concept called the auditory filter.
- *The excitation pattern.* The excitation pattern provides a psychological, internal representation of the stimulus spectrum. Its conceptualization has been integral to our understanding of what spectral information is accessible to the auditory system.
- *Masking by fluctuating sounds.* The healthy ear is able to receive a benefit from a fluctuating masker compared with a steady one. In this section, we review how this might happen.

Many of the early masking studies were critical in the development of the technologies associated with the telephone. The earliest masking studies provide information regarding how various stimuli influence auditory threshold and have provided a great deal of information regarding the representation of frequency in the auditory system, particularly in relation to the frequency-selective nature of the ear. Importantly, masking studies have also been crucial in the development of diag-

nostic audiological techniques. In this chapter, we discuss the role of masking studies in our understanding of auditory processing as well as how sensorineural hearing loss affects the ability to hear masked sounds. We will discuss the following concepts as they apply to masking in the auditory system:

- Acoustics of noise and filters
- Physiological representation of sounds
- Psychophysical masking in normal-hearing listeners
  - Simultaneous masking by tones and noise
  - Frequency selectivity in simultaneous and forward masking
  - Using masking to infer psychophysical representations of the spectrum
  - Masking by fluctuating sounds
- Effects of sensorineural hearing loss on masking
- Clinical application of masking

ACOUSTICS: NOISE AND FILTERS

Noise

Noise is often referred to as *any unwanted sound*. However, this definition is not terribly useful in the field of psychoacoustics because it is not associated with an acoustic characterization. This chapter will demonstrate that the acoustic representation of sound is an essential determinant in the ability of that sound to produce masking. Realistically, any sound can be a "noise" and can produce masking, but the amount of masking produced by that sound depends on the relationship between the masking sound (the *masker*) and the sound being detected (the *signal*). The relationship between the intensities, frequencies, and even the fluctuations within sounds are important. Common masking studies have employed noise maskers that are characterized by a random amplitude structure: white noise and narrowband noise, and so we review the acoustics of these sounds here.

White noise is a very specific type of noise, which is random in nature and has a constant power spectral density. Essentially, this means that when the power spectrum of white noise is plotted, it looks flat across frequency. Within the human hearing sciences, we generally assume that the frequencies contained within the white noise roughly correspond to the range of human hearing, or 20 to 20,000 Hz. Figure 3–1 illustrates the waveform and spectrum of a white noise. We can see large random amplitude fluctuations over time in the waveform represented in Figure 3–1. The spectrum also contains a representation of those fluctuations, but the fluctuations are relatively small and we generally treat the spectrum of white noise as being flat across frequency, particularly for long-duration white noise.

Unlike a pure tone, which is characterized by amplitude and frequency, we can characterize white noise with a single parameter describing its amplitude. We more commonly describe the amplitude of white noise by one of two primary metrics: the **total power** (dB SPL) and the **spectrum level** (dB SPL). The total power calculation weights all frequen-

cies equally and reflects the overall power in the noise. The total power of a noise stimulus can be calculated directly from the root mean square (rms) pressure using $20\log(P_{rms\text{-}noise}/P_{ref})$. The spectrum level reflects the power within a 1-Hz band and is also commonly referred to as the **level per cycle (LPC)** in the field of audiology.

Another important noise type is narrowband noise, essentially a band-restricted version of white noise. Because this noise does not contain all frequencies, narrowband noise must always be characterized by at least two parameters in addition to one that represents the power: the **bandwidth** and the **center frequency**. A narrowband noise is fully described by specifying the the bandwidth (the range of frequencies in the noise), the center frequency (the frequency at the center of the noise), and the LPC of the noise. A schematic of the spectrum of a narrowband noise is illustrated in Figure 3–2, which also shows the various parameters used to define the noise. A narrowband noise can also be described by the high and low **cutoff frequencies**, which define the highest and lowest frequencies before the noise amplitude is attenuated (often specified as 3 dB below the level at the center frequency). These parameters are also shown in Figure 3–2.

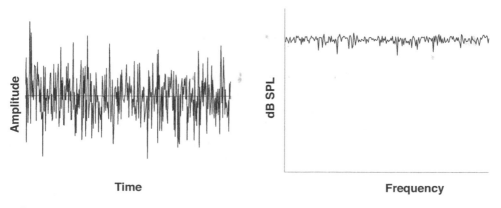

FIGURE 3–1. Plots of the waveform (*left panel*) and spectrum (*right panel*) of white noise.

FIGURE 3–2. Schematic of the spectrum of a narrow band of noise. The center frequency (f_C), cutoff frequencies (f_L and f_H), and bandwidth (BW) are specified.

It is fairly straightforward to switch between total power and LPC if the noise bandwidth is known, following the equation:

$$\text{Total Power} = 10 \log (\text{BW}) + \text{LPC},$$

Eq. 3–1

where BW = the bandwidth and LPC = the level per cycle.

In evaluating Eq. 3–1, we can see that the total power will be different for two noises with the same LPC but different bandwidths. For example, a white noise (about 20,000-Hz wide) at an LPC of 30 dB SPL will have a total power equal to 73 dB SPL [10log(20,000)+30], whereas a 200-Hz narrowband noise at an LPC of 30 dB SPL will have a total power of 53 dB SPL [10log(200)+30]. Notice how

the center frequency of the noise has no effect on the total power or the LPC. Because total power and LPC are representations of the physical characteristics of noise, their values are described in dB SPL.

Filters

Filters have an important role to play in both acoustics and perception, and they are used to modify sound. In many cases, models of auditory perception are based on the concept of filters. For example, hearing loss can be considered to be like a filter as some frequencies are attenuated by that hearing loss. Filters modify sound by attenuating certain frequency components of a stimulus. There are four major classes of filters:

- *Low-pass filter.* Passes the low frequencies and attenuates high frequencies.
- *High-pass filter.* Passes the high frequencies and attenuates low frequencies.
- *Band-pass filter.* Passes frequencies within a specified frequency region and attenuates all others.
- *Band-reject filter.* Attenuates frequencies within a specified frequency region and passes all others.

Because we describe filters in terms of their frequency characteristics, they are most easily represented in terms of their ***transfer function***, a representation of the gain provided by the filter as a function of frequency. Figure 3–3 illustrates the transfer functions of these four different filter types. The *y*-axis is gain in dB, which is an indication of how much a filter changes a sound. A 0-dB gain means no alteration in stimulus level, whereas negative gain implies attenuation. The power of the input (pre-filtered) sound has dB SPL units, and an output (post-filtered) sound has dB SPL units. However, the filter itself is not a representation of sound, and its gain is instead described using dB.

Figure 3–3 shows the transfer functions of the various filter types along with their acoustic descriptors. The cutoff frequencies and the slope of the filter skirt specify low-pass and high-pass filters. The cutoff frequency is a boundary in the filter's transfer function at which attenuation begins to occur. In many cases, the cutoff frequency is defined as the point that is 3 dB below the maximum gain, the 3-dB down point. The slope of the skirt indicates how rapidly the filter

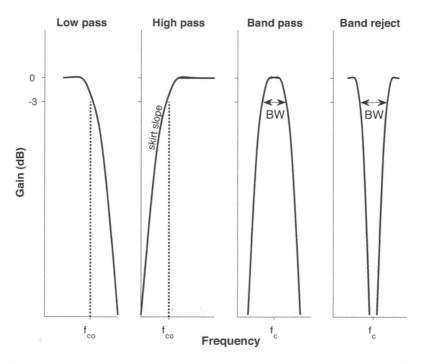

FIGURE 3–3. Schematic transfer functions of different filter types. Variables indicated are f_c=center frequency, f_{co} = cutoff-frequency, and BW = bandwidth. The cutoff frequencies are specified as 3-dB down points, and the slope of the filter skirt is also illustrated.

transitions from passing the signal to attenuating it.

We can observe in Figure 3–3 that the low-pass filter has 0 dB gain in the frequencies below the cutoff frequency (f_{co}) and begins attenuating sound at the cutoff frequency, whereas the high-pass filter does the reverse. The band-pass filter (illustrated second from the right in Figure 3–3), can be specified in one of two ways: using two cutoff-frequencies—the low- frequency and the high-frequency cutoff or the center frequency (f_c) and bandwidth (BW). The latter description is illustrated in Figure 3–3. Note that we often generate narrowband noise by filtering white noise with a band-pass filter. The band reject filter is described in the same manner but, in some sense, is the reverse of the band-pass filter. Here, the center frequency is the center of the rejection band, or the notch.

There are many ways in which we can use filter characterizations within the field of psychoacoustics and audiology. The outer and middle ears have transfer functions that are band-pass in nature. Although these systems serve to amplify sound, they do so in a way that amplifies the mid-frequencies more than higher or lower frequencies. In some cases, hearing loss can often be described using a filter transfer function: a conductive low-frequency hearing loss, for example, can be modeled as a high-pass filter. The filter analogy is extremely appropriate for conductive losses, as conductive losses tend to simply attenuate sound and do not contribute to additional perceptual distortions. On the other hand, it might seem appropriate to describe a sloping sensorineural hearing loss as a low-pass filter, due to the greater attenuation of high frequencies compared with the low frequencies. However, the distortions and perceptual deficits that accompany sensorineural hearing loss prevent the filter analogy from being wholly suitable. These distortions are discussed throughout this text.

PHYSIOLOGICAL FACTORS

We observed in Chapter 2 that the representation of vibration on the basilar membrane is primarily in the form of the traveling wave. The shape and size of the traveling wave are both important factors related to masking. Here, we review additional physiological measurements conducted in vivo that are relevant to masking. In these studies the experimenter measures the amount of displacement (or velocity) at a specific place on the basilar membrane in response to a stimulating tone. By presenting tones at different frequencies and then measuring the sound level that just noticeably vibrates the basilar membrane, the physiologist can obtain a *tuning curve*, which illustrates the lowest sound level that elicits a vibration plotted as a function of the stimulating frequency. These experiments have also been conducted in the auditory nerve, but rather than measuring vibration, they measure the signal level required to cause a single fiber to increase its firing rate.

Sellick, Patuzzi, and Johnstone (1982) measured basilar membrane tuning curves in the guinea pig cochlea. They measured the tuning curves when the cochlea was healthy, after threshold had deteriorated, and after death. Figure 3–4 illustrates their results, recorded initially at the place that responded best to an 18-kHz pure tone. Data obtained when the ear had a low threshold (filled circles), when the ear had a higher threshold (unfilled circles), and after death (unfilled squares) are shown. The curve obtained when the ear had low thresholds demonstrates *frequency selectivity*, a property in which the place on the basilar membrane responds to a very small range of frequencies, and a *band-pass* characteristic. Here, the stimulus level required to vibrate the 18-kHz place was very low, consistent with the low threshold. Higher and higher stimulus levels were needed to vibrate

FIGURE 3–4. Basilar membrane tuning curves measured in a healthy cochlea (*filled circles*), after threshold had elevated (*unfilled circles*), and after death (*unfilled squares*). Measurements are from the same basilar membrane location in a single animal. Adapted from Sellick et al. (1982).

that location as the stimulating frequency became lower and higher than 18 kHz. On the other hand, data from the impaired and the dead cochlea illustrated a shift in threshold: A 50 dB SPL stimulus was needed to achieve a response, compared with the 10 dB SPL level for the healthy cochlea. We also observe poorer frequency selectivity, indicated by the broader tuning curve, and we see a shift in the frequency that yields the lowest threshold, otherwise known as the ***best frequency***. For the dead and impaired cochlea, the best frequency was near 12 kHz, whereas it was 18 kHz for the healthy cochlea. Note that this shift is roughly 1/2 of an octave and indicates a shift in the peak of the traveling wave in the presence of hearing loss.

Numerous studies have followed that of Sellick et al. and have confirmed their results that frequency selectivity is much better than

initially reported by von Békésy, due to the damage to the cochlea caused by death in his experiments. Other physiological experiments have also reported tuning curves across a wide range of best frequencies for healthy mammalian species. Universally, those studies showed that the bandwidth (in hertz) of the tuning curves increases with increasing center frequency (Palmer, 1987).

These physiological measures have strong implications for masking, as we observe that a single cochlear location responds to multiple frequencies. Thus, if two frequencies are presented to the ear and they are similar to each other, these two frequencies will vibrate some of the same cochlear locations. We can think of this phenomenon as two tones competing for the same location on the cochlea, and the tone with the greater response would be the dominant one.

INTRODUCTION TO MASKING

Important Concepts

We define *masking* in two ways:

- The process by which sounds are made more difficult to hear by other sounds, or
- The amount by which the threshold of one sound is elevated by another sound.

Unlike physiological experiments, where we can measure the response elicited by a single stimulus, a masking study always involves at least two sounds: a *signal* and a *masker*. The signal is the sound being detected, whereas the masker is the interfering sound. Often the signal is a pure tone, but in principle, it can be any type of sound, such as speech and complex sounds. The same is true for the masker; it can be any type of sound such as noise, speech, or tones. In these studies, by measuring the influence of a masker on a signal, we can make inferences about how the signal or the masker is represented by the auditory system.

The amount of masking is typically measured using two conditions: an unmasked condition and a masked condition. The unmasked condition is essentially the same as detection in quiet, akin to measuring absolute threshold. In the masked condition, the threshold for the same stimulus is then measured in the presence of the masker. Many experiments measured masking using *simultaneous masking*, a paradigm in which the signal and masker completely overlap in time. The masker may start prior to and end after the signal, but the

entirety of the signal must fall within the duration of the masker stimulus. Figure 3–5 shows the time line for a single trial in a 2-Interval, 2-Alternative Forced Choice (2I–2AFC) masking experiment. In this figure, the signal is presented in the first of the two intervals. Recall in a 2I–2AFC experiment, there are two observation intervals: one interval contains the signal and the other does not. The interval containing the signal is selected at random. In a masking experiment, one interval contains the masker and signal, whereas the other interval contains the masker alone. The listener then selects which of these two intervals contains the signal. We can see from Figure 3–5 that the signal occurs within the extent of the masker and only occurs in one of the two intervals.

The main findings of psychophysical masking experiments quantify the effects of noise on the perception of sounds as well as measuring how different sounds are represented by the auditory system. A number of factors determine whether a sound has the capability of masking another sound: its intensity, its frequency content, and its temporal characteristics. Each of these properties will be discussed in turn.

Masking by Wide Bands of Noise

It is intuitive that the intensity of a masker should have a strong effect on its ability to mask sounds: A more powerful masker should produce more masking. This intuition, however, is not quantitative and requires further

FIGURE 3–5. Schematic of an experimental trial used in a 2I–2AFC task for simultaneous masking.

investigation. For example, intuition cannot address how much masking a given stimulus produces or how changes in the dB SPL of the masker alter the amount of masking.

Hawkins and Stevens (1950) reported a very simple but elegant study that addressed portions of these two questions. Their experiment measured the masking produced by a broadband noise (100 to 9000 Hz) on the detection of pure-tone stimuli with various frequencies. They tested eight different masker levels, ranging from –10 to 60 dB SPL. Data adapted from their experiment are illustrated in Figure 3–6, which shows the threshold of the pure tones measured in the presence of each of the eight maskers as a function of the frequency of the signal. The threshold in quiet is also shown.

The results of Hawkins and Stevens' experiment show the following patterns:

- *Frequency effects.* Masking effects across frequency, although small, were present. At the lowest levels, broadband maskers were able to mask the mid frequencies but not the low and high frequencies. For example, the –10 dB SPL masker raised the threshold of the 2000-Hz tone from about 7 dB SPL in quiet to about 11 dB SPL, but that same masker did not shift the threshold of the 250 Hz tone at all. At these low masker levels, these frequency effects could be attributed to audibility, as the level of the noise did not exceed the absolute threshold of the low-frequency tones. Once masking began, however, the same noise masked high frequencies slightly more than low frequencies: the 30 dB SPL masker raised the 500-Hz threshold to 48 dB SPL and the 4000-Hz threshold to 52 dB SPL. This trend was present across all masker levels and amounted

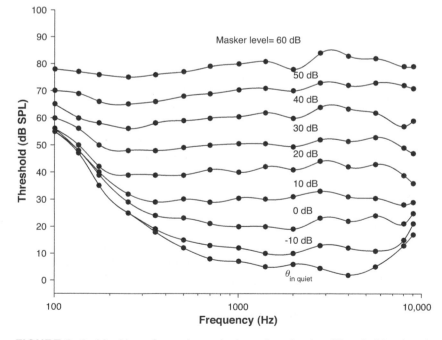

FIGURE 3–6. Masking of pure tones by broadband noise. Thresholds of various frequency tones presented in broadband maskers of different stimulus levels are shown. Solid lines represent curve fits to the data, and the masker levels are reported above the associated masking curve. Adapted from Hawkins and Stevens (1950).

to about a 5-dB increase in masking across the audible frequency range.

- *Intensity effects.* Increasing the masker dB SPL level increased the signal level necessary for detection. Figure 3–6 shows that once masking occurred (that is, once the masker was sufficiently powerful to mask the signal), a 10 dB increase in masker led to a 10 dB increase in masking. For example, at 1000 Hz, the 20 dB SPL masker was associated with a 40 dB SPL threshold, and the 30 dB SPL masker caused threshold to be 50 dB SPL.

We can calculate the amount of masking produced by each of these sounds by subtracting the threshold in quiet from the masked threshold. As an example, we can determine how much masking the 20-dB SPL noise masker will have at 2000 Hz:

The threshold in quiet at 2000 Hz is 7 dB SPL.

The 20-dB SPL masker elevates the 2000-Hz threshold to 42 dB SPL.

Amount of masking: 42 dB SPL – 7 dB SPL = 35 dB of masking

The same 20-dB masker, however, produces much less masking at 250 Hz: 39 dB SPL – 25 dB SPL = 14 dB of masking. If we completed this exercise for all frequencies, the resulting figure would be a *masking pattern*.

When referring to amount of masking, we use dB and not dB SPL. The decibel level of a sound always is in reference to a quantity, and 20 μPa is commonly used and is the typical reference for dB SPL. On the other hand, differences in dB between sounds are referred to using dB.

Masking by Frequency-Specific Sounds

The results from Hawkins and Stevens (1950) illustrate a small, but robust, effect of signal frequency. However, we can better observe the relationship between the frequency of maskers and the frequencies of the signals when experiments are conducted under variable frequency conditions. These experiments measure a property of the auditory system called *frequency selectivity*, or the ability of the auditory system to represent one frequency as independent of another. From the standpoint of perception, frequency selectivity is defined as the ability to hear one frequency as being separate from another, and is very similar, but not identical, in definition to the same term when applied to physiology.

The earliest experimental work that established the frequency selective nature of the auditory system was conducted in the early 1900s. Wegel and Lane (1924) measured the effects of the presence of one tone on the ability to detect a tone of a different frequency. They demonstrated that a masker produced the most masking when it had a frequency similar to that of the signal. Subsequent studies evaluated masking produced by narrow and wide bands of noise on the detection of pure tones and found similar results (Egan & Hake, 1950; Fletcher, 1940). Modern measurements, based on these seminal studies, now adopt somewhat different approaches, but are still based on the same principles. Together, these studies have formed the basis of our understanding of masking in the auditory system today. Here, we discuss a variety of different paradigms that have been used to measure the frequency selective nature of the ear and how well the ear represents the spectral content of sounds.

Egan and Hake (1950) measured *masking patterns* for a narrowband noise with center frequency of 410 Hz and bandwidth of 90 Hz. By fixing the noise masker and measuring the threshold of a tonal signal with a variable frequency, Egan and Hake were able to measure the amount of masking produced by that fixed stimulus as a function of signal frequency. We can consider the masking pattern as a psychological representation of an acoustic stimulus. In some ways, the masking pattern provides a picture of the internal psychological representation of the masker. Egan and Hake measured these masking patterns for this narrowband noise presented at three different levels: 40, 60, and 80 dB SPL in order to determine if the internal representation of sound was altered by the presentation level. Figure 3–7 illustrates their data and shows the amount of masking plotted as a function of the signal frequency.

Figure 3–7 shows a number of important findings from Egan and Hake's seminal experiment:

- *Frequency selectivity.* Masking was greatest at signal frequencies nearest the frequencies encompassed by the masker. Signal frequencies that were very distant from those in the masker often experienced no masking.
- *Upward spread of masking.* More masking occurred at signal frequencies higher than the masker than at signal frequencies lower than the masker. This is observed in Figure 3–7 by the asymmetrical shape of the masking patterns. When the signal was lower in frequency than the masker (i.e., signal frequencies <410 Hz), the amount of masking was less than when the signal was higher in frequency than the masker

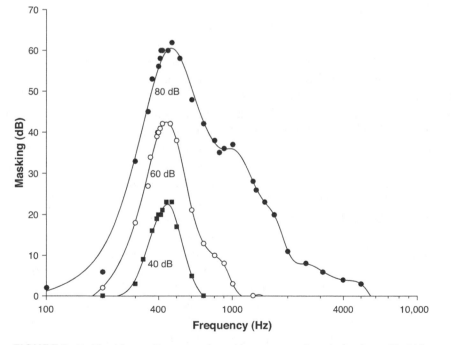

FIGURE 3–7. Masking patterns produced by a narrow band of noise with 410-Hz center frequency and 90-Hz bandwidth. Data obtained at different noise levels (40, 60, and 80 dB SPL) are shown as the different symbols. Adapted from Egan and Hake (1950).

(i.e., signal frequencies >410 Hz). Across all levels tested, more masking was produced when the masker was lower in frequency than the signal than the reverse.

- *Intensity affected frequency selectivity.* Increasing the intensity of the masker led to more masking and produced greater upward spread of masking. The frequency selectivity of the ear was worse at high levels compared with low. The level-dependent nature of auditory frequency selectivity has been replicated on numerous occasions (e.g., Lutfi & Patterson, 1984; Rosen, Baker, & Darling, 1998).

The work of Egan and Hake (1950) allows an estimate of how well the ear is able to resolve different frequencies in the stimulus. Their data illustrate the ***frequency selective*** nature of the ear in that only frequencies near a signal were able to mask it and ***upward spread of masking***, in which low-frequency sounds masked high-frequency sounds greater than the reverse. We can also see substantial nonlinearity: More intense sounds produced greater upward spread of masking. It is impressive how far masking extends for a fairly narrow band of noise, particularly at the high stimulus levels where masking extended multiple octaves!

THE CRITICAL BAND AND THE AUDITORY FILTER

The Critical Band

Fletcher (1940) used a different technique from that of Egan and Hake and used his data to provide the foundation for our modern theory of masking. Rather than measure the masking effects of a fixed masker and varying the frequency of the signal being detected, Fletcher fixed the frequency of the signal and measured the signal's threshold in the presence of different maskers. In this work, Fletcher measured the threshold of a pure tone in the presence of a masker with increasing bandwidth. Importantly, he kept the spectrum level of the noise constant, which led to increases in total noise power as the bandwidth increased. Recall from the section on acoustics in this chapter that the total power of a stimulus is determined by two factors: the spectrum level and the bandwidth. A 10-fold increase in bandwidth leads to a 10 dB increase in the total power. Thus, a 5000-Hz wide noise band is 10 dB more intense than a 500-Hz wide noise band and is 20 dB more intense than a 50-Hz wide noise band. If masking were determined only on the basis of total power, the threshold of a signal added to a band of noise should increase by 10 dB for each 10-fold increase in bandwidth.

Figure 3–8 illustrates an example taken from Fletcher's band-widening experiment, which plots the signal level at threshold (for a 2000-Hz signal) as a function of masker bandwidth. The masker was a narrow band of noise centered at 2000 Hz presented at a variety of different bandwidths. Fletcher, however, did not find that the threshold of the signal increased by 10 dB per 10-fold increase in bandwidth! Rather, his experiment showed a very striking finding: For relatively narrow noise bandwidths, signal thresholds did increase as predicted by the power calculation. However, for all of the frequencies he tested, there was always a bandwidth beyond which increases in the masker bandwidth did not lead to further increases in masking. Fletcher dubbed this bandwidth the ***critical band.***

Fletcher's data point to ***frequency selectivity*** of the ear, just as do the data from Egan and Hake. Fletcher intuited that power at masker frequencies distant from the signal do not produce masking because those masker components do not interact with the signal in the auditory system. Therefore, a band-pass filter

FIGURE 3–8. Band-widening data. The threshold of a 2000-Hz signal is plotted as a function of the bandwidth of a masking noise. The dashed line indicates the estimated critical bandwidth. Adapted from Fletcher (1940).

analogy might be a great way to describe this aspect of auditory processing. A filter, centered at the signal frequency, only passes certain frequencies that are defined by the critical band. Any frequency outside of the critical band surrounding the signal cannot mask that signal. This is why thresholds did not change as the masker bandwidth was widened beyond the critical band.

Fletcher also noted that the size of the critical band tended to increase with increasing frequency. Data that illustrate the bandwidth of the critical band are plotted as a function of frequency in Figure 3–9. For frequencies up to about 500 Hz, the size of the critical band is fairly constant, but then it increases with increasing frequency. As a result, frequency selectivity of the ear is not constant and gets worse as frequency is increased, as long as frequency selectivity is characterized in terms of hertz.

The Power Spectrum Model of Masking

Using his experiments on the critical band, Fletcher developed the ***power spectrum model of masking,*** which first posits that the ear functions like a bank of *band-pass auditory filters*, with many individual filters tuned to specific center frequencies. Secondly and importantly, after filtering, the <u>only determining factor</u> of masking effectiveness is the power of the masker that falls within the critical band (or filter) surrounding the signal being detected. Increases in the power within the critical band will yield increases in the signal level needed for detection. This model accounts for Fletcher's original (1940) data, and is still in use today due to its success in predicting masking data for experiments that have used steady-state maskers.

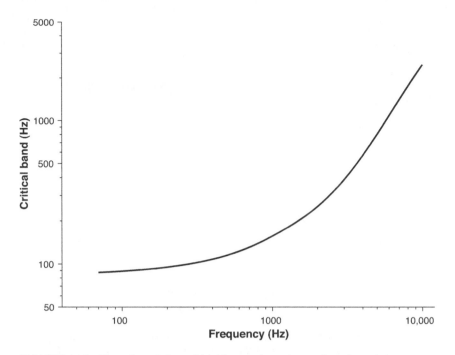

FIGURE 3–9. The size of the critical band plotted as a function of the center frequency. Adapted from Zwicker (1961).

We will note failures of this model in later sections of this chapter, particularly for fluctuating sounds. However, some of the limitations of this model are already apparent: First, Fletcher defined the critical band as a single value used to represent frequency selectivity for each frequency. However, even in the early experiments, we knew that *frequency selectivity worsens with increasing stimulus level* (as illustrated in Egan and Hake's data in Figure 3–7). Thus, the size of the critical band should be wider at higher stimulus levels. Second, Fletcher defined the critical band as being symmetrical around the signal frequency. However, studies have also demonstrated a robust upward spread of masking, in which low-frequency sounds mask high-frequency sounds to a greater degree than the reverse. Although Fletcher's critical band concept has substantial limitations, it has been

Fletcher's description of the critical band assumed band-pass characteristics and rectangular shape. This filter would pass all noise components within the passband equally as well as fully remove all components that fall outside of the passband. This assumption greatly simplifies the calculation for determining the amount of masking produced by a noise stimulus. Fletcher was acutely aware that his definition of the critical band did not fully describe masking data, but remember that Fletcher did not have computers to easily model his data. As a result, he made these simplifying assumptions, but those assumptions still allowed him to robustly predict data on masking by steady sounds.

extremely effective in predicting the amount of masking of steady-state sounds, like white noise, on the detection of pure tones. This topic and its application to the field of audiology is discussed in more detail in Chapter 8. Unfortunately, however, the power spectrum model of masking has not been as successful at predicting masking by fluctuating sounds, as we will discuss later.

Beyond the Critical Band: The Auditory Filter

To date, Fletcher's views and theories have stood the test of time. Although there are some limitations to his theories, the fundamental concept remains: the auditory system can be treated as a bank of band-pass *auditory filters*, and energy falling within one of those filters determines the amount of masking. Modern descriptions of auditory frequency selectivity have addressed some of the limitations of Fletcher's critical band measurement. First, modern techniques and computers now allow us to characterize the auditory filters using many parameters, such as their asymmetry and their dependence on stimulus level. Second, auditory filters are typically measured using a variation of Fletcher's band widening experiment, called the *notched-noise method*.

Patterson (1976) developed the notched-noise method to measure the shape of the auditory filter. This method uses a masker that is two bands of noise (~300-Hz wide or so) with a spectral notch placed between them. The tone to be detected (the signal) has a frequency that falls within the spectral notch. Rather than vary the bandwidth of the noise like Fletcher did, the bandwidth of the spectral notch is varied. Larger notches will lead to less masking compared with smaller notches, due to fewer masking components falling within the theoretical auditory filter surrounding the signal frequency. One advantage of this method is that asymmetrical placement of the notch around the center frequency can allow measurement of a filter that is asymmetrical.

A schematic illustrating this experiment and the type of data resulting from this experiment are shown in Figure 3–10. The left panel shows four schematics of the stimuli used. In all cases, a signal tone (illustrated by the line spectrum) is plotted with the notched noise (indicated by the dark gray shaded areas). The different panels illustrate increasing notch bandwidths from panel 1 (top) to panel 4 (bottom). Increasing the size of the notch bandwidth leads to less noise falling in the filter (illustrated by the light gray shading) and a better detection threshold. The signal level at threshold is illustrated by the decreasing signal amplitude. The right panel of the figure illustrates the signal threshold as a function of increasing notch bandwidth as we progress from panel 1 to panel 4, as obtained by Patterson (1976). The specific examples shown in the left panel of Figure 3–10 are indicated by the corresponding numbers on the data graph. We see from the right panel of Figure 3–10 that thresholds decreased with increasing notch bandwidth.

The auditory filter can be calculated by applying the power spectrum model of masking to estimate the shape and characteristics of the auditory filter. To estimate the auditory filter, one must make some initial assumptions about the auditory filter, such as an approximation of the shape and size of the filter. We then pass the stimuli through this hypothetical filter, and using the power at the output of the filter, estimate the signal level at threshold for various notch bandwidths. By comparing the predicted data with the actual obtained data, we can revise the parameters selected for the auditory filter. When the predicted data yield a good match to the obtained data, we have an estimate of the auditory filter. Parameters that are commonly estimated are the bandwidth of the filter and the slope of the high- and low-frequency skirts.

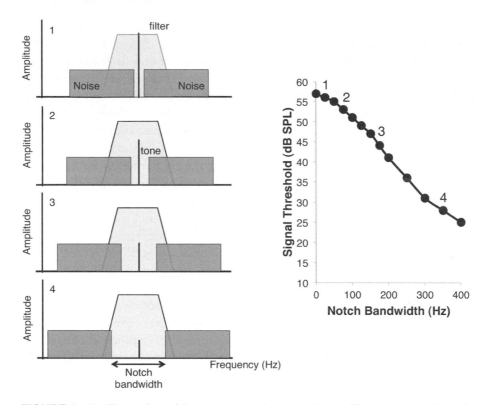

FIGURE 3–10. Illustration of the notched-noise experiment. The panels on the left illustrate various acoustic conditions used in the notched-noise method, from a narrow notch (panel 1) to a wide notch (panel 4). The right panel illustrates data obtained from the notched-noise method at 1000 Hz with signal thresholds from the various notch bandwidths indicated from #1 to 4. These thresholds decrease with increasing notch bandwidth. Data are adapted from Patterson (1976).

Figure 3–11 illustrates estimates of the auditory filter obtained by Rosen and Baker (1994), who used the notched-noise method at multiple stimulus levels to estimate the shape of the auditory filter centered at 2000 Hz. Following convention, auditory filters are plotted in terms of gain, and are normalized to 0 dB gain at their center frequency. From this figure, we see that at low levels, the auditory filter is relatively symmetric. However, as level increases, the auditory filter becomes increasingly shallower on the low-frequency side than the high-frequency side (Glasberg & Moore, 2000). This asymmetry accounts for upward spread of masking, as the low-frequency side of the auditory filter allows more low-frequency

masker energy to pass through and mask the tone being detected, which in this case is a 2000-Hz tone. We also note that as the intensity of the stimulus increases, auditory filters become broader and more asymmetric (Rosen et al., 1998). These changes with level occur exclusively on the low-frequency skirt of the auditory filter and result in greater upward spread of masking at higher stimulus levels.

Frequency selectivity measures have physiological correlates that can be traced down to cochlear physiology. Physiological estimates of frequency selectivity have also demonstrated *asymmetry* (Sellick et al., 1982; see Figure 3–4), *increasing bandwidth with level* (Ruggero, Narayan, Temchin, & Recio, 2000), and

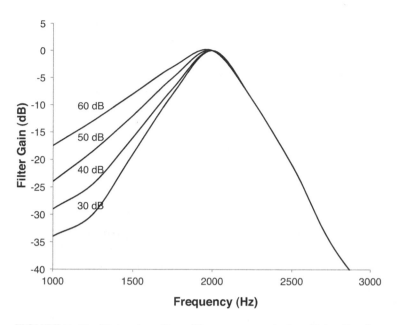

FIGURE 3–11. Plots of auditory filters measured at multiple stimulus levels at 2000 Hz. Adapted from Rosen and Baker (1994).

increasing bandwidth with frequency (Palmer, 1987). The correlation between physiological measurements and psychophysical measurements supports the idea that the frequency selectivity measured psychophysically is a consequence of basilar membrane tuning.

> Auditory filter bandwidths are commonly reported in terms of their equivalent rectangular bandwidth, or ERB. This value quantifies the bandwidth in terms of an equivalent filter that is rectangular in shape. Other measurements of bandwidth can also be used, such as one defined using the 3-dB down points, which correspond to measures from the filter skirts defined by the frequency at which the attenuation is 3 dB. However, the ERB is much more commonly adopted in psychoacoustic literature.

THE EXCITATION PATTERN

Auditory filters provide a unique opportunity for illustrating the representation of sounds from a perceptual standpoint. In particular, by using the power spectrum model of masking, we can approximate the spectral information as it is represented in the auditory system. Because auditory filters are not perfectly frequency selective (that is, they pass more than one frequency), each spectral component of a stimulus is not represented with perfect fidelity by the ear.

One method of representing sounds to illustrate their *internal* rather than acoustic representation is the ***excitation pattern***, a representation of the excitation evoked by a sound stimulus plotted as a function of the filter center frequency (Zwicker, 1970). The excitation pattern is essentially a multichannel implementation of the power spectrum model of masking. An excitation pattern is generated by passing any stimulus though a bank of auditory filters with varied center frequencies. The excitation is calculated as the power in dB at the output of each auditory filter. This excitation value in dB is then plotted as a function of the center frequency of that auditory filter, yielding the excitation pattern.

Figure 3–12 illustrates the spectrum (solid lines) and excitation pattern (dotted lines) for a synthetic vowel /i/ with a fundamental frequency of 150 Hz and an overall level of approximately 70 dB SPL. Notice the spectrum and excitation patterns are plotted on a logarithmic frequency axis; this is a common practice due to the logarithmic spacing of the basilar membrane. The spectrum in Figure 3–12 illustrates a robust representation of many of the 150-Hz harmonics—we see separate lines at least up to 2000 Hz. We also can see a robust presence of the formants: There are distinct spectral peaks around 300 Hz, 2200 Hz, and 3000 Hz.

The excitation pattern, on the other hand, provides a smoothed representation of the power spectrum. The representation of the individual harmonics and the formants, although easily visible in certain frequency regions, are not nearly as pronounced as in the spectrum. Figure 3–12 illustrates two major differences between the spectral representation and the excitation patterns:

- *Individual harmonics represented only in the low frequencies.* The representation of the low-frequency harmonics is not as robust as present in the spectrum. Harmonics 1 through 8 are visible as distinct bumps in the excitation pattern, and these bumps gradually smooth as frequency increases. Harmonics 1 to 8 are considered ***resolved***, whereas harmonics 9 and above are considered ***unresolved***.
- *Smoothed representation of the formants.* The formants are still well represented in the

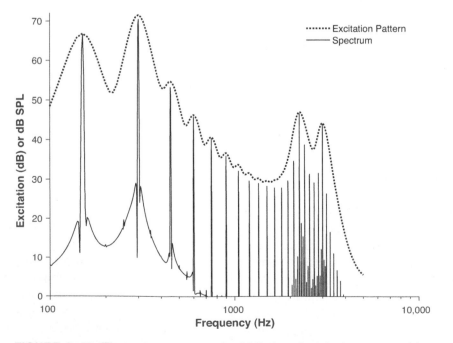

FIGURE 3–12. The power spectrum (*solid line*) and excitation pattern (*dotted line*) of a harmonic complex modeled after the vowel /i/ for normal hearing listeners.

excitation pattern, though they are not as pronounced as in the stimulus.

The excitation pattern can also illustrate the impact of masking on the internal representation of the spectrum. Figure 3–13 illustrates the excitation pattern for the /i/ illustrated in Figure 3–12, but in the presence of a moderate-level noise. In the spectrum (solid line), we observe evidence of harmonics 1 to 5 or so, and the formants at 300, 2200, and 3000 Hz. Regarding the excitation pattern, however, each individual auditory filter passes a portion of vowel as well as a portion of the noise stimulus. The result is a smoother excitation pattern compared with the one obtained without noise and has a representation of only a few harmonics, which are smeared in comparison to the spectrum. The excitation of the first formant is relatively unaffected by the noise, as the level of formant is well above the

level of the noise. However, formants 2 and 3 have less pronounced representations in the excitation pattern, and the effects of noise on their representations are drastic. Within the excitation pattern, both formants are smeared and reduced in amplitude, and the spectral valley is not as deep.

The excitation pattern provides a great deal of intuition about the representation of sound by the ear, as it reflects the imperfect frequency selectivity of the ear as well as the changing frequency selectivity with increasing frequencies. The imperfect frequency selectivity of the ear is illustrated by the overall smoothing of the spectrum in the excitation pattern. The frequency effects are also illustrated, as the individual harmonics become more smeared together in the high versus the low frequencies.

In summary, the excitation provides a model representation of the spectrum and

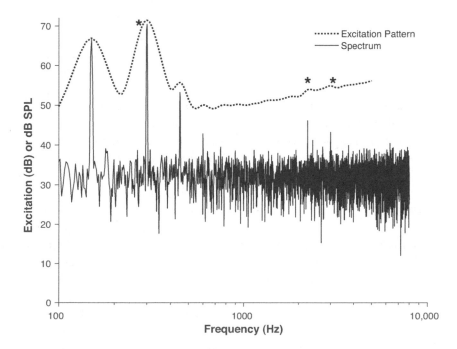

FIGURE 3–13. The power spectrum (*solid line*) and excitation pattern (*dotted line*) for the vowel /i/ when presented in noise. The locations of the formants are shown with asterisks for reference.

simply reflects the information that *may be available* to the ear using known estimates of frequency selectivity. The excitation pattern, however, does not reflect the information that the ear actually uses in perceptual tasks or how the ear uses that information.

Excitation patterns have been extremely valuable for making inferences about auditory processing. With the example shown here, we could predict that vowel perception can be altered by the presence of large noise, but that the perception of the high-frequency formants would be the most degraded. In one application of the excitation pattern, Leek and Summers (1996) used the excitation pattern to generate a stimulus that masked the spectral valley, but not the formants. This noise had a lower level relative to the vowel than the one just illustrated. Leek and Summers found that noise had only a small effect on vowel identification. This finding suggests that the spectral valley is not nearly as important for vowel identification as the representation of the formants. Such results provide fuel for a hot debate in the speech-perception literature, as there is also evidence in support of a whole-spectrum model for vowel perception (Ito, Tsuchida, & Yano, 1999; Molis, 2005). Excitation patterns have also been greatly helpful in our understanding of auditory representations of listeners with hearing loss, as discussed in a later section of this chapter.

Implications

Excitation patterns provide a representation of the spectrum from a psychological perceptive. However, an excitation pattern is only a representation of a "best case" scenario and does not measure how well the ear is able to *use* the information that is represented. As we have observed, many sounds in the environment are broadband in nature, and the acoustic cues are often distributed across frequency. One specific example of this is the vowel, which is a broadband stimulus containing spectral peaks, or formants. The frequencies associated with these formants provide information about the identity of the vowel, but successful identification of a vowel requires the presence of at least two of the formants. Consequently, the ear must have some ability to integrate information across frequency, but how much? and over what frequency range?

Profile analysis, a technique developed in the 1980s by David Green and his colleagues (Green, 1988; Spiegel, Green, & Picardi), provided answers to some of these questions. Profile analysis measured the ability to discriminate between sounds with different *spectral profiles,* sounds with different shapes in the power spectrum. For example, two vowels have very different spectral profiles because they have formants at different frequencies. In particular, Green's experiments showed that we can discriminate spectral profiles across a very wide frequency range (effectively the entire audible bandwidth) and that our perception benefits from distributed spectral information across frequency. Yet, Berg and Green (1990) expanded on the profile-analysis technique and showed that while human listeners indeed benefited from added information across the audible bandwidth, they did not use all of the spectral information for discrimination. In general terms, they found that listeners performed more poorly than "best-performance" models, suggesting loss of some spectral information in the perceptual process.

While profile-analysis experiments support the view that the ear represents the entire stimulus spectrum, they also demonstrate that the ear does not always use this information efficiently, and essentially loses some of the spectral information in the coding process. We can view this interpretation in light of the excitation pattern, which only provides a picture of the information available to the ear. In many cases, listeners are unable to efficiently and effectively use all of the information present in the excitation pattern.

PSYCHOPHYSICAL TUNING CURVES AND SUPPRESSION

A different type of masking experiment called the *psychophysical tuning curve (PTC)*, a measurement of frequency selectivity similar in concept to the physiological tuning curve, has been used to illustrate additional nonlinear effects of auditory processing. Measuring the PTC uses tone-on-tone masking, in which the signal and the masker are both tones. In a typical PTC measurement task, the tone to be detected is fixed in frequency and in intensity, usually around 10 dB above threshold. Then, for various masker frequencies, the experimenter measures the masker level that just masks the tone. When masking is measured in this way, low masker levels are associated with maskers that produce a lot of masking; they are very effective. We generate a PTC by plotting the masker level needed to just mask the tone versus the frequency of the masker.

Importantly, PTCs have been measured in two different experimental paradigms: *simultaneous masking* and *forward masking*. Up to this point, all of our discussion has revolved around simultaneous masking, a paradigm in which masker and signal are presented at the same time. In forward masking, the masker is always presented before the signal and the masker and signal never overlap in time. Using forward masking illustrates an important consequence of nonlinear auditory processing on the masking process, which occurs only when two sounds are presented simultaneously. Here, we are specifically concerned with how frequency selectivity is measured under both simultaneous and forward-masked scenarios.

Yet, due to the temporal nature of the method, additional information about forward masking is provided in Chapter 5 on temporal processing.

To illustrate this type of masking, Figure 3–14 shows an experimental trial of a forward masking experiment. Although the masker comes before the signal, the masker can make that signal more difficult to hear.

Measuring PTCs under forward and simultaneously masked conditions illustrates why we must consider both situations. Moore, Glasberg, and Roberts (1984) measured PTCs for a tone presented at 10 dB SL and at four different frequencies under both simultaneous and forward masked conditions. They found that that simultaneous- and forward-masked PTCs have a very similar shape, as shown in Figure 3–15. However, we see a striking difference between the two types of PTCs. The PTC measured using simultaneous masking was broader than the PTC measured using forward masking. We also observe evidence of upward spread of masking in the shallower low-frequency tail in both simultaneous- and forward-masked conditions, suggesting that upward spread of masking is a robust property of the auditory system. Although comparisons between psychological and physiological tuning curves can be difficult due to species differences and measurement differences, note how similar the PTCs are in comparison to the physiological tuning curve measured from the basilar membrane in Figure 3–4.

The difference in frequency selectivity obtained using the two methods is a consequence of a nonlinear physiological phenomenon called *two-tone suppression* (Sachs & Kiang, 1968; later measured psychophysically by Houtgast, 1974). In brief, the excitation produced by a single tone can be reduced (i.e., suppressed) by the simultaneous presence of a stronger second tone, with the largest effects occurring when the two tones are nearby in

FIGURE 3–14. Schematic of the stimulus presentation sequence used in a 2I–2AFC task for forward masking.

FIGURE 3–15. Example psychophysical tuning curves measured under forward (*dotted lines*) and simultaneous (*solid lines*) masking for four different frequencies. Adapted from Moore et al. (1984).

frequency, but not immediately adjacent (Shannon, 1976). In masking, then, a strong masker suppresses the signal, effectively lowering the excitation of the signal. Because the masker suppresses the signal, the level of the masker that is needed to mask the signal will be lower than if the signal were not suppressed. As a result, the masker level at threshold is lower in the simultaneous condition than the same masker in the forward-masked condition, where suppression is not active. If we apply this principle to the simultaneously masked PTC, the masker components that fall within the suppressive region around the signal require lower masker levels to mask the signal, causing tuning to appear to be broader than when measured under forward-masking conditions.

Implications

Two-tone suppression may appear to be a negative aspect of auditory processing. In fact, however, it has a number of benefits related to auditory perception. Under some circumstances, components within a masker can suppress each other, rendering the entire masker less effective. It also leads to improved spectral contrast for broadband stimuli. For example, formants within a vowel suppress components within the valleys, enhancing the spectral representation of the vowel spectrum. If we consider two-tone suppression in light of the excitation pattern, the representation of spectral information would be even better than is described by the excitation pattern. Auditory filters used for the excitation pattern are measured using simultaneous masking, and therefore might actually underrepresent the spectral information available to the ear!

As a result, we must consider the method used when describing the frequency selectivity of the ear. A fair amount of everyday listening occurs in simultaneous masking situations, and consequently, frequency selectivity measured under these conditions may be most appropriate to include in auditory models. On the other hand, the effects of two-tone suppression are not negligible, and comparison with physiological measurements requires psy-

chophysical measures to be conducted under forward-masked conditions.

MASKING BY FLUCTUATING SOUNDS

Up to this point, our discussion of masking has focused on the masking produced by steady-state sounds. However, as we know, the sounds we encounter in the environment vary considerably in their amplitude. That is, they fluctuate. An important class of masking experiments focuses on the effects of these fluctuating maskers that have amplitude variations that occur over time. Hall, Haggard, and Fernandes (1984) demonstrated that masking by steady-state noise can be much greater than masking by fluctuating noise, and their data are illustrated in Figure 3–16. In a set of conditions very similar to that conducted by Fletcher (1940), listeners detected a 1000-Hz tone added to bands of steady noise of

FIGURE 3–16. Thresholds for detecting a pure tone added to a steady band of noise (*filled circles*) and a fluctuating band of noise (*unfilled circles*) as a function of the bandwidth of the noise. Adapted from Hall et al. (1984).

varied bandwidths. Like Fletcher, Hall et al. found that thresholds increased with increasing bandwidths up to the critical bandwidth and then did not increase more with increasing bandwidth, as shown by the filled circles in Figure 3–16. Hall et al. then imposed fluctuations upon the noise (a process called *modulation*) and measured thresholds again. In contrast to the results of Fletcher, Hall et al. found that increasing the bandwidth of the modulated noise first increased thresholds but then thresholds decreased as the bandwidth was further increased, as shown by the unfilled circles in Figure 3–16.

We see from Figure 3–16 that the decrease in threshold provided by the fluctuating masker did not begin until the masker bandwidth was greater than the critical band, or around 60 to 100 Hz. The difference in threshold between the steady masker and the fluctuating masker is the *fluctuating masker benefit*. The size of the benefit increased as the bandwidth of the masker increased, with a benefit of over 10 dB for the 1000-Hz

wide masker. When the fluctuations across frequency were synchronous, a release from masking occurred. Data such as these point to problems with Fletcher's power spectrum model of masking, which would have predicted the same thresholds regardless of stimulus fluctuations.

To understand Hall et al.'s results, we must first consider how a fluctuating masker may provide benefits to a listener. A fluctuating masker has "dips" or "valleys" in the waveform. These dips provide brief epochs in time that have high signal-to-noise ratios (SNRs), compared with the waveform peaks, and a listener with normal hearing can take advantage of these dips to detect a signal (Buus, 1985). Steady maskers do not have pronounced dips and therefore do not provide opportunities for *dip listening*. To illustrate how this might work, Figure 3–17 illustrates how the valleys in a masker provide regions of high SNR. This figure illustrates a fluctuating masker, plotted along with a signal. The signal is only visible in the masker dips, which therefore have a high

FIGURE 3–17. Illustration of dip listening. A fluctuating masker is shown with a pure tone signal. Arrows indicate epochs with a high signal-to-noise ratio.

SNR. A sophisticated detection system, like the ear, can take advantage of those dips to facilitate detection. Benefits of a broadband modulated masker are not restricted to detecting pure tones, as they have also been demonstrated for detecting and understanding speech (Miller & Licklider, 1950).

MASKING AND SENSORINEURAL HEARING LOSS

Listeners with sensorineural hearing loss have a common complaint of having great difficulty communicating in noisy environments. This complaint can be partially traced to a greater susceptibility of masking that results from cochlear damage. Deficits in detecting masked sounds have been measured repeatedly in listeners with sensorineural hearing loss.

Physiological Factors

Sensorineural hearing loss can be associated with a loss of both outer and inner hair cells within the cochlea. Most listeners with sensorineural hearing loss have either outer hair cell loss or a combination of outer and inner hair cell loss. Loss of the outer hair cells, which are responsible for sharpening the tuning of the traveling wave, leads to a reduction in frequency selectivity in these listeners. This result is evident in the basilar membrane tuning curves provided by Sellick et al. (1982) and illustrated in Figure 3–4, where threshold elevation led to a broadening of frequency selectivity on the basilar membrane. These physiological measurements may be expected to have a direct consequence on the psychoacoustical measurement of frequency selectivity, and we would expect a broadening of the auditory filter in the presence of the loss of outer hair cells. Although loss of the inner hair cells would not affect basilar membrane tuning, their loss may also broaden the psycho-

physical auditory filter (depending on pattern of fibers that are damaged) and will most definitely raise the threshold for detection.

Frequency Selectivity

A number of studies have evaluated the effects of masking in listeners with hearing loss, with a general consensus being that listeners with hearing loss experience poorer frequency selectivity and a greater susceptibility to masking than their normal-hearing counterparts (e.g., Florentine, Buus, Scharf, & Zwicker, 1980; Leek & Summers, 1993). The high stimulus levels used may be part of the reason for poor frequency selectivity in listeners with hearing loss, due to the worsening of frequency selectivity with increasing level. However, even when stimuli are equated between the two groups of listeners and threshold elevation is taken into account, listeners with hearing loss appear to experience an additional reduction in frequency selectivity due to their auditory pathology (Dubno & Schaefer, 1995).

To illustrate the range and variation of auditory filters measured in listeners with hearing loss, five examples of auditory filters obtained from listeners with normal hearing and listeners with hearing loss are illustrated in Figure 3–18 (from Glasberg & Moore, 1986). Auditory filters obtained from the normal-hearing listeners (top panel) are fairly symmetrical but tend to have a shallower low-frequency skirt compared with the high-frequency skirt, as we have already observed. Note too that there is some variability across listeners in terms of the overall bandwidth and shape. The bottom panel, which plots the auditory filters for the listeners with hearing loss shows:

- *Broadening of the auditory filter.* The auditory filters for the listeners with hearing loss are broader than for those with normal hearing. One consequence of the broader

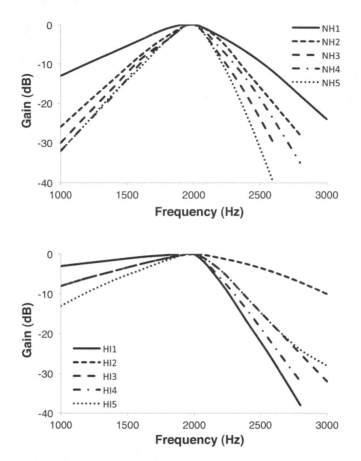

FIGURE 3–18. Auditory filters centered at 2000-Hz are plotted for five listeners with normal hearing (*top panel*) and five listeners with sensorineural hearing loss (*bottom panel*). Adapted from Glasberg and Moore (1986).

filter is additional masking in these listeners. Changes to the bandwidth are typically assumed to be approximately two or three times the width of auditory filters measured in listeners with normal hearing. Consequently, listeners with hearing loss will need a better signal-to-noise ratio in order to detect a sound embedded in noise.

- *A shallower low-frequency skirt of the filter.* Auditory filters measured in listeners with hearing loss tend to be more asymmetric than in listeners with normal hearing. Typically, the low-frequency side of the auditory filter is much broader than the high-

frequency side of the filter, although individual differences exist. The consequence is that these listeners with a shallower low-frequency auditory filter skirt tend to experience greater upward spread of masking.

- *Large variability across listeners.* Measurements of frequency selectivity in listeners with hearing loss demonstrate considerable variation in the bandwidth and asymmetry of the filter, especially compared with listeners with normal hearing. While many listeners present with broader auditory filters, one cannot easily predict from audiometric thresholds how poor frequency selectivity might be (Glasberg & Moore, 1986). The degree of asymmetry exhibited in the auditory filters of listeners with hearing loss is extremely variable (Glasberg & Moore, 1986), and some listeners (like HI2 in Figure 3–18) might exhibit broadening of the high-frequency skirt as well as the low-frequency skirt.

Psychophysical tuning curves obtained in listeners with hearing loss demonstrate poor frequency selectivity as well. The poorer frequency selectivity of the impaired listeners becomes even more apparent when PTCs are measured under conditions of forward masking, as tuning is not sharper under forward masked conditions for listeners with sensorineural hearing loss (Moore & Glasberg, 1986). Wightman, McGee, and Kramer (1977) found that the suppression mechanism is not effective in listeners with sensorineural hearing loss. Recall that in normal-hearing listeners, suppression caused the simultaneously obtained PTCs to be broader than the forward-masked PTCs. Thus, loss of suppression explains why the PTCs are so similar

between forward-masked and simultaneously masked conditions.

Poor frequency selectivity and loss of suppression would cause listeners with hearing loss to experience more masking and a loss of the important contrasts present in the spectrum.

Excitation Patterns

To illustrate how broadening the auditory filter affects the excitation pattern, the left panel of Figure 3–19 plots the excitation patterns for the vowel /i/ in a healthy ear (solid lines) and an impaired ear with filters twice as wide (dotted line). The right panel illustrates the excitation patterns for the vowel presented in noise. When comparing the excitation patterns for the vowel stimuli in quiet, we see that the excitation pattern with simulated impairment (dotted lines) shows that the peaks associated with the individual low-frequency harmonics and the formants are greatly smoothed compared with the normal-hearing excitation pattern. On the whole, the broadened auditory

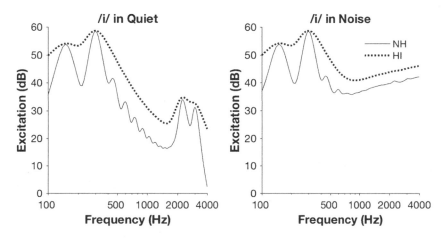

FIGURE 3–19. Excitation patterns for the vowel /i/ presented in quiet (*left panels*) and in noise (*right panel*). Excitation patterns based on a normal ear are shown with the solid line and excitation patterns for the impaired ear are shown as the dotted line.

filters provide less access to the spectral information present in a stimulus.

Wider auditory filters also allow more noise to pass through and obscure spectral contrasts present in sounds. We observe this in the right panel of Figure 3–19, in which the impaired excitation pattern is severely smeared by the presence of the noise, to a much greater extent that the normal-hearing excitation pattern. The two high-frequency formants are essentially completely obscured by the noise. Note that these effects would be further intensified if this simulation included the reduced audibility that is associated with sensorineural hearing loss.

Many stimuli in the environment contain relatively small spectral contrasts, and this illustration of the excitation pattern suggests that reduced frequency selectivity can have a real impact on the perception of sounds in our environment. Further, even small reductions of spectral contrast may be problematic when stimuli are masked. Thus, reduced frequency selectivity by listeners with sensorineural hearing loss is generally considered to translate into difficulties understanding both speech in quiet and speech in noise, as demonstrated by Baer and Moore (1993). They showed that simulated reduced frequency selectivity negatively impacted speech perception in noise. However, while reduced frequency selectivity is a clear problem for listeners with hearing loss, it is much less important to speech perception than the reduction in audibility caused by their hearing loss (Humes & Roberts, 1990).

Masking by Fluctuating Maskers

The difficulties imposed by sensorineural hearing loss are not restricted to steady noise. Listeners with hearing loss have been demonstrated to receive much less benefit from fluctuating maskers than those with normal hearing, and in some cases receive no fluctu-

ating masker benefit at all (Bacon, Opie, & Montoya, 1998; Festen & Plomp, 1990). The reduced benefit can be attributed to a number of different factors, with a primary factor being that the dips in the fluctuating stimulus are rendered inaudible by the sensorineural hearing loss. Thus, the impaired ear does not have the opportunity to take advantage of high-SNR temporal epochs. Other factors related to the hearing loss are also likely involved, such as alterations in the representation of amplitude variation over time, which is discussed in more detail in Chapter 5. The inability to take advantage of temporal fluctuations in a masker leads to substantial deficits for everyday listening and is a major contributor to difficulties understanding speech in noise.

Summary of Effects of Hearing Loss on Masking

Taken together, we see that listeners with hearing loss experience a reduction in frequency selectivity, a greater susceptibility to masking, and reduced effects of two-tone suppression compared with listeners with normal hearing. Impaired frequency selectivity directly contributes to a reduced representation of the spectrum and leads to the greater susceptibility to masking. Loss of two-tone suppression also reduces the representation of spectral contrast, and the inability to take advantage of stimulus fluctuations significantly degrades the ability to detect and understand sounds in a variety of noisy environments.

CLINICAL IMPLICATIONS OF MASKING

The principles of masking are an integral component to an audiological assessment. Whenever a patient presents with an asymmetry between the ears, audiologists apply the principles of masking. Both types of transducers used in audiometry (headphones and the bone vibrator) can allow sound to "cross over" via bone conduction from the test earphone to the non-test (contralateral) cochlea. Any time a patient has an asymmetry in hearing, the audiologist evaluates whether cross-hearing (in which the non-test ear responds to the sound rather than the test ear) can occur. If necessary, the audiologist applies the principles of masking to ensure that the threshold measurements reflect the sensitivity of the ear being tested. When masking is used in audiogram measurement, it is used to shift the threshold of the non-test ear to a level that does not allow the non-test ear to detect the tone presented to the test ear. The maskers used for clinical masking are derived explicitly from Fletcher's work on the critical band, and critical band theory governs masking in audiology in the following ways:

- *Masker bandwidth.* When masking pure tones in clinical applications, the maskers used must exceed the critical band. A masker narrower than the critical band would be insufficient as a masker for diagnostic audiology. Typical maskers used in audiometry are wider than the critical band in order to take into account individual differences and to ensure sufficient masking even at high stimulus levels.
- *Masker effectiveness.* The size of the critical band is a necessary component to determine how effective a masker can be. Because the audiologist is interested in the effectiveness of the masker rather than its total power, maskers are considered in terms of their **effective masking level**, dB EML. The effective masking level is the dB HL value to which threshold is shifted in the presence of a noise at that dB EML.

For example, if a patient's absolute threshold is measured in quiet at 10 dB HL, and then this patient's threshold is measured in the presence of a 40-dB EML noise, his threshold will become 40 dB HL in that noise. On the other hand, a patient with an absolute threshold of 60 dB HL will not experience any masking by this noise, as his absolute threshold is greater than the dB EML of the noise. It is likely that, in this case, the patient will not be able to hear the noise. However, if his threshold were 45 dB HL, he may be able to hear the noise, but in principle, it should not mask his threshold.

Effective masking level is determined by the spectrum level of the noise, the critical band at the test frequency, and a conversion from dB SPL to dB EML, which can be calculated in the following way:

$$dB\ EML = 10\log(CB) + LPC - RETSPL,$$
$$Eq.\ 3\text{–}2$$

where CB = critical bandwidth, LPC = level per cycle of the noise, and RETSPL = the reference threshold in SPL. Both RETSPL values and critical band values are given in Table 3–1.

TABLE 3–1. Reference Thresholds in dB SPL and Critical Band Values in Hz

Frequency (Hz)	Reference Threshold in dB SPL	Critical Bandwidth (Hz)
125	45.5	70
250	25.5	50
500	11.5	50
1000	7	64
2000	9	100
4000	9.5	200
8000	13	400

Source: RETSPL values are from ANSI (2010) and critical bandwidth values are from Hawkins and Stevens (1950).

Using Eq. 3–2 as a guide, we can see that increases in the LPC of the noise will increase its masking effectiveness. However, we also see that increasing the noise bandwidth beyond the critical band will not lead to increases in masker effectiveness. The noise bandwidth is not a component of Eq. 3–2. However, note that this equation only applies for maskers that have bandwidths greater than the size of the critical band.

We can calculate the dB EML of the following stimulus: a 1000-Hz wide noise, centered at 500 Hz, presented at a 40-dB LPC. Using Eq. 3–2 and Table 3–1, dB EML = 10log(50) + 40 – 11.5 = 45.5 dB EML. This masker has the ability to shift any threshold for a pure tone in quiet that is <45.5 dB HL to 45.5 dB HL.

SUMMARY AND TAKE-HOME POINTS

A variety of different stimuli can mask other stimuli. The relationship between the frequencies, intensity, and fluctuations of the masker and the signal being detected are important. Higher-intensity maskers with frequencies near the signal have the greatest effect in elevating the signal's threshold. Upward spread of masking also increases as stimulus intensity increases. Listeners with normal hearing receive a release from masking when makers fluctuate, as they can rely on brief temporal epochs with high signal-to-noise ratios in order to detect signals or identify speech sounds. Hearing loss greatly impacts masking, with listeners experiencing greater masking effects, increased upward spread of masking, and a reduction in the fluctuating masker benefit. The psychoacoustic principles discussed

in this chapter are important determinants in the design and application of maskers used in clinical audiometric assessment.

We should give a shout out to Fletcher, whose findings have had far-reaching impact on our understanding of masking by the ear and its ability to represent the spectrum of sounds. His critical band theory and the power spectrum model of masking are still used to calculate masking effectiveness for audiological applications, and excitation patterns use his principles to characterize how a sound might be represented by the auditory system. Although Fletcher's theory was not perfect, it has had a profound impact on our understanding of the frequency selective nature of the ear.

The following are key take-home points of this chapter:

- Masking experiments have demonstrated that the intensity, frequency, and fluctuations of a masker are influential in its ability to mask a signal. Experiments which have manipulated the bandwidth of stimuli and other acoustic characteristics have illustrated that healthy ears are very frequency selective and have a robust ability to represent the spectral content of a stimulus. These findings have influenced the selection of maskers used in clinical audiometry.
- Frequency selectivity in the healthy ear worsens with increasing stimulus level and with increasing center frequency.
- All listeners experience upward spread of masking, in which low-frequency sounds mask high-frequency sounds greater than the reverse.
- The excitation pattern provides a representation of the internal spectral information available to the auditory system.
- Sensorineural hearing loss causes a reduction in frequency selectivity, leading to a greater susceptibility to masking and greater upward spread of masking.

- Listeners with normal hearing receive benefits from fluctuating maskers; these benefits are lost to listeners with sensorineural hearing loss.

EXERCISES

1. Calculate the total power for three different noises all having an LPC = 40 dB SPL. Bandwidth = 100 Hz, 1000 Hz, and 10,000 Hz. Using your calculations, discuss how increasing the bandwidth by a factor of 10 alters the total power in the noise.

2. You are outside doing a hearing screening by measuring the ability of a patient to detect a 1000-Hz pure tone. However, there is an annoying sound in the background, in particular a tonal sound with a frequency of roughly 8000 Hz. You can hear this sound, but it is likely at a moderate sound pressure level. Do you think that the presence of this background sound influence your threshold measurement at 1000 Hz? Discuss.

3. In a general sketch, convert (approximately) the 20 and 60 dB masking functions represented in Figure 3–6 to a masking pattern. This will be a graph showing *amount of masking in dB*, plotted as a function of the frequency of the signal being detected. Using your result, discuss how increasing the masker level affects masking at the different signal frequencies.

4. Sketch predicted data for a normal-hearing listener for the following notched noise experiment. The signal to be detected is 1000 Hz in a noise with a notch. Thresholds for this signal are measured at different notch bandwidths (placed symmetrically around the signal frequency): 0, 25, 50, 75, 100, and 200 Hz. The experiment is conducted at two masker levels: one high (e.g., 80 dB SPL) and one low (e.g.,

30 dB SPL). Your sketch should illustrate the following:
   a. The condition (high or low level) that produces the most masking for the 0-Hz notch (i.e., no spectral notch)
   b. The condition (high or low level) that yields less frequency-specific data
   In your sketch, you should consider the size of the auditory bandwidth at 1000 Hz and the effects of level on masking and the auditory bandwidth.

5. Sketch excitation patterns for a pure tone for the following types of listeners. Be sure to pay attention to your axis labels and consider both the effects of audibility and frequency selectivity.
   a. A listener with normal hearing
   b. A listener with 40 dB of conductive hearing loss
   c. A listener with 40 dB of sensorineural hearing loss

6. Sketch excitation patterns for a harmonic complex containing frequencies of 300, 600, 900, 1200, 1500, 1800, 2100, 2400, 2700, and 3000 Hz (all harmonics have the same amplitude) for the following types of listeners. Be sure to pay attention to your axis labels and consider both the effects of audibility and frequency selectivity.
   a. A listener with normal hearing
   b. A listener with 40 dB of conductive hearing loss
   c. A listener with 40 dB of sensorineural hearing loss

7. Using your sketches from Exercise 3–6, discuss which listener will experience the most detrimental effects of noise on perceiving this harmonic complex and why.

8. Auditory filters provide straightforward ways to determine how much a single tone will influence the detection of another tone. Using the auditory filter for a normal-hearing listener shown in Figure 3–11 (the 60-dB curve), calculate the level of the following tones that are passed

through this filter. Using the numbers, discuss whether the 1500-Hz tone or the 2500-Hz tone will have a greater masking effect on the 2000-Hz tone. Explain whether your calculations are consistent with upward spread of masking.

   a. 1500 Hz presented at 60 dB SPL
   b. 2000 Hz presented at 60 dB SPL
   c. 2500 Hz presented at 60 dB SPL

9. Discuss the concept of upward spread of masking and explain why this concept might lead to problems with low-frequency amplification in hearing aids.

10. Discuss whether simple, linear amplification would be expected to assist a listener who has reduced frequency selectivity.

11. Discuss whether simple linear amplification could increase the fluctuating masker benefit for listeners with hearing loss.

12. Calculate the total power and the dB EML for a noise band 500 Hz wide centered at 2000 Hz with an LPC = 30 dB SLP. Do the same for a noise band that is 5000 Hz wide and centered at 2000 Hz. Discuss which of these noises is a more effective masker. After that discussion, consider whether one of these maskers is more efficient at masking than the other. Discuss the factors that you considered.

REFERENCES

ANSI/ASA S3.6-2010. American National Standard Specification for Audiometers. New York: American National Standards Institute.

Bacon, S. P., Opie, J. M., & Montoya, D. Y. (1998). The effects of hearing loss and noise masking on the masking release for speech in temporally complex backgrounds. *Journal of Speech, Language, and Hearing Research, 41*(3), 549–563.

Baer, T., & Moore, B. C. (1993). Effects of spectral smearing on the intelligibility of sentences in noise. *Journal of the Acoustical Society of America, 94*(3), 1229–1241.

Berg, B. G., & Green, D. M. (1990). Spectral weights in profile listening. *Journal of the Acoustical Society of America, 88*(2), 758–766.

Buus, S. R. (1985). Release from masking caused by envelope fluctuations. *Journal of the Acoustical Society of America, 78*(6), 1958–1965.

Dubno, J. R., & Schaefer, A. B. (1995). Frequency selectivity and consonant recognition for hearing-impaired and normal-hearing listeners with equivalent masked thresholds. *Journal of the Acoustical Society of America, 97*(2), 1165–1174.

Egan, J. P., & Hake, H. W. (1950). On the masking pattern of a simple auditory stimulus. *Journal of the Acoustical Society of America, 22*(5), 622–630.

Festen, J. M., & Plomp, R. (1990). Effects of fluctuating noise and interfering speech on the speech-reception threshold for impaired and normal hearing. *Journal of the Acoustical Society of America, 88*(4), 1725–1736.

Fletcher, H. (1940). Auditory patterns. *Reviews of Modern Physics, 12*((1), 47–66.

Florentine, M., Buus, S., Scharf, B., & Zwicker, E. (1980). Frequency selectivity in normally-hearing and hearing-impaired observers. *Journal of Speech, Language, and Hearing Research, 23*(3), 646–669.

Glasberg, B. R., & Moore, B. C. (1986). Auditory filter shapes in subjects with unilateral and bilateral cochlear impairments. *Journal of the Acoustical Society of America, 79*(4), 1020–1033.

Glasberg, B. R., & Moore, B. C. (2000). Frequency selectivity as a function of level and frequency measured with uniformly exciting notched noise. *Journal of the Acoustical Society of America, 108*(5), 2318–2328.

Glasberg, B. R., Moore, B. C., & Nimmo-Smith, I. (1984). Comparison of auditory filter shapes derived with three different maskers. *Journal of the Acoustical Society of America, 75*(2), 536–544.

Green, D. M. (1998). *Profile analysis: Auditory intensity discrimination.* New York, NY: Oxford Science.

Hall, J. W., Haggard, M. P., & Fernandes, M. A. (1984). Detection in noise by spectro-temporal pattern analysis. *Journal of the Acoustical Society of America, 76*(1), 50–56.

Hawkins Jr., J. E., & Stevens, S. S. (1950). The masking of pure tones and of speech by white noise. *Journal of the Acoustical Society of America, 22*(1), 6–13.

Houtgast, T. (1974). Lateral suppression in hearing. Doctoral dissertation. Free University, Amsterdam.

Humes, L. E., & Roberts L. (1990). Speech-recognition difficulties of the hearing-impaired elderly: The contributions of audibility. *Journal of Speech, Language, and Hearing Research, 33*(4), 726–735.

Ito, M., Tsuchida, J., & Yano, M. (2001). On the effectiveness of whole spectral shape for vowel perception. *Journal of the Acoustical Society of America, 110*(2), 1141–1149.

Leek, M. R., & Summers, V. (1993). Auditory filter shapes of normal-hearing and hearing-impaired listeners in continuous broadband noise. *Journal of the Acoustical Society of America*, *94*(6), 3127– 3137.

Leek, M. R., & Summers, V. (1996). Reduced frequency selectivity and the preservation of spectral contrast in noise. *Journal of the Acoustical Society of America*, *100*(3), 1796–1806.

Lutfi, R. A., & Patterson, R. D. (1984). On the growth of masking asymmetry with stimulus intensity. *Journal of the Acoustical Society of America*, *76*(3), 739–745.

Miller, G. A., & Licklider, J. C. (1950). The intelligibility of interrupted speech. *Journal of the Acoustical Society of America*, *22*(2), 167–173.

Molis, M. R. (2005). Evaluating models of vowel perception a. *Journal of the Acoustical Society of America*, *111*(2), 2433–2434.

Moore, B. C., & Glasberg, B. R. (1986). Comparisons of frequency selectivity in simultaneous and forward masking for subjects with unilateral cochlear impairments. *The Journal of the Acoustical Society of America, 80*(1), 93–107.

Moore, B. C., Glasberg, B. R., & Roberts, B. (1984). Refining the measurement of psychophysical tuning curves. *Journal of the Acoustical Society of America*, *76*(4), 1057–1066.

Palmer, A. R. (1987). Physiology of the cochlear nerve and cochlear nucleus. *British Medical Bulletin*, *43*(4), 838–855.

Patterson, R. D. (1976). Auditory filter shapes derived with noise stimuli. *Journal of the Acoustical Society of America*, *59*(3), 640–654.

Rosen, S., & Baker, R. J. (1994). Characterising auditory filter nonlinearity. *Hearing Research, 73*(2), 231–243.

Rosen, S., Baker, R. J., & Darling, A. (1998). Auditory filter nonlinearity at 2 kHz in normal hearing listeners. *Journal of the Acoustical Society of America*, *103*(5), 2539–2550.

Ruggero, M. A., Narayan, S. S., Temchin, A. N., & Recio, A. (2000). Mechanical bases of frequency tuning and neural excitation at the base of the cochlea: Comparison of basilar-membrane vibrations and auditory-nerve-fiber responses in chinchilla. *Proceedings of the National Academy of Sciences*, *97*(22), 11744–11750.

Sachs, M. B., & Kiang, N. Y. (1968). Two-tone inhibition in auditory-nerve fibers. *Journal of the Acoustical Society of America*, *43*(5), 1120–1128.

Shannon, R. V. (1976). Two-tone unmasking and suppression in a forward-masking situation. *Journal of the Acoustical Society of America*, *59*(6), 1460–1470.

Sellick, P. M., Patuzzi, R., & Johnstone, B. M. (1982). Measurement of basilar membrane motion in the guinea pig using the Mössbauer technique. *Journal of the Acoustical Society of America*, *72*(1), 131–141.

Spiegel, M. F., Picardi, M. C., & Green, D. M. (1981). Signal and masker uncertainty in intensity discrimination. *Journal of the Acoustical Society of America*, *70*(4), 1015–1019.

Wegel, R., & Lane, C. E. (1924). The auditory masking of one pure tone by another and its probable relation to the dynamics of the inner ear. *Physical Review*, *23*(2), 266.

Wightman, F. L., McGee, T., & Kramer, M. (1977). Factors influencing frequency selectivity in normal and hearing-impaired listeners. In E. F. Evans & J. P. Wilson (Eds.), *Psychophysics and physiology of hearing* (pp. 295–306). New York, NY: Academic Press.

Zwicker, E. (1961). Subdivision of the audible frequency range into critical bands (Frequenzgruppen). *Journal of the Acoustical Society of America*, *33*(2), 248.

Zwicker, E. (1970). Masking and psychological excitation as consequences of the ear's frequency analysis. In R. R. Plomp & G. F. Smoorenburg (Eds.), *Frequency analysis and periodicity detection in hearing* (pp. 376–394). Leiden, Netherlands: Sijthoff.

4

Loudness and the Perception of Intensity

LEARNING OBJECTIVES

Upon completing this chapter, students will be able to:

- Apply appropriate methodology to loudness measurement
- Compare the strengths and weaknesses of the different methods used to assess loudness perception
- Describe the effects of intensity, frequency, and bandwidth on loudness
- Discuss the implications of Weber's law for tones and noises
- Relate the effects of hearing loss to loudness perception

INTRODUCTION

Sounds in our environment are associated with numerous perceptual dimensions, and to fully understand perception, we must evaluate our perception in terms of more than just the ability to detect sounds. One of these perceptual dimensions is the *loudness* of sounds, defined as the attribute of auditory sensation by which sounds can be ordered on a scale ranging from soft to loud. Loudness is a primary component of auditory sensation and its concept is intuitive to anyone who can hear. In our everyday lives, we assess how loud a sound is and whether one sound is louder than another.

Loudness is a perceptual correlate of sound intensity, and the mechanisms by which sound intensity is coded by the ear are of fun-damental importance to understanding the loudness percept. We have already captured one of these facets in our discussions of absolute threshold, but the relationship between loudness and intensity and frequency is also relevant to our understanding of auditory function. For example, degraded perceptions of intensity can lead to speech identification errors, particularly for speech elements that contain varied intensities across frequency, such as vowels or fricatives.

The healthy ear has an exceptional ability to represent many sound intensities—from approximately 0 dB SPL (threshold) to 120 dB SPL (the level above which damage generally occurs). This 120-dB range of hearing maps to a range of audible intensities of a **trillion to 1**! Yet, even though our ear can code intensities across this range, our ear is able to detect changes in intensity that are smaller than 1 dB! Taken together, the studies on the representations of intensity by the ear, via loudness and *intensity discrimination* experiments, illustrate the truly exceptional abilities of the ear.

The perception of loudness has been measured in multiple ways and is affected by a number of acoustic variables. The following chapter discusses the following aspects of loudness:

- *Loudness growth.* In this section, we will evaluate the relationship between loudness and sound intensity, including the techniques and the measurement units.
- *Equal loudness contours.* The loudness of a sound also depends on its frequency. Here, we review how we know that mid-frequency sounds are louder than high- and low-frequency sounds when presented at the same sound pressure level.
- *Loudness summation.* In this section, we evaluate the role that stimulus bandwidth has on the loudness of sounds.
- *Intensity discrimination.* The previously mentioned aspects of loudness all establish the relationship between acoustic variables and the loudness of sounds. Intensity discrimination experiments, on the other hand, measure the just noticeable difference in intensity between two sounds.

It is worth noting that loudness and intensity are two distinct concepts. Loudness is a psychological perception associated with sound, and is therefore a perceptual variable. We cannot measure it directly—we can only measure the loudness of a sound in the context of other sounds. Further, loudness measurements rely on human reports of loudness. Consequently, the techniques employed to measure loudness are quite different from those used to measure sound level. This chapter will review a number of the psychoacoustic

tools that have been developed to assess the perception of loudness.

On the other hand, intensity is an acoustic variable, and we can quantify it directly using a sound level meter. We do not need a human listener in order to make measurements of sound level. The difference in how we measure loudness versus sound level has implications for how we interpret loudness data as well as highlighting why the terms *loudness* and *intensity* are not interchangeable.

> Note, the sound level meter actually measures sound pressure, not intensity. However, because there is a known relationship between sound pressure and sound intensity, we can calculate intensity and dB SPL from the sound level measurement.

In this chapter, we will discuss the following concepts, as they apply to loudness perception:

- Acoustics—Intensity and the decibel
- Physiological representation of stimulus level
- Loudness measures in normal-hearing listeners
- Intensity discrimination
- Loudness and intensity discrimination in listeners with sensorineural hearing loss

ACOUSTICS: INTENSITY AND THE DECIBEL

The decibel is a very important acoustic parameter for this chapter. In Chapter 2, we discussed the relationship between the decibel and sound pressure, but we did not discuss the relationship between the decibel and intensity. As mentioned in the introduction to this chapter, sound intensity and sound pressure are related to one another. Sound pressure is defined as force per unit area (pascals or N/m²), and can be measured via movement of the diaphragm of a microphone used in a sound level meter. In contrast, sound intensity is the power carried by the sound waves per unit area and has units of watts/m². For the purposes of this course, intensity and pressure can be calculated from one another following this equation:

$$I = p^2/Z,$$

where I is the intensity of sound, p is the pressure of the sound, and Z is the impedance of air. The impedance of air is a constant, and is roughly 415 rayls at 20° C. Because intensity and pressure are related, we can calculate decibels using either the pressure (P_1) or intensity (I_1) of that sound using either dB SPL = 20 $\log(P_1/P_{ref})$ or dB IL =10 $\log(I_1/I_{ref})$, where P_{ref} is the reference pressure 20 µPa and I_{ref} is the reference intensity of 1×10^{-12} W/m². Note that dB SPL is the **sound pressure level** in decibels and dB IL is the **intensity level** in decibels. However, for the applications in this text, dB SPL = dB IL, and dB SPL will be used exclusively throughout this text.

As an aside, we often see the term **sound level** used to describe how big a sound is. This term is purposely general, and does not reference units of sound pressure, intensity, or decibels. It is similar to the term "amplitude," in that it refers to the size of the sound but can be used without reference to the specific units of measurement.

PHYSIOLOGICAL REPRESENTATION OF STIMULUS LEVEL

Because it is well-established that the perception of loudness and the intensity of sound are intimately related to one another, we should discuss the representation of sound intensity in the auditory system. Although physiological measures will never be able to measure loudness, as loudness is a perception, physiological measurements are crucial for understanding the auditory mechanisms that ultimately lead to loudness. Coupling psychophysical with physiological measurements can facilitate our understanding of loudness perception.

Basilar Membrane Vibration

Stimulus intensity is represented within the cochlea by the size and velocity of the vibrations on the basilar membrane. Johnstone and Boyle (1967) made some of the first in vivo measurements of basilar membrane responses, and Rhode (1971) reported the first in vivo input-output (I-O) functions.

To illustrate the characteristics of basilar membrane response, in vivo measurements from Ruggero and Rich (1991) are plotted in Figure 4–1. They placed a small bead on a chinchilla's basilar membrane and measured the vibration of that bead when the basilar membrane was stimulated with sound. By stimulating the ear with sound presented at various sound levels (in dB SPL) and measuring the velocity of the bead as a function of the dB levels, Ruggero and Rich obtained basilar membrane (BM) I-O functions in the chinchilla. They measured basilar membrane responses in two important conditions. The first measurement was conducted in a healthy, intact chinchilla cochlea. They then treated the cochlea with furosemide, a reversible ototoxic agent that altered the function of the outer hair cells, and measured the basilar membrane response again. Examining Figure 4–1, we see:

- *A compressive function in the healthy ear.* In the healthy cochlea, basilar membrane velocity increased rapidly at the low stimulus levels. Once a moderate stimulus level

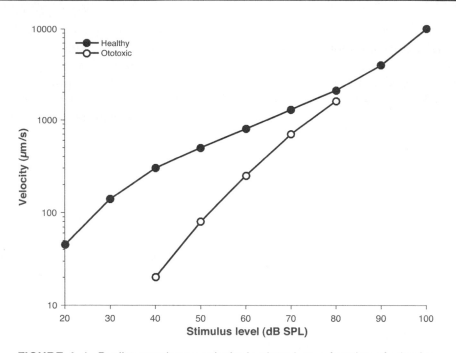

FIGURE 4–1. Basilar membrane velocity is plotted as a function of stimulus level. The solid line indicates the basilar membrane Input-Output (I-O) function in a healthy cochlea. The dashed line indicates the I-O function after treatment with the ototoxic agent. Adapted from Ruggero and Rich (1991).

was reached, velocity increased more slowly, and then increased quickly again at the highest levels. The region at moderate levels is considered the ***compressive nonlinearity*** of the ear, as basilar membrane vibration grows more slowly than at the lower levels.

- *Damage linearized velocity growth.* Damage to the outer hair cells altered the lowest level at which a velocity could be recorded (e.g., it elevated the threshold of response at this location). Damage also altered the slope of the I-O function, which became steeper than in the healthy cochlea.

Because the shape of the basilar membrane I-O function changes when outer hair cells are selectively altered, we can infer that healthy outer hair cell function is responsible for the compressive nonlinear shape of the basilar membrane I-O function. When dam-

age to the outer hair cells occurs (such as via treatment by furosemide or another mechanism), we can expect that the shape of the basilar membrane I-O function will change and become steeper. The sound pressure level associated with the smallest amount of detectable vibration (e.g., the threshold of vibration) also increases. The place of maximum excitation also shifts basally as the intensity of a stimulus increases (McFadden, 1986).

Auditory Nerve Responses

The auditory nerve is responsible for coding the vibration of the basilar membrane and provides a neural representation of stimulus level in the auditory system. Rate-level functions for the different fibers types are shown in Figure 4–2, to reiterate how the different fibers in

FIGURE 4–2. Auditory nerve rate/level functions for the three different type I auditory nerve fibers, classified by their spontaneous firing rate (SR).

the auditory nerve code for different stimulus levels. Auditory nerve fibers are characterized based on their spontaneous firing rate (SR), with low (15% of fibers), medium (25% of fibers), and high (60% of fibers) spontaneous firing rates.

Figure 4–2 illustrates that each of the three different fiber types (low-, medium-, and high-SR fibers) increase their firing rate as the stimulus level increases. The threshold of each of the fiber types, the stimulus level that causes a detectable increase in firing rate from spontaneous, is also different. As a result, different fibers will respond by different amounts depending on the level of the stimulus. For example, a sound at 15 dB SPL will only cause the high-SR fibers to fire. On the other hand, a stimulus presented at 50 dB SPL will cause all three fiber types to fire: The high-SR fiber will be in saturation, or firing at its highest possible rate. The low-SR fiber will not yet be in saturation, and will fire at a lower firing rate

than the high-SR fiber. Although all fibers will fire to a 50 dB SPL stimulus, they will not all code an increase in stimulus level. Only the medium and high threshold fibers will have an increase in firing rate if the stimulus level increased from 50 dB SPL. In this way, we see two physiological codes for stimulus level: the firing rate of individual fibers and the pattern of firing rates across the three different fiber types.

INTRODUCTION TO MEASURING LOUDNESS

A primary question in the loudness literature is how loud one sound is compared with another sound. As we have discussed, we cannot measure the loudness of a sound directly, but we do have techniques that allow the assessment of the relative loudness between sounds. Stanley S. Stevens pioneered the study of measuring the subjective quantity of loudness and had great interest in the relationship between intensity and loudness. It is easy to intuit that increasing stimulus intensity will increase loudness, but Stevens was interested in quantifying how loudness varied with intensity. He asked questions such as:

- If sound pressure level changes by 10 dB, how much does loudness change?
- Is a 10 dB difference in sound pressure level associated with the same loudness difference if a stimulus is presented at a low level versus a high level?

At the time Stevens was conducting his research, there were no psychophysical tools available to measure the loudness of sounds. Consider the difficulty he faced: How would you measure sound pressure level if you didn't have a sound level meter, your weight without a scale, or length without a ruler? Not only did Stevens not have any tools to measure loudness, there was no unit for loudness either. Consider again the implications of not having a measurement unit: How would you quantify sound pressure level without the pascal, your weight without pounds, or length without inches? In his impressive body of work, Stevens developed both the measurement tools to quantify loudness as well as a unit that allowed the quantification of loudness.

Measuring loudness has been approached from two different directions: rating the relative loudness of sounds and matching the level of one sound to be equally loud as another sound. Because these approaches have been used to address somewhat different questions in the loudness literature, we discuss the different procedures in the context of their experimental questions. Rating methods have been typically used to measure how loudness changes with intensity, whereas matching has been used to measure how loudness changes with frequency.

LOUDNESS AND INTENSITY

In one of Stevens' many accomplishments, he developed the ***magnitude estimation*** technique, which allowed listeners to estimate the magnitude of sounds by providing numerical values corresponding to the size of their perception as the intensity of the stimulus was varied. When the magnitude estimation technique is applied to measuring loudness, listeners hear a sound and assign a number (or rating) to that sound according to its perceived loudness. Consequently, we sometimes also call these procedures ***rating*** or ***scaling***. When loudness is measured in this way, the resulting function that relates the ratings to stimulus intensity is a ***loudness growth function***. In his early experiments, listeners were often presented with a reference sound, and listeners judged the relative loudness of the test sounds in reference to that one. Recent work often omits the reference sound and listeners assign any numbers they like, as Stevens (1957) demonstrated that a reference sound was not necessary. Perhaps this result should not surprise us, as our daily listening experiences include very soft and very loud sounds, and so we have references already in our perceptual experience.

Stevens' Power Law

Using magnitude estimation, Stevens (1956) and later investigators measured the growth of loudness in healthy human listeners for 1000-Hz pure tones. In this type of experiment, listeners hear two tones: a reference tone (a 40 dB SPL tone) followed by a test tone. In different experimental conditions, test tones are presented at a range of levels. Listeners are told that the reference tone (a 1000-Hz tone presented at 40 dB SPL) should be assigned a rating of 1. Stevens defined this reference sound as one ***sone***, the unit of loudness. They then rate the relative loudness of other tones compared with that reference. For example, a sound twice as loud would be assigned a value of 2 and a sound half as loud would be assigned a value of .5. Using this approach, the numbers resulting from magnitude estimation only have meaning in the context of each other and in the context of the number assigned to the reference. If a listener assigned a value of 2 in a magnitude estimation experiment, we could determine that 2 is double that of 1, but the 2 by itself is meaningless. A sound with a loudness of two sones is twice as loud as a sound with a loudness of one sone, but we do not know the absolute loudness of either of those sounds.

Data adapted from experiments such as this are illustrated in Figure 4–3 as the filled symbols, which shows that the loudness ratings increase as the sound level increases.

For levels above about 30 dB SPL, the function also looks like a straight line, so we might be tempted to conclude that there is a proportional, linear relationship between loudness and sound level in dB SPL. However, notice that the *y*-axis is plotted on a logarithmic scale, and a 10-dB change in dB SPL is associated with a *doubling* of loudness. As a result, Stevens (1956) noted that loudness and intensity (in W/m^2) have a ***power law*** relationship at moderate to high stimulus intensities.

Together, the loudness growth function of Figure 4–3 illustrates a number of striking findings when we evaluate the data obtained between 30 and 90 dB SPL:

- *Increasing sound level increases loudness.* This is exactly what we would expect as consistent with our intuition.

FIGURE 4–3. A typical loudness growth function. Loudness in sones is plotted as a function of stimulus level in dB SPL as the filled symbols. The dotted line represents growth predicted by Stevens' power law. Data are similar to those reported by Hellman and Zwislocki (1961), but who used dB SL.

- *Increasing sound by 10 dB doubles the loudness.* For any dB SPL value above 40, increasing 10 dB doubles the sones. For example, if we increase the decibel level of a sound from 40 to 50 dB SPL, the loudness goes from one sone to two sones, a doubling of loudness. Changing the sound level 50 to 60 dB, the loudness changes from 2 to 4 sones, and so on. Decreasing the sound level by 10 dB also halves the loudness.

- *A power relationship between sound intensity and loudness.* When loudness ratings are plotted on a logarithmic scale against sound pressure level in dB SPL, the data fall on a straight line. This indicates that there is a *power relationship* between the perceived loudness of a stimulus and the intensity.

Whether data are plotted on logarithmic or linear scales is important for making inferences about the relationships between dependent (the measured) and independent (the experimentally manipulated) variables. In the case of loudness growth functions, we could plot either axis on linear scales. The different ways of plotting the data would yield different shapes of the same function.

Today, we refer to the relationship between loudness and stimulus intensity as **Stevens' power law**, which follows the following equation:

$$L \propto I^{0.3}, \qquad \text{Eq. 4-1}$$

where L is the perceived loudness and I is the physical intensity. Note that α is a symbol indicating proportionality. Equation 4-1 indicates that a 10 dB change in sound level produces a doubling of loudness.

The power relationship between loudness and intensity predicts a straight line on log-log axes (note that dB SPL is calculated by taking the log of an intensity, so in a sense, the x-axis is logarithmically spaced), we can take the logarithm of both sides of the equation:

$$\log (L) \propto \log (I^{0.3})$$

using the law of logarithms: $\log(x^y) = y*\log(x)$, then

$$\log(L) \propto 0.3*\log(I).$$

This equation has a similar format to a straight line: y=mx, where m is the slope (0.3). Thus, if we plot this relationship on log-log axes, we will see a straight line.

Referring back from Figure 4–3, we also must consider the change in the loudness growth function that occurs at low levels. We observe here that the loudness growth function has a steeper slope at low sound levels compared with the slope at the moderate levels. The dotted line on Figure 4–3 shows the predictions for Stevens' power law, and we observe that for low levels, loudness growth is more rapid than growth at the higher stimulus levels and does not follow Stevens' power law. It is now well established that the growth of loudness is more rapid at low levels than at moderate ones (Hellman & Zwislocki, 1961).

Relationship to Physiological Measures

Notably, the pattern of loudness growth follows a similar pattern to that observed in basilar membrane input-output functions of healthy mammalian cochlea. The BM I-O functions presented in Figure 4–1 illustrate a rapid growth of vibration amplitude at levels below 30 to 40 dB SPL and a slower growth of vibration at moderate to high levels. Such similarity between these two measurements suggests that the magnitude of basilar membrane vibration contributes strongly to the perception of loudness and that there is a strong correlation between the amount of basilar membrane vibration and loudness for pure tones. Thus, sounds that yield more vibration on the basilar membrane should be louder than sounds that yield less vibration.

However, we must also consider that loudness is a perception that is not only a consequence of basilar membrane vibration. The central auditory system has a clear role in the representation of loudness and includes mechanisms that transform basilar membrane vibration into perception. The next step in the pathway, of course, is that of the auditory nerve. Unlike the pattern observed for vibration measured at a single place on the basilar membrane, however, there is no obvious correlate contained within a single auditory nerve fiber that can immediately explain loudness growth.

One of the issues here is the very large **dynamic range of hearing**, which encompasses sound levels ranging from those near threshold (e.g., 0–10 dB SPL) to the level at which damage or uncomfortably loud sounds are experienced (e.g., 100–120 dB SPL). A single locus on the basilar membrane is able to code this large range, as we observed in Figure 4–1. The auditory nerve also codes for stimulus intensity: Figure 4–2 illustrates that increasing stimulus level increases the firing rate of auditory neurons. However, each individual fiber cannot, by itself, provide sufficient information to code the entire dynamic range of the auditory system. If we look more closely at the rate-level functions shown in

Figure 4–2, the following observations indicate why a single fiber cannot provide the code for all stimulus levels represented by the auditory system:

- *Dynamic ranges of fibers are less than 60 dB.* None of the auditory nerve fibers that are depicted have a dynamic range that approaches 100 dB. In fact, Palmer and Evans (1979) showed that only about 10% of fibers have a dynamic range greater than 60 dB.

- *Most auditory nerve fibers are saturated at high stimulus levels.* That is, when the stimulus level is high, increases in stimulus level do not increase the firing rate. A fiber that is in saturation will not be able to indicate when the stimulus level has changed. Because most auditory nerve fibers (60%) are low-threshold fibers and another 25% are mid-threshold fibers, most are in saturation at moderate and high levels.

- *Different fibers are needed to code for low and high stimulus levels.* The high-SR fibers code for low levels and the mid- and low-SR fibers represent the higher stimulus levels. All fiber types are necessary to represent the level of sound across 0 to 100 dB SPL.

Taken together the code for loudness must be more sophisticated than a simple increase in firing rate within a single fiber, and the responses to multiple fibers must be involved in the coding of the dynamic range of the auditory system. Low stimulus levels can only be coded by low-threshold fibers, and except for the very lowest stimulus levels, multiple fibers will fire in response to even a low-level stimulus. Higher stimulus levels will lead to the involvement of multiple fibers, including the high-threshold fibers. Psychophysical modeling also implicates the involvement of many fibers to code the full dynamic range of hearing (Viemester, 1988).

An implication of this work, then, is that damage to any of the various types of auditory nerve fibers should alter the perception of loudness. Although we currently have no mechanism to assess the health of various fiber types, damage to the low-threshold fibers will impact threshold measurements and loudness near threshold. Abnormal loudness perception of high-level sounds might implicate loss or damage to high- and mid-threshold fibers.

Other Measurement Techniques

Magnitude estimation is known to have a number of problems, particularly related to the poor reliability of the measurements and large variability in results across listeners (Algom & Marks, 1984). Many experimenters have attempted to circumvent such issues by using a variety of different procedures. Loudness growth functions can also be measured using a *magnitude production* technique. In contrast to magnitude estimation, where the listener rates the loudness of a sound, the listener adjusts the level of a sound to a certain loudness. For example, one might adjust the level of a test sound so that it is twice as loud as a reference sound. Typically, the method of adjustment is used for this approach, as the listener has control over the test stimulus. Results tend to be similar to those collected using magnitude estimation.

Today, magnitude estimation is more likely to be conducted using *cross-modality scaling*, in which a listener rates the loudness of a stimulus by adjusting the length of string or a slider on a computer monitor. The advantage of this procedure is that length is represented using a true ratio scale (for example, 2 inches is double the length of 1 inch), whereas rating (assigning a number) does not necessarily result in a ratio scale even if listeners are instructed to use one (e.g., a loudness rating of 2 is twice as loud as a rating of 1). However,

these methods remain fairly time consuming, and these procedures do not eliminate all of the criticisms of magnitude estimation techniques.

In cases where more rapid estimates are needed (such as clinical applications), another alternative is *categorical loudness scaling*, in which there is no explicit reference (e.g., Allen, Hall, & Jeng, 1990; Garner, 1953). These procedures are commonly used to measure the level at which sound is uncomfortably loud (the uncomfortable loudness level) or the level at which sound is most comfortable. In this procedure listeners are given a set of terms ranging from "very soft" to "painfully loud," and they use those terms to categorize the loudness of the sounds they hear. This procedure has been adapted for clinical use due to its ease and speed of administration, and an example of the categories commonly used in clinical applications is shown in Figure 4–4 (Hawkins, Walden, Montgomery, & Prosek, 1987). Here, the different categories are also illustrated with different sized boxes to reinforce the differences between the categories for patients. In these procedures, a clinical version of this procedure would begin testing at a low stimulus level and the stimulus level would be increased until the listener rates the sound as comfortable or uncomfortably loud, depending on the application.

LOUDNESS AND FREQUENCY

Equal-Loudness Contours

Other methods are also commonly used to assess loudness, with a *matching*, or *loudness balancing*, procedure being one of the easiest to implement and interpret. In this procedure, rather than measure the relative loudness of a sound using a rating procedure, the level of a sound is adjusted so that its loudness matches that of a reference sound.

FIGURE 4–4. Categories used in categorical loudness scaling procedures. These are the categories used by Hawkins et al. (1987), and are now commonly illustrated with changes to the box and font sizes.

In a common implementation of the *loudness balancing procedure*, we measure the level of a sound of interest (the test stimulus here) that matches the level of a 1000-Hz stimulus (the reference stimulus). For these studies, a 1000-Hz tone is always the reference sound, and it is presented at some fixed stimulus level (e.g., 40 dB SPL). The two sounds (the 1000-Hz reference and the test stimulus) are always presented in succession (never simultaneously) and sometimes to opposite

ears if the listener has normal hearing. In a typical experiment, the method of adjustment is used where the listener adjusts the level of the test sound so that its loudness is equal to that of the reference sound. The level of the 1000-Hz tone in dB SPL is the *loudness level* of the test sound, measured in *phons*. If the reference sound is a 40-dB SPL 1000-Hz tone, the test sound would have a loudness level of 40 phons. However, if the reference were 70 dB SPL, the test sound would have a loudness level of 70 phons.

If tones are used as the test stimuli, this procedure allows measurement of *equal-loudness contours*, functions that illustrate the sound level as a function of frequency associated with equal loudness, and first measured by Fletcher and Munson (1933). In their experiment, Fletcher and Munson fixed the level of a 1000-Hz reference tone and, using loudness balancing, asked listeners to adjust the level of a test tone until it was perceived as being equally loud to the reference tone. They repeated this measurement for multiple frequencies and reference levels. For a given reference level, then, they achieved a single equal-loudness contour. Data adapted from Fletcher and Munson are illustrated in Figure 4–5.

Each function in Figure 4–5 represents a set of sounds that have the same loudness level. For example, sounds on the 40-phon curve were equally loud and had a loudness level of 40 phons. Note in particular that the equal-loudness contours were not flat and depended on frequency. For example, a 3000-Hz tone presented at 35 dB SPL had the same loudness level as a 10,000-Hz tone presented at 48 dB SPL. From Fletcher and Munson's data, we can conclude that the frequency of a sound impacts its loudness, with mid-frequency sounds being perceived as louder when presented at the same dB SPL level as low- and high-frequency sounds. This simple illustration demonstrates that sound pressure level (or intensity) and loudness are not the

FIGURE 4–5. Equal-loudness contours. Each contour represents a series of stimuli having the same loudness in phons, with the bottom-most curve labeled absolute threshold as $\theta_{in\ quiet}$. Adapted from Fletcher and Munson (1933).

same. Taking any curve for reference, we can make a number of inferences:

- *Strong frequency effects are present.* Sounds in the mid frequencies (about 3000 to 6000 Hz) can be presented at lower sound pressure levels than sounds at other frequencies to be equally loud. Generally speaking, then, we consider tones at these frequencies to be louder than tones at many other frequencies.
- *Patterns follow middle and outer ear amplification.* Equal-loudness contours follow similar patterns to the amplification provided by the outer and middle ears. There are some subtle differences in the shape of the equal-loudness contours as the stimulus level is increased, particularly at low frequencies. However, generally speaking, the patterns are similar across the different levels.

Over the years, numerous experiments have revised the equal-loudness contours.

Modern measurements are now included in the international standard (ISO 226-2003), which report equal-loudness contours very similar to Fletcher and Munson's data illustrated in Figure 4–5. Even today, these contours are commonly called "Fletcher-Munson" curves.

There are many practical implications for equal-loudness contours. First, the data above suggest that the loudness of sounds across frequency is predominantly determined by the characteristics of the outer and middle ear. Disorders in these structures will alter the relationship between the loudness of sounds across frequency. Second, equal-loudness contours have many practical implications and are used in the design of alarms and sirens and in numerous audio production applications. Further, the A-weighted decibel (dB A) uses the 40-phon loudness contour to calculate a decibel metric that is more similar to the sound level as represented by the human ear.

Interestingly, dB A provides a better assessment of a specific sound's potential for hearing loss than dB SPL, and is therefore often used to describe the sound level in industrial environments and for noise dosing.

Bandwidth Effects: Spectral Loudness Summation

The intensity and frequency of sound are not the only factors that determine the loudness—the bandwidth is also a factor. The influence of bandwidth on loudness is referred to as *spectral loudness summation*. It is important to also understand the effects of changing stimulus bandwidth on the loudness of sounds, particularly because we listen to a variety of different sounds with different bandwidths on a regular basis and we use both narrow-band and broadband sounds in audiometric testing. Zwicker, Flottorp, and Stevens (1957) first demonstrated that loudness depends on bandwidth, using the loudness balancing technique. Their listeners adjusted the level of a comparison noise (centered at 1420 Hz with a 2300-Hz bandwidth) so that it matched the level of a test noise centered at 1420 Hz, but had a variable bandwidth. A subset of their data is presented in Figure 4–6, which shows data collected at four levels. Note that Zwicker et al. had listeners adjust the level of the *comparison* stimulus, rather than the test stimulus. As a result, within single curve, louder sounds are plotted <u>higher</u> on the *y*-axis in Figure 4–6.

Figure 4–6 illustrates the following effects:

- *Loudness increased with increasing bandwidth.* For the smallest bandwidths, the loudness level of the test stimuli was relatively

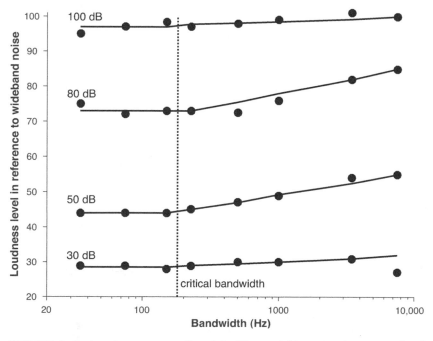

FIGURE 4–6. Loudness summation data. The matching sound pressure level in dB SPL of a comparison noise (2300-Hz wide centered at 1420 Hz) is plotted a function of the bandwidth of a test noise centered at 1420 Hz. Data from four different test stimulus levels (30, 50, 80, and 100 dB SPL) are indicated. Adapted from Zwicker et al. (1957).

constant with increasing bandwidth. However, at a certain bandwidth (corresponding to a value very similar to but somewhat greater than the critical band), the loudness level of the test stimuli began to increase as the bandwidth increased. It is worth pointing out that the dB SPL of the test stimuli remained constant, so the increase in loudness was not associated with an increase in the power present in the stimuli. The increase in loudness must be created by the auditory system.

- *Loudness changes with bandwidth are greatest at moderate stimulus levels.* The rate of change of loudness with bandwidth was not constant across levels. It was most rapid for the moderate levels and less rapid at high and low levels.

The take-home message, then, is that wide bandwidth stimuli are louder than narrow bandwidth stimuli <u>when presented at the same dB SPL level</u>. These results again highlight that loudness and sound pressure level are not the same. Further, when assessing the loudness of sounds, we must consider more than the power or dB SPL of the stimulus. These issues are taken into consideration in loudness models, which allow computation of a sound's loudness of sounds, using the spectral characteristics and dB levels.

CALCULATING LOUDNESS

There are many practical situations where it would be helpful to estimate the loudness of sounds. For example, using loudness models has impacted the design of alarms and acoustic spaces. Because loudness and sound level are not the same, using decibel calculations is not sufficient to determine the loudness of a particular sound source.

Models of loudness have been demonstrated to provide reasonable ballpark esti-

mates of the loudness of steady sounds. The work of Brian Moore (in Moore, Glasberg, & Baer, 1997 and Glasberg & Moore, 2006) now forms the basis of a standard for calculating the loudness of steady sounds, published by the Acoustical Society of America (ANSI 3.4-2007). These models are based on the premise that the loudness of a sound is based on the total neural activity evoked by the sound: Greater neural activity leads to a louder sound. Because we have no direct way to measure or quantify total neural activity in the human auditory system, a model of neural activity forms the basis of the loudness estimate. These models are psychophysical in nature and are based on psychophysical, not physiological, data. Figure 4–7 illustrates the steps involved to calculate the loudness of sounds.

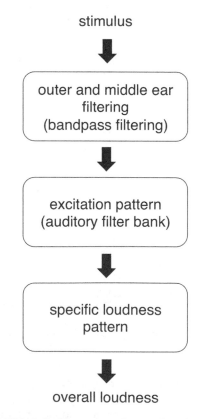

FIGURE 4–7. Flow chart illustrating the steps involved in models used to calculate loudness.

The steps of the loudness model are as follows:

1. *Stimulus filtering by outer and middle ear transfer functions.* The consequence of this step is amplification of the mid frequencies.
2. *Filtered stimulus transformed into an excitation pattern.* Recall that an excitation pattern is calculated by passing a stimulus through a bank of auditory filters consisting of different center frequencies. The power at the output of each auditory filter is calculated.
3. *Excitation pattern transformed into a specific loudness pattern.* This process essentially converts the excitation pattern into a loudness density pattern. The decibel level in each filter band is converted into a specific loudness, which has the units of sones per equivalent rectangular bandwidth (ERB, a measure of auditory filter bandwidth). Essentially, the compressive nonlinearity of the ear and the width of the auditory filter are taken into consideration to establish the specific loudness for each auditory filter.
4. *Loudness is calculated from the area under the specific loudness pattern.* This calculation gives the total loudness of a sound.

To illustrate the process of the loudness model, two example stimuli are shown as they are passed through the different steps of the model in Figure 4–8. Each of these example stimuli has a similar loudness, in order to show how the loudness model might predict the loudness of two sounds that are very different in overall level and bandwidth. The first sound is a 57 dB SPL, 1000-Hz tone, and the second is a band-limited noise with a total power of about 43 dB SPL. These two sounds are similar in their loudness and loudness levels, which are 3.4 sones and 56.8 phons, respectively, as determined by the loudness model.

The top panel of Figure 4–8 illustrates the acoustic representation of these sounds in the form of the spectrum. The middle panel shows the excitation patterns of these two sounds, which is a model of the internal representation of these two stimuli. Finally, the bottom panel illustrates the specific loudness pattern. The pure tone has a higher dB SPL level, excitation, and maximum specific loudness than the noise. However, the noise has a wider bandwidth and is therefore subject to spectral loudness summation. The area under the two specific loudness pattern curves is the same for the tone and the noise, which is why the two stimuli have the same loudness.

The loudness model is based on many decades of psychophysical data, and it predicts the loudness of steady-state sounds rather well. It is also clear from the loudness model that sounds can be loud because of multiple reasons: Sounds may be loud because of high presentation levels or because of a wide bandwidth. As the field progresses, we may be able to use loudness models to estimate how loud sounds might be for a listener with sensorineural hearing loss or for sounds that fluctuate. The applications are numerous: We could use such models to select the best ring tone that would allow you to hear an emergency phone call or to program a hearing aid for attending a symphony versus a lecture.

REACTION TIME AS A MEASURE OF LOUDNESS

Reaction time is a correlate of loudness that has garnered favor in the past few years, and reaction time has the potential to provide a less subjective correlate of loudness than magnitude estimation. If reaction time, the time it takes to respond to a stimulus, varies in a predictable way with loudness, then reaction time could be used as a fast and possibly more reliable estimate of the loudness of sounds. It

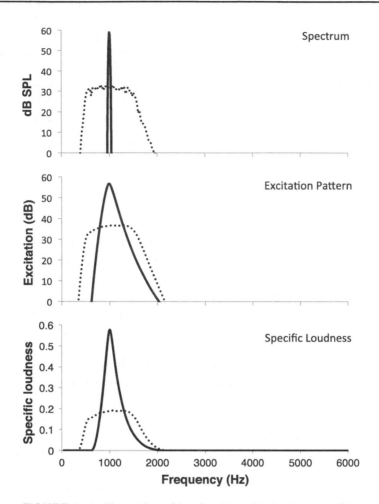

FIGURE 4–8. Illustration of loudness model calculations. Two stimuli (a pure tone and band of noise) that have the same loudness are passed through the model. Each panel represents the output at a different stage of the loudness model.

has strong potential application for animal studies, as animals cannot provide loudness estimates, but animal studies are critical to understanding the physiological mechanisms that underlie loudness perception.

In a detection experiment, the reaction time is defined as the amount of time required for a listener to detect a stimulus (e.g., by pressing a button), and it is generally measured from stimulus onset. Although reaction time is not commonly considered a psychoacoustic measure, reaction time measurements have become increasingly valuable for assessing components of auditory processing. Notably, reaction time experiments allow measurements for detection of sounds across a large range of stimulus levels. Psychoacoustic detection experiments do not allow this, as the relevant measures for detection are either absolute threshold or percent detection. A typical psychometric function only covers a range of about 10 to 15 dB. Reaction times, on the other hand, can be measured to sounds presented at levels across the full dynamic range of hearing.

In the simplest reaction time experiment, a listener responds to a stimulus as accurately and as quickly as possible. Chocholle (1940) was one of the first to demonstrate that the reaction time to a stimulus decreases (gets faster) as the sound pressure level increases, as shown in Figure 4–9. Chocholle also demonstrated that equal-loudness contours obtained using reaction times closely resemble those measured using the loudness balancing technique adopted by Fletcher and Munson (1933). Many years later, Humes and Ahlstrom (1984) showed that loudness growth measured using magnitude estimation was correlated with loudness growth measured using reaction time. Recent measurements show that the correlation between reaction time and loudness only holds for moderate to high stimulus levels, but not so for low stimulus levels (Schlittenlacher, Ellermeier, & Avci, 2017). Wagner, Florentine, Buus, and McCormack (2004) further demonstrated that spectral loudness summation measured using reaction times also follows patterns similar to those observed using loudness balancing. Taken together, there is converging evidence that reaction time provides an indirect measure of loudness, at least for moderate to high stimulus levels.

Because loudness can be difficult to measure, using alternative methods such as reaction time to characterize loudness has value for research and clinical purposes. Certain populations, like animals or people with significant language disabilities, cannot always provide loudness judgments like those described in this chapter. Consequently, using reaction time as a correlate of loudness has been gaining traction in animal models and has proven valuable in establishing animal models for auditory disorders (e.g., Lauer & Dooling, 2007). Reaction time measures are beginning to become more widespread in human testing as well. For example, recent studies have applied reaction time techniques in the development of models of *hyperacusis*, an increased sensitivity to sounds. Reaction times would be expected to be faster in the presence of hyperacusis (Hébert, Fournier, & Noreña, 2013), and therefore reaction time may provide a fast and reliable way to measure loudness in large groups of people.

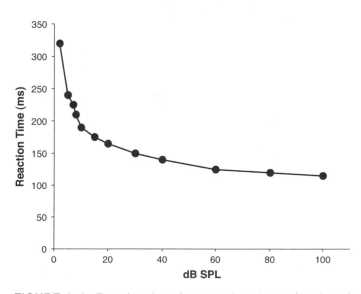

FIGURE 4–9. Reaction time data are plotted as a function of stimulus level in dB SPL. Adapted from Chocholle (1940).

INTENSITY DISCRIMINATION

Due to many of the problems with both rating and matching studies, other investigators have approached the study of the auditory representation of intensity by using discrimination experiments. In these cases, the researchers measure the *just noticeable difference* (JND) in intensity. Recall that the JND is the smallest difference that is discriminable by the ear, and is also referred to as the *difference limen*. These experiments fall in a long line of psychoacoustic studies that evaluate the capabilities of the ear. In these experiments, the primary question is, "What is the smallest intensity change that the ear can detect?" These experiments also ask whether the JND is a constant across intensities or whether it varies.

Weber's Law

A common method to measure the JND for intensity is to conduct an *intensity discrimination* experiment in which a listener hears two sounds, and one of the stimuli (the reference) has a specific intensity (I) and the other (the test stimulus) has a higher intensity (I+ ΔI), where ΔI is the change in intensity between the reference and the test stimulus. An example of an experimental trial for an intensity discrimination experiment is illustrated in Figure 4–10. Although the intensity of the stimulus is varied, the listener's task is perceptual, and so selects the stimulus that is perceived as being louder. The experimenter

uses standard psychophysical techniques (such as 2I–2AFC and an adaptive staircase procedure) to measure the JND in terms of ΔI. When only the intensity of stimulus is varied, we can also call this experiment *increment detection*.

It can be difficult to generate an intuition for this type of experiment, so rather than considering intensity discrimination of sound for the time being, let's consider a weightlifting experiment. A weight lifter is given a weight and is asked to determine the next size weight needed to determine that one of the weights is bigger than the other. The weightlifter experiments with numerous weights and determines that he can tell the difference between a 10- and an 11-lb weight. Next, that same weight lifter is given a 50-lb weight and determines the size of the weight that is just noticeably heavier. Again, he experiments and determines that he can tell the difference between a 50- and a 55-lb weight. Finally, he does this at 100 lbs and discovers that he can differentiate between 100 and 110 lbs.

Note that there is a trend here: As the size of the weight increases, the amount needed to differentiate between weights increases. However, the increase occurs in a systematic way —for each weight lifted, the just noticeable weight difference is a change of 10% (a proportion of 0.1) in the weight. In this case, the pattern is 10 versus 11, 50 versus 55, and 100 versus 110 lbs, or a 10% difference in weight across the various baseline weights. If the JND is defined as the just noticeable difference in weight, the JND equals 1, 5, and 10 lbs for the

FIGURE 4–10. Illustration of an experimental trial in an intensity-discrimination experiment.

various weights. However, if we describe the JND as a percentage, the JND equals 10%, 10%, and 10% for the various weights. This pattern is now commonly known as **Weber's law**, which states that the just noticeable change in a stimulus is a constant ratio (or percentage) of the original stimulus. Weber's law is characterized by the following equation:

$$\Delta S/S = k,$$

where ΔS is the just detectable change, S is the size of the original stimulus, and k is a constant. This quantity, $\Delta S/S$, is commonly called the **Weber fraction**.

Ernst Heinrich Weber (pronounced Vay-burr) conducted the experiments needed to formulate the law. However, his student Gustav Fechner formulated the law mathematically and named it after his mentor.

Weber's Law Applied to Intensity Discrimination

Now that the weightlifting analogy provides an intuition of Weber's law, we can apply the same concept to an intensity discrimination experiment. Note that in these experiments, the size of the stimulus is characterized by the intensity (I) of the sound in W/m^2, not the decibel value of the sound, as this is important for understanding and interpreting Weber's law. Here, the JND is defined as ΔI, or the difference in intensity between two sounds. Applied to intensity discrimination, then, the Weber fraction is $\Delta I/I$.

Intensity discrimination has been measured as a function of stimulus intensity for both tonal and noise stimuli, with surprising results. However, in order to fully understand and appreciate the results, we must consider the different ways of representing performance. A number of metrics are commonly used in the research literature, and a brief overview of them is provided here. Understandably, the use of multiple acoustic descriptors can be frustrating to a student, but it is often unclear to a researcher which metric is the best to describe auditory perception, as there is not always a standard unit to use. Predictions of Weber's law are illustrated in Figure 4–11.

- *JND reported as ΔI.* We can report the JND as ΔI and plot that JND as a function of intensity, I. If we plot data in this way, the JND would increase as the stimulus level increases and the line relating ΔI

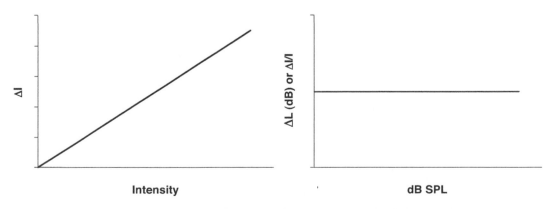

FIGURE 4–11. Predictions of Weber's law using different acoustic quantities. The left panel illustrates ΔI plotted as a function of I. The right panel illustrates ΔL or $\Delta I/I$ plotted as a function of dB SPL.

to I would be an <u>increasing line</u>. The left panel of Figure 4–11 illustrates this prediction.

- *JND reported as the Weber fraction.* We can also report the JND in terms of the Weber fraction, $\Delta I/I$, and plot the Weber fraction as a function of intensity or dB SPL. Because Weber's law predicts that the Weber fraction is a constant, the resulting plot would be a <u>straight, horizontal line</u> regardless of whether the *x*-axis was plotted using intensity units or dB SPL, as shown in the right panel of Figure 4–11.

- *JND reported as a decibel difference.* It can also be convenient to plot the JND as a dB transformation of the Weber fraction, such as $10\log(\Delta I/I)$ or $10\log[(\Delta I/I)+1]$. Conveniently, the latter transformation is the decibel difference between two sounds, often called ΔL in dB. For these transformations, Weber's law again predicts the plot would still be a <u>straight, horizontal line</u> regardless of the units for the *x*-axis (e.g., they could be intensity units, I, or dB SPL). This pre-

diction is shown in the right panel of Figure 4–11 and occurs because the Weber fraction is a constant.

To test whether Weber's law holds for auditory intensity discrimination, Miller (1947) measured intensity discrimination for a noise stimulus across a large range of stimulus levels. Data adapted from his report are shown in Figure 4–12 as the filled, black symbols. Figure 4–12 plots the JND in terms of the decibel difference (ΔL in dB) as a function of the intensity of the noise stimulus in dB sensation level (SL). Note that the other data plotted on this figure are discussed next.

Miller's data illustrate the following:

- *Weber's law held for noise at moderate-to-high levels.* That is, the function relating ΔL to dB SL was a straight line, as long as sound levels were above about 20 dB SL. We observe no change in the Weber fraction as the stimulus level increases. We can interpret these data to indicate that the JND in

FIGURE 4–12. Intensity discrimination data for white noise stimuli and pure tones. ΔL in dB is plotted as a function of the dB SL of the stimuli. Noise data are adapted from Miller (1947). Tone data are adapted from Jesteadt et al. (1977).

intensity is a **proportion of the intensity** of the stimulus.

- *Weber's law did not hold at low stimulus levels.* Here, the Weber fraction decreased with increasing level, suggesting that intensity discrimination became proportionally easier with increasing level. Miller's listeners were particularly poor at intensity discrimination for the very low level sounds.

Humans are exceptional at their ability to tell whether two sounds are louder than one another—note that these thresholds are less than ½ of a decibel, particularly in light of the dynamic range of the auditory system being over 100 dB!

Twenty years before Miller made his measurements for noise, Riesz (1928) measured whether Weber's law holds for tones. However, his experiment did not use a standard intensity discrimination paradigm and instead relied on modulation detection. Yet, Reisz's experiment suggested that Weber's law may not hold for tonal stimuli and that intensity discrimination continues to improve proportionally as stimulus level increases, even for moderate and high levels. Jesteadt, Wier, and Green (1977) conducted a comprehensive follow-up study that adopted a standard intensity discrimination procedure. They measured the Weber fraction for tones at multiple stimulus frequencies and stimulus levels. Data obtained at 400 and 2000 Hz are plotted along with Miller's in Figure 4–12 as the square symbols.

Jesteadt et al.'s data look rather different from those of Miller, as the functions for pure tones are not horizontal lines, but rather they have negative slopes. Jesteadt et al. actually measured seven different tone frequencies, with the same results for all frequencies. From their data, along with those of Reisz, we conclude that:

- *Weber's law did not hold for tones.* In fact, the JND, when expressed as a proportion

of the intensity of the stimulus, decreased with increasing intensity across the audible range. This phenomenon is called the ***near miss*** to Weber's law. Note that we observe this result only for tones and not noise at levels greater than 20 dB SL.

- *The Weber fraction was not dependent on frequency.* The overall sensitivity for intensity discrimination did not vary with frequency, and the slope of the near miss to Weber's law was constant across the frequencies up to about 10 kHz.

Explanations for the Near Miss

The near miss to Weber's law is a consequence of the ability of the central auditory system to take advantage of multiple pieces of information across frequency, and it highlights that basilar membrane vibration and auditory nerve firing rate together do not provide enough information to understand the perception of loudness. The central auditory system has a clear role.

To better understand why the near miss happens, consider the following example. For a pure tone at 2000 Hz presented at 60 dB SL, the JND for intensity discrimination (ΔL) is approximately 0.9 dB (see Figure 4–12). The JND for this pure tone is not nearly as small as the JND for noise, suggesting that when noise is presented, the auditory system uses multiple frequency regions to discriminate between sounds with different intensities. To illustrate how the ear might be able to improve its detection with increasing stimulus level, we look to the excitation pattern, which provides a psychoacoustical representation of the spectral information available to the ear.

Figure 4–13 illustrates two excitation patterns, one calculated from a 60-dB SPL tone and another for a 64-dB SPL tone at 1000 Hz. Figure 4–13 illustrates that the 64-dB excitation pattern has a higher maximum excitation

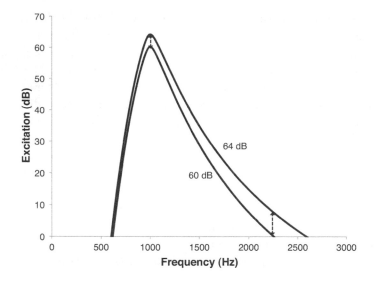

FIGURE 4–13. Excitation patterns for two tones presented at 60 and 64 dB SPL are shown. The difference between the excitation patterns is larger for the high-frequency side of the excitation pattern when compared with the peak, illustrated by the two arrows on the figure.

and extends across more frequencies than the 60-dB excitation pattern. At 1000 Hz, the difference between the two excitation patterns is about 4 dB. However, as the auditory filter center frequency increases, the difference between the two excitation patterns also increases. The excitation pattern associated with the higher-level stimulus has a greater spread of excitation, and due to upward spread of excitation, the spread of excitation is most pronounced on the high frequency side. As an illustration, the high frequency edge of the excitation pattern corresponding to 2250 Hz represents an excitation difference of about 8 dB.

Using these patterns, we can envision how the ear may be able to use information across frequency in order to determine which of the two tones is more intense than the other. The auditory filters higher in frequency contain much more information about the intensity difference than the one centered at the signal frequency. The auditory filters greater than 2250 Hz, however, do not have any representation of the 60-dB stimulus, but there is a small amount of power passed through the auditory filters in the 64-dB stimulus. These auditory filters are considered "off-frequency" and provide a very robust representation of the dB difference between two sounds. As more and more auditory filters become involved in representing the stimulus, the ear effectively has more and more information with which to determine whether one sound is more intense than another.

Note that because the excitation pattern of a pure tone is asymmetric and spreads to higher-frequency regions more than low-frequency regions, the high-frequency edge has been hypothesized to be the most important. This idea has been tested in a number of different experiments, all of which used experimental manipulations designed to block the high-frequency spread of excitation. The logic is that if the high-frequency edge provides additional information cueing an intensity change, blocking this information should restore Weber's law.

Schroder, Viemeister, and Nelson (1994) measured intensity discrimination in which they blocked the high-frequency spread of excitation using noise bands. They also tested Weber's law using listeners with steeply sloping hearing losses, losses which increase rapidly as frequency increases. Both experimental manipulations restored Weber's law: that is, the Weber fraction did not improve with increasing stimulus level in either experiment. Florentine, Buus, and Mason (1987) measured intensity discrimination for the extended high frequencies, where spread of excitation could not occur due to basilar membrane mechanics. Their results at the very high frequencies also demonstrated support for Weber's law. Taken together, there is strong support for the notion that the near miss results from the ear's ability to use multiple frequency regions across the excitation pattern to code for intensity.

EFFECTS OF SENSORINEURAL HEARING LOSS ON LOUDNESS

Loudness Recruitment

Sensorineural hearing loss (SNHL) has a robust and profound effect on loudness, with a primary effect being abnormally rapid growth of loudness. Fowler (1928) was the first to report that listeners with SNHL experienced a similar range of loudness (from very soft to uncomfortably loud) but over a smaller range of decibel levels due to reduced audibility. He dubbed this phenomenon *loudness recruitment*. Numerous studies have followed Fowler's initial observations, and an illustration of loudness growth in listeners with SNHL is illustrated in Figure 4–14, which shows a sample loudness growth function for a listener with 40 dB hearing loss plotted along with a loudness growth for a listener with normal hearing. Loudness growth functions like this one are typically measured using pure tones

FIGURE 4–14. Loudness growth functions a normal-hearing listener (*filled circles*) and for a listener with a 40-dB HL sensorineural hearing loss (*unfilled circles*) are shown. The dynamic ranges of hearing of the two listeners are labeled.

as stimuli. The dynamic range of each listener (from threshold to about 100 dB HL) is also illustrated on the figure.

Figure 4–14 shows some clear differences between the loudness growth functions in these two listeners, summarized as follows:

- *Rapid growth of loudness in SNHL compared with normal hearing.* The slopes of the two functions are strikingly different. Loudness for listeners with sensorineural hearing loss grows much more quickly than loudness for listeners with normal hearing.
- *Similar loudness at very high stimulus levels.* Regardless of the presence of hearing loss, the loudness at high levels is similar for the two groups of listeners. The functions tend to converge at levels around 80 to 90 dB HL. The consequence of this is that the level at which sound becomes uncomfortable (the **loudness discomfort level** or the **uncomfortable loudness level**) is similar for listeners with normal hearing and those with sensorineural hearing loss.

The slope of the loudness growth functions (loudness in sones vs. dB SPL), then, is steeper for the listeners with SNHL than for listeners with normal hearing. Hellman and Meiselman (1993) found that the slopes of loudness functions increased with the degree of sensorineural hearing loss. For losses of 60 dB of greater, slopes were at least twice that in normal hearing listeners, but more typically were four or five times greater. They also noted considerable variability in loudness growth across listeners, suggesting that we cannot exactly predict loudness growth from degree of hearing loss. However, all listeners with hearing loss experienced some degree of loudness recruitment. Taken together, there is clear experimental evidence for loudness recruitment in listeners SNHL, although wide variability exists across listeners.

Although we commonly accept that listeners with SNHL experience loudness recruitment, recent experiments have questioned this finding. A somewhat controversial idea is related to the loudness of sounds at and near threshold for listeners with SNHL. These measurements can be difficult to make, but work by Buus and Florentine (2002) suggests that the loudness of sounds at and near threshold may be higher for listeners with SNHL than for those with normal hearing. Essentially, listeners with SNHL appear to perceive sounds near their threshold as being louder than listeners with normal-hearing. Buus and Florentine have named this particular phenomenon **softness imperception**. This phenomenon occurs in conjunction with the abnormally rapid growth of loudness observed for levels between 10 dB SL and about 80 dB SPL.

A complementary way to think about loudness recruitment is to consider the dynamic range of the impaired and the healthy auditory systems. The dynamic ranges, illustrated in Figure 4–14, are rather different between a listener with SNHL and one with normal hearing, with the dynamic range being much smaller for the listener with SNHL. Data from the normal-hearing listener illustrates a threshold of 5 dB HL and a **loudness discomfort level** (LDL, defined as the level of sound in dB at which sound becomes uncomfortably loud) of around 100 dB HL. Although magnitude estimation techniques do not allow measurement of the LDL, we assume here that it occurs at a loudness of about 100 to 200 sones. With this assumption, this listener's dynamic range is 95 dB. On the other hand, the listener with SNHL has a threshold of 40 dB HL and an LDL of 100 dB HL. This listener's dynamic range is then 60 dB. Yet, there is a similar range of loudness encompassed across that same range—from about 0.02 sones to about 100 sones.

It is important to recognize that the dB level associated with loudness discomfort does not change with SNHL. Listeners with mild to moderately severe hearing losses generally have LDLs very similar to listeners with normal hearing. Although LDLs can be highly variable across listeners (even with normal hearing), we do not consider listeners with sensorineural hearing loss to be more sensitive to high-level sounds. Thus, the full range of loudness—from very soft to very loud—is squeezed into a dynamic range much smaller than that of normal-hearing listeners. The consequence, then, is a steeper slope for the function relating loudness to stimulus level in dB.

> Diagnostic audiology has capitalized on the different growth of loudness measured in listeners with normal hearing and those with SNHL to assess retrocochlear disorders. It is expected that listeners with SNHL have recruitment if their loss is cochlear in origin. However, if a listener with SNHL does not present with recruitment, the loss may be caused by retrocochlear pathology, like an auditory nerve tumor. Such tests are now replaced by physiological tools.

Loudness growth functions have shapes very similar to BM I-O functions measured in animals with healthy cochlea, but we also observe a correlation in the shape of damaged input-output functions and the loudness growth measured in listeners with SNHL. Note the strong similarity between the loudness growth data of Figure 4–14 and the data

on BM vibration in an animal with impaired hearing (e.g., Figure 4–1) due to loss of outer hair cells. Loss of outer hair cells impacts the shape and slope of the basilar membrane I-O function in a way very similar to loudness growth functions measured in listeners with SNHL. This correlation and the presence of loudness recruitment in listeners with mild and moderate hearing losses, who presumably have predominantly outer hair cell loss, suggest that loss of outer hair cells contributes to loudness recruitment.

On the other hand, loss of inner hair cells, as they do not interact with basilar membrane vibration, has no effect on the shape of the BM I-O function. Psychophysically, however, loss of inner hair cells will elevate the threshold and may also impact the perception of loudness because of a reduced input to the auditory nerve. While there is no current way to assess the relative contribution of inner and outer hair cells to a specific listener's hearing loss, severe and profound hearing losses likely involve inner hair cell loss in addition to outer hair cell loss. For many of these listeners, the loudness of sounds, even at high levels, does not approach the loudness measured in listeners with normal hearing. This phenomenon is sometimes called ***underrecruitment***, or ***partial recruitment***. These listeners will

> We can use loudness growth data to emphasize why caution must be taken to not interchange the terms loudness and intensity. Consider Figure 4–14 and a stimulus presented at 20 dB HL. This stimulus is soft to the listener with normal hearing but inaudible to a listener with sensorineural hearing loss. Thus, it would be a mistake to refer to this stimulus as soft—it is only soft to the person who is able to hear it!

constantly experience soft sounds compared with listeners with less hearing loss. As a result, it can be extremely difficult, and sometimes impossible, to restore full loudness perception for some of these listeners using amplification.

To summarize, listeners with mild-moderate hearing losses typically experience loudness recruitment, in which the loudness of sounds tends to grow more rapidly than for listeners with normal hearing. Yet, sensorineural hearing loss is not typically associated with abnormal loudness discomfort levels. On the other hand, listeners with severe-to-profound losses can experience underrecruitment and may perceive all sounds as being relatively soft compared with the perception of listeners with normal hearing and mild-moderate losses.

Measuring Loudness Discomfort and Hyperacusis

As we just discussed, hypersensitivity to sounds, or **hyperacusis**, is not a common consequence of SNHL. That is, most people with SNHL do not experience hyperacusis. Hyperacusis is typically considered a separate pathology from SNHL, and it can also be present in listeners with normal hearing. Hyperacusis can, and often does, occur in the presence of sensorineural hearing loss, and it is also commonly, but not always, associated with tinnitus. Many patients are aware that they have a heightened sensitivity to sounds, but patients may also believe that they have hyperacusis, even if their experiences fall within normal ranges. Thus, it is important to fully document a patient's response to intense and moderate-level sounds to verify whether hyperacusis is indeed present.

To assess whether a patient is experiencing hyperacusis, a measurement of loudness discomfort levels (LDLs) should be made. LDLs are also often measured as a component of hearing aid fitting in order to establish maximum hearing aid output levels. A common clinical approach to measuring LDLs is to apply a straightforward ascending method of limits, with clear instructions and loudness anchors that are easy for patients to understand (Cox, Alexander, Taylor, & Gray, 1997). Aspects of this procedure are similar to categorical loudness scaling, discussed previously. In this case, the tester is specifically looking for the level at which a sound is deemed "uncomfortably loud." A common procedure initially developed by Hawkins, Walden, Montgomery, and Prosek (1987) provides a listener with seven-to-nine loudness categories with words ranging from "very soft" to "painfully loud," as illustrated in Figure 4–5. Presentation begins at a level that targets the "soft" category (a level approximately 20 dB SL, but may be lower depending on the degree of hearing loss). Upon hearing the sound, the patient categorizes the loudness using the scale provided. Stimulus level is increased in 5-dB steps (or possibly 2 dB for a patient with a very small dynamic range) until the patient indicates that the sound is uncomfortably loud.

> Note that there are other terms in operation with the same meaning as LDLs: uncomfortable loudness levels (UCLs or ULLs) or threshold of discomfort (TD). Which term to use is a large discussion among scientists and professionals. If one follows the convention to use the term that corresponds with the measurement, UCL or ULL is probably more appropriate than LDL or TD, because patients are typically asked to find a level at which sound is *uncomfortable*. That being said, it is most common in the United States to use LDL.

Measurement of LDLs can help with the diagnosis of hyperacusis. Patients with hyperacusis will typically have LDLs that are below

85 to 90 dB SPL, although recent work by Sheldrake, Diehl, and Schaette (2015) suggests that LDLs alone may not be sufficient to diagnose hyperacusis.

SUMMARY AND TAKE-HOME POINTS

Loudness is a perceptual quantity that, although correlated with stimulus intensity, is also influenced by other acoustic factors such as frequency and stimulus bandwidth. Loudness is measured using techniques based on rating and matching, and these different techniques can be used to make inferences about the growth of loudness with increasing intensity (rating experiments) and the influence of frequency on loudness (matching experience). In comparison to listeners with normal hearing, listeners with hearing loss experience a more rapid growth of loudness with increasing intensity but do not generally experience different loudness discomfort levels. As rating and matching experiments adopt methods that yield variable and sometimes biased results, intensity-discrimination experiments are also commonly used to assess the representation of intensity in the auditory system.

The following points are key take-home messages of this chapter:

- Loudness is measured using magnitude estimation and quantified in sones. It increases with intensity and follows patterns very similar to basilar membrane input-output functions. Loudness and intensity have a power law relationship, and a 10-dB change in sound level corresponds to a doubling of loudness.
- The loudness level measured using loudness balancing is quantified in phons. The loudness level depends on frequency and follows patterns very similar to the frequency/gain characteristics of the outer and middle

ears. The loudest sounds, when presented at equal SPLs, are in the 2 to 6 kHz range.
- Loudness depends on stimulus bandwidth: For bandwidths greater than a critical band, loudness increases with increasing bandwidth, a phenomenon called spectral loudness summation. A sound can be loud because of a high sound level or because it has a broad bandwidth.
- Weber's law predicts that the just detectable amount of intensity is proportional to the intensity of the sound ($\Delta I/I = k$). Weber's law holds for noise at moderate-to-high levels but not for low levels or for tones. Tones exhibit a near miss, in which $\Delta I/I$ or ΔL decreases with increasing intensity.
- Listeners with sensorineural hearing loss experience rapid growth of loudness, referred to as recruitment. Their loudness discomfort levels are the same as those of listeners with normal hearing, except among those with severe hearing loss who experience underrecruitment. Loss of outer hair cells is the primary contributor to recruitment.

EXERCISES

1. Using loudness growth functions, determine how much louder a 50 dB SPL sound is than a 30 dB SPL sound. Is this the same relationship for 50 dB versus 70 dB SPL? Or 70 dB versus 90 dB SPL? (all have a 20 dB range). Discuss. In your answer, be sure to consider the implications of the units for loudness: a sound at 4 sones is twice as loud as a sound at 2 sones, and a sound at 8 sones is twice as loud as a sound at 4 sones.
2. Using equal-loudness contours, determine the dB SPL values of 200, 2000, and 8000 Hz tones when they are equally loud at 60 phons.
3. Using equal-loudness contours, determine the loudness level (in phons) of

200, 2000, and 8000 Hz tones when they are presented at 40 dB SPL. Which of these tones is louder when presented at the same sound pressure level? Discuss.

4. You are going to a concert next week, and you expect that sound levels will exceed 100 dB SPL. To protect your hearing, you purchase a set of musicians' earplugs, which have a constant attenuation of 25 dB at all frequencies.

   a. Using the equal-loudness contours given in Figure 4–5, discuss whether these earplugs will change the natural loudness relationships across frequency that will occur in the concert.

   b. Your friend purchases foam earplugs with the following attenuation characteristics (Table 4–1). Do you expect that he will have the same experience at the concert that you will? Again, use the equal-loudness contours to discuss. Consider, in particular, whether his perception will be dominated more by low or high frequencies.

5. Using equal-loudness contours, sketch a loudness growth function (in phons) for a 250-Hz tone. Compare that loudness growth function to that at 1000 Hz. Using your results, discuss why we would not use phons as a unit to measure loudness growth.

6. Provide three different examples indicating why loudness and intensity are not interchangeable terms.

7. Sketch loudness growth functions for a listener with 50 dB of conductive hearing loss. When drawing your sketch, pay attention to use correct axis labels. From your sketch, what is the dynamic range? What is the LDL? Explain your answers using your knowledge of auditory physiology.

8. Sketch loudness growth functions for a listener who demonstrates partial recruitment. In this case, the patient has 60 dB of sensorineural hearing loss. Label the dynamic range on your sketch. Using only loudness as a guide, discuss the impact on loudness perception of providing the same amount of gain in a hearing aid as for a patient who does not experience partial recruitment but has the same degree of hearing loss.

9. Sketch a loudness growth function consistent with a listener (with normal hearing) who experiences hyperacusis at all stimulus levels. Label the dynamic range on your graph.

TABLE 4–1. Attenuation Characteristics of Earplugs

	Frequency (Hz)					
	250	500	1000	2000	4000	8000
Attenuation (dB)	15	15	20	25	30	40

REFERENCES

Algom, D., & Marks, L. E. (1984). Individual differences in loudness processing and loudness scales. *Journal of Experimental Psychology: General, 113*(4), 571.

Allen, J. B., Hall, J. L., & Jeng, P. S. (1990). Loudness growth in 1/2-octave bands (LGOB)—a procedure for the assessment of loudness. *Journal of the Acoustical Society of America, 88*(2), 745–753.

ANSI 3.4-2007. *Procedure for the computation of loudness of steady sounds.* New York, NY: American National Standards Institute.

Buus, S., & Florentine, M. (2002). Growth of loudness in listeners with cochlear hearing losses: Recruitment reconsidered. *Journal of the Association for Research in Otolaryngology, 3*(2), 120–139.

Chocholle, R. (1940). Variation des temps de réaction auditifs en fonction de l'intensité à diverses fréquences. *L'année psychologique, 41*(1), 65–124.

Cox, R. M., Alexander, G. C., Taylor, I. M., & Gray, G. A. (1997). The contour test of loudness perception. *Ear and Hearing, 18*(5), 388–400.

Fletcher, H., & Munson, W. A. (1933). Loudness, its definition, measurement and calculation. *Bell Labs Technical Journal, 12*(4), 377–430.

Florentine, M., Buus, S. R., & Mason, C. R. (1987). Level discrimination as a function of level for tones from 0.25 to 16 kHz. *Journal of the Acoustical Society of America, 81*(5), 1528–1541.

Fowler, E. P. (1928). Marked deafened areas in normal ears. *Archives of Otolaryngology, 8*(2), 151–155.

Garner, W. R. (1953). An informational analysis of absolute judgments of loudness. *Journal of Experimental Psychology, 46*(5), 373–380.

Glasberg, B. R., & Moore, B. C. (2006). Prediction of absolute thresholds and equal-loudness contours using a modified loudness model. *Journal of the Acoustical Society of America, 120*(2), 585–588.

Hawkins, D. B., Walden, B. E., Montgomery, A., & Prosek, R. A. (1987). Description and validation of an LDL procedure designed to select SSPLSO. *Ear and Hearing, 8*(3), 162–169.

Hébert, S., Fournier, P., & Noreña, A. (2013). The auditory sensitivity is increased in tinnitus ears. *Journal of Neuroscience, 33*(6), 2356–2364.

Hellman, R. P., & Meiselman, C. H. (1993). Rate of loudness growth for pure tones in normal and impaired hearing. *Journal of the Acoustical Society of America, 93*(2), 966–975.

Hellman, R. P., & Zwislocki, J. (1961). Some factors affecting the estimation of loudness. *Journal of the Acoustical Society of America, 33*(5), 687–694.

Humes, L. E., & Ahlstrom, J. B. (1984). Relation between reaction time and loudness. *Journal of Speech, Language, and Hearing Research, 27*(2), 306–310.

ISO 226-2003. International Standard normal equal-loudness contours. Geneva: Switzerland: International Standards Organization.

Jesteadt, W., Wier, C. C., & Green, D. M. (1977). Intensity discrimination as a function of frequency and sensation level. *Journal of the Acoustical Society of America, 61*(1), 169–177.

Johnstone, B. M., & Boyle, A. J. F. (1967). Basilar membrane vibration examined with the Mössbauer technique. *Science, 158*(3799), 389–390.

Lauer A. M., & Dooling, R. J. (2007). Evidence of hyperacusis in canaries with permanent hereditary high-frequency hearing loss. *Seminars in Hearing, 28*(4), 319–326.

McFadden, D. (1986). The curious half-octave shift: Evidence for a basalward migration of the traveling-wave envelope with increasing intensity. In *Basic and applied aspects of noise-induced hearing loss* (pp. 295–312). New York, NY: Springer.

Miller, G. A. (1947). Sensitivity to changes in the intensity of white noise and its relation to masking and loudness. *Journal of the Acoustical Society of America, 19*(4), 609–619.

Moore, B. C., Glasberg, B. R., & Baer, T. (1997). A model for the prediction of thresholds, loudness, and partial loudness. *Journal of the Audio Engineering Society, 45*(4), 224–240.

Palmer, A. R., & Evans, E. F. (1979). On the peripheral coding of the level of individual frequency components of complex sounds at high sound levels. *Hearing Mechanisms and Speech, 19*–26.

Rhode W. S. (1971). Observations of the vibration of the basilar membrane in squirrel monkeys using the Mössbauer technique. *Journal of the Acoustical Society of America, 49,* 1218–1231.

Riesz, R. R. (1928). Differential intensity sensitivity of the ear for pure tones. *Physical Review, 31*(5), 867.

Ruggero, M. A., & Rich, N. C. (1991). Application of a commercially-manufactured Doppler-shift laser velocimeter to the measurement of basilar-membrane vibration. *Hearing Research, 51*(2), 215–230.

Schlittenlacher, J., Ellermeier, W., & Avci, G. (2017). Simple reaction time for broadband sounds compared to pure tones. *Attention, Perception, and Psychophysics, 79*(2), 628–636.

Schroder, A. C., Viemeister, N. F., & Nelson, D. A. (1994). Intensity discrimination in normal-hearing and hearing-impaired listeners. *Journal of the Acoustical Society of America, 96*(5), 2683–2693.

Sheldrake, J., Diehl, P. U., & Schaette, R. (2015). Audiometric characteristics of hyperacusis patients. *Frontiers in Neurology, 6*, 1–7.

Stevens, S. S. (1956). The direct estimation of sensory magnitudes: Loudness. *American Journal of Psychology, 69*(1), 1–25.

Stevens, S. S. (1957). On the psychophysical law. *Psychological Review, 64*(3), 153.

Viemeister, N. F. (1988). Intensity coding and the dynamic range problem. *Hearing Research, 34*(3), 267–274.

Wagner, E., Florentine, M., Buus, S., & McCormack, J. (2004). Spectral loudness summation & simple reaction time. *Journal of the Acoustical Society of America, 116*(3), 1681–1686.

Zwicker, E., Flottorp, G., & Stevens, S. S. (1957). Critical band width in loudness summation. *Journal of the Acoustical Society of America, 29*(5), 548–557.

5

Temporal Processing

LEARNING OBJECTIVES

Upon completing this chapter, students will be able to:

- Discuss the strengths and weaknesses of various measures of temporal processing
- Differentiate between temporal acuity, temporal masking, and temporal integration
- Evaluate the mechanisms of temporal integration
- Explain the relationship between temporal integration and tone durations used for audiometry
- Describe the influence of hearing loss on temporal processes

INTRODUCTION

The representation of the temporal features of sounds is a key component to auditory processing. Time is an extremely important aspect of both sound and its perception, as all sounds vary over time to some degree, and information in sounds unfolds over time. Note that because sound is a vibration, all sounds, by definition, are characterized by pressure changes occurring over time. However, if the overall intensity and frequency of a sound remain constant over time (e.g., a pure tone or white noise), the sound is considered a steady one. Sounds with changes in intensity over time are considered time-varying, and the limits on the perceptual ability to represent those variations is the focus of this chapter.

This ability to represent the variations in intensity over time is referred to as *temporal processing*. Temporal processing is a key component in coding natural sounds and the information contained in them. Consider speech, for example, which contains temporal elements that are important for the differentiation of speech sounds. An ear that can represent the temporal aspects of speech is able to gather more information about a speech signal than an ear that cannot represent the temporal changes across time. Music also contains important temporal elements, as the pattern of note duration and timing between notes yields rhythm. To illustrate the variety of temporal changes that occur in natural stimuli, Figure 5–1 plots a waveform of a speech sentence, which is plotted to illustrate the pattern

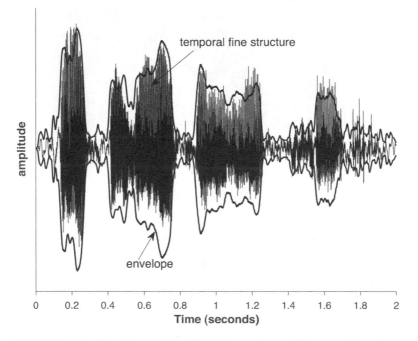

FIGURE 5–1. Waveform of an English sentence. The waveform has numerous amplitude fluctuations over time, demonstrating the nature of fluctuating stimuli in the natural world. The carrier (*fine structure*) and envelope (*modulation*) are also shown.

of high- and low-amplitude variations that occur over time. The waveform illustrates a fluctuating sound, which, by definition, has large amplitude changes over time.

The waveform in Figure 5–1 is plotted along with its envelope, which is a representation of the slow temporal variations in the stimulus. This waveform illustrates two aspects of the stimulus that are time dependent: rapid individual pressure variations, commonly called *temporal fine structure* or the *carrier*, and slower changes in the pressure variations, referred to as the *envelope* or the *modulator*. Both of these aspects are labeled in Figure 5–1 for reference. The rapid variations are very important for auditory perception, but we do not typically perceive them as temporal events, like we do the envelope. Thus, the perception of temporal fine structure is usually not treated as an aspect of temporal processing. On the other hand, we consider the ability to represent stimulus envelope as a component of temporal processing.

There are a number of different aspects of temporal processing, and we will discuss the following in this chapter:

- *Temporal resolution or temporal acuity.* This aspect of temporal processing measures the ability of the ear to represent changes in the envelope of sound.
- *Temporal masking.* Temporal masking is sometimes considered an aspect of temporal resolution, and is measured using forward-masking techniques. However, because temporal masking uses masking techniques, whereas the other measures of temporal acuity do not, it is sometimes considered as separate to temporal resolution.
- *Temporal integration.* In this section, we review the ability of the ear to take advantage of an increased duration of sound.

Perceptual aspects of temporal processing are key elements contributing to our ability to decode both speech and musical signals, and degradations in temporal processing can undermine the ability to understand speech and appreciate music. In addition, the concept of temporal integration plays a role in experimental design for psychoacousticians, but audiologists should be knowledgeable of temporal integration, as the concept is foundational to audiometric testing. Additionally, hearing loss can impact some of these abilities, and its influence should be considered when designing experiments or conducting audiometric tests.

In this chapter, we will discuss the following concepts, as they apply to temporal processing:

- Temporal resolution: gap detection and modulation detection
  - Psychoacoustic experiments and methods
  - Acoustic implications
- Temporal masking: forward masking
- Temporal integration and its implications for audiology
- Effects of sensorineural hearing loss (SNHL)
  - Temporal resolution and temporal masking
  - Temporal integration

TEMPORAL RESOLUTION: GAP DETECTION

There have been numerous investigations into temporal resolution using a variety of different procedures. Today, we use *gap detection* to provide a rapid and general assessment of the temporal resolution of the auditory system. In a gap detection task, we measure the just noticeable duration of a silent gap embedded into a stimulus.

The Gap Detection Paradigm

Plomp (1964) developed an intuitive paradigm to assess the temporal acuity of the auditory system. Plomp reasoned that perception of a stimulus persists, even after cessation of the acoustic signal. He suggested that the perception of sound decays over time and that persistence of the perception could interfere with the perception of a subsequently occurring sound. Plomp measured this decay using two broadband noise pulses, separated by a silent period, Δt. Plomp measured the minimum detectable silent period, the "gap"—Δt—between the two noise pulses and varied the levels of the two pulses. We now call his paradigm *gap detection*. Figure 5–2 illustrates how gap detection might be implemented in a 2I–2AFC task. One interval contains the stimulus with the gap, whereas the other interval does not. The listener selects which of the two intervals contains the brief gap. Essentially Plomp asked, "What is the smallest gap that can be detected?"

In order to get a feel regarding why gap detection reflects temporal processes, a schematic adapted from Plomp's paper is illustrated in Figure 5–3, which shows how gap detection provides a measure of the decay of auditory sensation. The upper panel shows a schematic of the stimulus characteristic: two

FIGURE 5–2. Illustration of an experimental trial in a gap detection experiment.

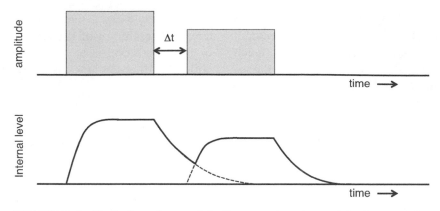

FIGURE 5–3. Illustration of a gap detection experiment, as originally conceptualized by Plomp (1964). The top panel illustrates a schematic of two pulses separated by a silent gap with duration Δt. The bottom panel illustrates the "internal representations" of the two pulses and how they build up and decay over time.

noise pulses separated by a silent gap, Δt. The lower panel shows Plomp's visualization of how the amplitude of these stimuli might be represented in the auditory system. This diagram also illustrates how an internal psychological representation of one sound can decay into the representation of a following sound. If the gap between the two sounds is not sufficiently long, a listener will hear the second sound blend into the first sound. In this case, the two sounds may fuse together, and the gap will not be perceived. However, if the gap is sufficiently long, a listener will hear the interruption of the pulse pair. The just detectable gap reflects how much temporal separation can be between the two sounds before the first sound has decayed enough to allow for the listener to hear the silent gap in between them.

Although Plomp's original experiment varied the levels of the noise pulses, today we typically set the levels of the noises to be equal, and we measure the minimum detectable gap between two sounds. The longer the gap needed for detection, the greater the decay produced by the first stimulus. Plomp measured gap detection thresholds (the just detectable gap) in white noise to be approxi-

mately 2 to 3 ms (Plomp, 1964), and a number of investigators have followed using sounds rather different from those tested by Plomp.

The type of sound used in a gap detection task, be it a pure tone, narrow band of noise, or white noise, has a strong influence on the gap detection threshold. The following sections will discuss the factors that are necessary to interpret the gap detection threshold for only a subset of these sounds, but gap detection has been measured for numerous different stimulus types. For the purposes of this chapter, we place gap detection in two categories: gap detection in steady sounds, such as white noise and pure tones, and gap detection in fluctuating sounds, such as narrowband noise. Note that we consider white noise to be a steady sound, even though it contains random fluctuations, due to the rapid nature of the fluctuations. The envelope of white noise is effectively flat, as white noise contains no slow amplitude variations over time. Experimenters testing both types of stimuli have also attempted to measure gap detection in a frequency-specific way, although with less success. This body of work has demonstrated that the gap detection threshold depends on a number of stimulus characteristics, and is not always 2 to 3 ms. In fact, it is often much higher. The gap detection threshold is affected by stimulus level, stimulus bandwidth, and whether a stimulus is fluctuating or not. These factors are discussed in the sections to follow.

Before we can discuss the experimental results, however, we must first consider the acoustic effects of inserting a brief quiet gap in the waveform of a sound stimulus. As we will see below, introducing a temporal gap into a stimulus can alter the spectral characteristics of that sound. Experimenters testing both steady and fluctuating stimuli must consider whether spectral cues are present in their sounds. Should this happen, the gap detection threshold no longer reflects temporal processing, but is actually a spectral processing measure. As we will see, this phenomenon can make it difficult to measure gap detection in a frequency-specific manner.

Gap Detection: Acoustics

Anyone interested in evaluating temporal processing must be mindful of the relationship between the waveform and spectrum— changes to the temporal characteristics of a stimulus can lead to changes in the spectrum, just as the reverse can occur. An example we have already discussed is the time-frequency trade-off: Sounds cannot be brief in time as well as frequency specific. Shortening a sound will lead to additional frequencies present in the sound (i.e., spectral splatter). Applying this same concept to gap detection, abruptly stopping and starting a sound, as might happen when a gap is inserted into a stimulus, can also produce spectral splatter.

If we consider the relationship between the waveform and spectrum, we can observe that placing a silent gap within a stimulus has the potential to introduce spectral changes. Effectively, we can consider a stimulus with a gap as two sequential stimuli. However,

because the just noticeable gap between two sounds may be very short (e.g., 2–3 ms), the first sound must be rapidly turned off and the second sound must be rapidly turned on. Depending on the characteristics of the two sequential sounds, spectral changes can occur. To illustrate how these effects might manifest, Figure 5–4 illustrates the spectra of noise stimuli (*top panels*) and 2000-Hz tone stimuli (*bottom panels*) without gaps (*left panels*) and with a 2-ms temporal gap (*right panels*).

As we observe in the top panels of Figure 5–4, when a gap is introduced into a white noise, spectral splatter is negligible, as white noise already has a wide frequency range. The two spectra contain the same frequency components. Although the two noise spectra are very slightly different from each other, using a random sample of white noise each time a stimulus is presented (with or without the gap) prevents the listener from using slight spectral differences to detect the presence of the gap. We can do this because every sample of white noise is different with unique amplitude fluctuations.

For pure tones, however, the frequencies introduced by the gap greatly change the spectral characteristics of the stimulus. Although tone without the gap is not fully frequency specific (because its duration is not infinite), the spectral differences between the stimulus with the gap and the one without are readily visible. We observe that the 2000-Hz tone has a broader bandwidth than the long duration tone. For this particular gap scenario, the *side lobes* and the broader primary lobe may be audible to a listener. As a result, that listener may be able to detect the spectral changes associated with a gap, rather than detecting the temporal interruption itself. If this were to happen in an experiment, the gap detection thresholds may not reflect temporal processing at all. The consequence of these spectral changes is that getting extremely frequency-specific measures for gap detection can be difficult.

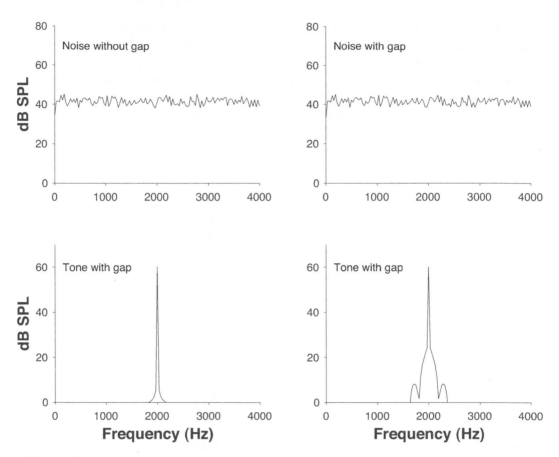

FIGURE 5–4. Illustration of spectra for sounds without 2-ms gaps inserted (*left panels*) and with gaps inserted (*right panels*). The spectra in the top panels are for noise without and with the temporal gap, and the spectra in the bottom panels are for a 2000-Hz tone without and with the temporal gap.

Psychophysical Findings

Gap detection is a fairly straightforward task —a listener is asked to determine which of two sounds has a brief temporal disruption. Gap detection experiments can provide a relatively rapid estimate of temporal processing abilities in the form of a single number representing temporal processing ability. As a result, this experiment would be very appealing to include in a clinical test measuring temporal acuity. Yet, Plomp's initial experiments and those of other investigators have illustrated that the gap detection threshold depends on a number of stimulus characteristics, including the level

and the bandwidth of sound. Thus, it is not straightforward to interpret gap detection from a clinical perspective—whether a listener can hear the frequencies present in the stimulus contributes substantially to whether a large or a small gap detection threshold is measured.

Level Effects

Plomp's original study demonstrated that gap detection thresholds for white noise are strongly dependent on stimulus level but only for low stimulus levels. Figure 5–5 shows data adapted from Plomp's experiment in which he measured gap detection thresholds at different

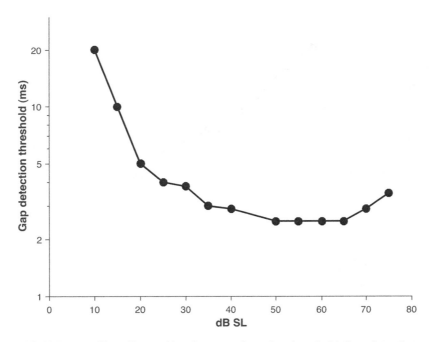

FIGURE 5–5. The effects of level on gap detection threshold. Gap detection thresholds (ms) are plotted as function of sensation level in dB. Adapted from Plomp (1964).

sensation levels (defined as the sound level in dB above threshold). At very low stimulus levels, gap detection thresholds decreased (they improved) with increasing level. At 10 dB sensation level (SL), gap detection thresholds were around 20 ms and decreased to slightly less than 3 ms between 10 and 30 dB SL. Once the stimulus level reached about 30 dB SL, further increases in stimulus level were not associated with increased performance.

The effect of level on the gap detection threshold has clear implications for the ultimate utility of using gap detection as a clinical test of temporal acuity. A listener must be presented with a stimulus that is *well above* his threshold in order to achieve the lowest threshold possible. Thus, gap detection thresholds can be difficult to interpret when measured in listeners who have large amounts of hearing loss. If a patient were to have a high gap detection threshold, we have to ask, "Is the gap detection threshold high because the

patient can't hear it? Or is it because of poor temporal processing?" This is a problem if this test were used diagnostically in isolation—a high gap detection threshold does not automatically imply poor temporal processing, particularly if the patient has a hearing loss.

Bandwidth and Frequency Effects

The bandwidth of a stimulus also has a profound effect on the ability to detect a gap. In short, gap detection thresholds decrease (get better) as the bandwidth of a stimulus is increased. Across a large number of studies, we observe that gap detection thresholds depend greatly on stimulus bandwidth. Data from Eddins et al. (1992), who measured gap detection thresholds in high-pass filtered bands of noise with bandwidths ranging from 50 to 1600 Hz, are plotted in Figure 5–6. Eddins et al. also varied the high-frequency cutoff frequencies of the noises, and data for the dif-

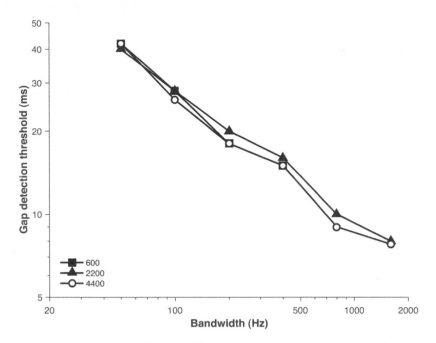

FIGURE 5–6. Effects of bandwidth on gap detection. Gap detection thresholds (ms) are plotted as function of stimulus bandwidth (Hz) for three different high-frequency cutoff frequencies. Adapted from Eddins et al. (1992).

ferent cutoff-frequencies are illustrated using different symbols. Note that the two largest bandwidths could not be tested for the 600-Hz cutoff frequency. By manipulating frequency region and bandwidth, Eddins et al.'s experiment tested both the effects of bandwidth and frequency region at the same time.

There are a number of notable features in the data presented in Figure 5–6. First, we clearly see that the gap detection threshold decreased with increasing bandwidth. The best (lowest) thresholds were achieved when the bandwidth of the stimulus is the widest. We also observe that the frequency region did not influence gap detection abilities. As a result, we can conclude that the bandwidth affects the measurement of the gap detection threshold, but not the frequency region.

We interpret the effects of stimulus bandwidth on gap detection as support for a hypothesis that, even for temporal processing, the ear is able to utilize information across many fre-

quency bands. A similar finding was discussed in Chapter 3 in which we discussed the auditory representation of sound spectrum, but we now observe this ability applied to temporal processing measures. Although this interpretation may not immediately be obvious, consider the following: When we introduce a gap into the time course of a stimulus, there is a con-comitant spectral effect: All of the stimulus frequencies are stopped simultaneously. For a white noise stimulus that contains all audible frequencies, a temporal gap causes a temporal disruption down the full length of the basilar membrane. From a psychoacoustical perspective, the temporal information is represented in the bank of auditory filters, with each auditory filter containing information about the temporal disruption. This effect is illustrated in Figure 5–7, which shows the output of multiple auditory filters plotted as a function of time for a noise with a 10-ms temporal gap. This format is similar to a spectrogram, only each individ-

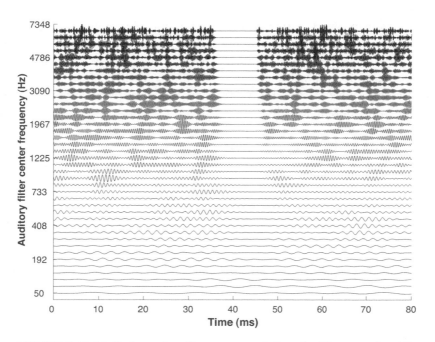

FIGURE 5–7. Multi-channel auditory representation of a 10-ms gap in white noise. Similar to a spectrogram, this plot represents the output of multiple auditory filters as a function of time.

ual trace represents the output of a single auditory filter with bandwidths estimated from human psychophysical studies. Here, we can see that the gap is represented across the frequency range, as each auditory filter processes a signal that is turned on and turned off very quickly. All but the very low frequency filters (<250 Hz or so) represent the gap very well.

Considering the example illustrated in Figure 5–7, we can evaluate two possibilities for detecting the presence of the gap in a noise. In one of those possibilities, the auditory system could "listen" to the output of only one auditory filter, essentially "picking" one of the auditory filter outputs. On the other hand, "listening" across multiple auditory filters would be a viable alternative, and multiple auditory filters code for the gap extremely well. If the ear always listened to the same auditory filter, or even switched which auditory filter was used, regardless of stimulus bandwidth, gap detection thresholds would not change

with increasing bandwidth. However, if the ear listened to more and more auditory filters as the bandwidth increased, gap detection thresholds would improve with increasing bandwidth, as there would be more and more opportunities to detect the gap. In this way, we observe that the ear has access to multiple frequency regions when the stimulus has a wide bandwidth in order to detect a gap.

Gap detection experiments usually ask a listener to detect a silent gap between two sounds. However, experimenters can ask the listener whether one or two sounds are present. If the experimenter asks the listener to report the order of two different sounds, the experiment becomes a ***temporal ordering*** experiment. Thresholds for reporting the temporal order of two sounds are much higher than those for detecting a gap between two sounds. This task is more difficult than gap detection, as the listener must store the identity of the two sounds in memory.

In summary, then, gap detection experiments provide an intuitive way to measure temporal resolution. They are limited in their scope of measuring temporal processing, however, because only a single threshold value is obtained. Thus, they only reflect the ability to detect whether a stimulus is "on" or "off" and are not sensitive to the ability of the ear to code for different stimulus fluctuation rates. Furthermore, the thresholds themselves depend on the frequency span of the stimulus, and a fully audible stimulus is needed in order to obtain the best gap detection thresholds.

Gap Detection in Fluctuating Sounds

The previous two sections discussed gap detection in steady stimuli, stimuli that do not have large amplitude variations over time. However, many sounds have inherent fluctuations that are also represented by the auditory system. Gap detection experiments that use these sounds help us to understand the representation of slowly fluctuating sounds by the ear. Although there are many types of sounds that contain slow fluctuations, here we discuss a specific class of sound: a narrowband noise. Narrowband noises are filtered versions of white noise—they contain fewer frequencies and also have greater fluctuations.

Before we discuss the data on gap detection in narrow bands of noise, we must first understand the acoustic representation of these sounds. Figure 5–8 illustrates the effects

of filtering white noise using filters with a very wide (*left panel*), a moderately narrow (*middle panel*), and a narrow (*right panel*) bandwidth. As the bandwidth of the noise decreases (*left to right panels*), the rate of the fluctuations also decreases. Thus, narrower bandwidth stimuli are associated with slower fluctuation rates.

Shailer and Moore (1985) demonstrated that gap detection abilities degraded substantially when the bandwidth of noise was very narrow and less than a critical band. They argued that these very narrow bandwidth sounds have robust fluctuations that can be easily confused with the gap. Figure 5–9 illustrates this idea. The left panel shows the stimulus with its natural fluctuations, and the right panel illustrates that stimulus with a gap inserted. In this figure, the gap is inserted near one of the waveform valleys. One can see that if the gap, as in this case, is presented near or in one of the temporal valleys of the waveform, it would be difficult to detect, particularly in comparison to a gap inserted near a peak.

Glasberg and Moore (1992) explicitly tested whether gap detection was made more difficult by the presence of stimulus fluctuations. They used a clever stimulus, originally developed by Pumplin (1985), to determine whether the fluctuations make gap detection more difficult. This stimulus, commonly called low fluctuation noise (LFN), contains the same frequencies present in white noise, but undergoes an algorithm designed to reduce the fluctuations present in the stimu-

FIGURE 5–8. Effects of filtering noise on the waveform. Going from the left panel to the right panel, each waveform reflects a noise band with the same center frequency with a wide (1000 Hz), medium (200 Hz), and narrow (50 Hz) bandwidth, respectively.

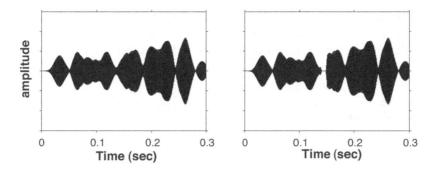

FIGURE 5–9. Illustration of a gap inserted into a fluctuating stimulus. The left panel shows a narrowband noise without a gap, whereas the right panel shows the same noise with a gap inserted at 130 ms into the stimulus.

lus. LFN does not completely eliminate temporal fluctuations in a stimulus, but it greatly reduces them, particularly in comparison to natural narrow bands of noise with the same bandwidth. Glasberg and Moore showed that gap detection thresholds were much better in LFN than in narrowband noise, supporting the hypothesis that fluctuations can make gaps difficult to detect. Because listeners have difficulty detecting gaps in fluctuating sounds, we know that those fluctuations are robustly represented in the auditory system.

Gap Detection: Summary and Implications

Taken together, the ear can follow relatively quick changes in amplitude, as the gap detection threshold for white noise is 2 to 3 ms. The following factors influence temporal gap detection:

- *Stimulus level.* Gap detection thresholds decrease (improve) with increasing sound level, but only for low-level sounds. Once a moderate level is reached, stimulus level has little effect on gap detection thresholds. Poor gap detection at low levels may suggest a necessity to present stimuli well above auditory threshold in order to give the ear full access to the temporal variations

present in stimuli. For example, speech presented near threshold, or even at 20 dB SL, may not provide sufficient representation of the temporal variations in everyday sounds.

- *Stimulus bandwidth.* The wider the stimulus bandwidth, the better the gap detection threshold. The auditory system is able to use information across a wide frequency range to gather information, even temporal information. We can infer from this result that providing access to stimuli with the widest bandwidth possible is important for robust coding of acoustic temporal information. Consider how the telephone, which only represents frequencies up to about 3500 Hz, or a hearing aid with a bandwidth of 6000 kHz, might impair the representation of temporal information present in speech, which has a bandwidth of closer to 8000 Hz, and music, having a bandwidth of 14,000 Hz. In both cases, a listener is in an impoverished auditory environment. By not having access to the full bandwidth of environmental stimuli, the ability to take advantage of broadband temporal changes may be impacted in a negative way. Note that we may not notice a large decrease in speech understanding, but decoding the information in the impoverished speech signal may require more effort on the part of the listener.

- *Stimulus fluctuation.* Fluctuations in the stimulus are associated with poorer gap detection thresholds. This result indicates that the ear represents these fluctuations and may use these fluctuations to benefit perception. An example is the *fluctuating masker benefit*, in which the ear is able to "listen" in low-frequency temporal epochs to improve speech understanding and detection abilities.

At face value, gap detection experiments may seem fairly contrived and have no obvious application to our understanding of everyday listening. However, the ability to represent temporal information in a stimulus is clearly important for communication, and gap detection tasks provide a measurement, albeit coarse, of the ability of the auditory system to follow temporal variations.

TEMPORAL RESOLUTION: AMPLITUDE MODULATION DETECTION

When a more thorough method of temporal resolution assessment is desired, we use a method based on **amplitude modulation detection**. Amplitude modulation is defined as the process by which a steady sound is turned into a sound with variable amplitude. In these types of experiments, the listener detects the presence of modulation that is imposed on a stimulus. Before psychoacoustic studies using this method are discussed, we review the acoustics of amplitude modulation.

Amplitude Modulation: Acoustics

An amplitude-modulated sound is described in two parts: the *envelope* (or *modulator*), the portion of the stimulus that slowly varies over time, and the *fine structure* (or *carrier*),

the portion of the stimulus with rapid pressure fluctuations. One formula to generate a modulated stimulus, *y*, is given by the following equation:

$$y(t) = [1+m^*\text{mod}(t)]\ \text{car}(t), \qquad \text{Eq. 5–1}$$

where *m* refers to the modulation depth, $\text{mod}(t)$ is the modulator, $\text{car}(t)$ is the carrier, and *t* is time. The modulator and carrier can be any type of stimulus, and in many psychoacoustic experiments, the modulator is a pure tone and the carrier is either a pure tone or a noise.

A special case referred to as a **sinusoidally amplitude modulated (SAM)** tone occurs when both the modulator and carrier are pure tones. For a SAM tone, Equation 5–1 becomes $y(t)=[1+m\sin(2\pi f_m t)]\sin(2\pi f_c t)$, where f_m and f_c are the frequencies of the modulator and the carrier, respectively.

The amount of modulation is controlled by the parameter, *m*, which ranges between 0 (an unmodulated sound) and 1 (a fully modulated sound). To facilitate an intuition of modulation, the top panels of Figure 5–10 illustrate the waveforms of three different SAM tones. The left panel shows an unmodulated tone, the middle panel shows a 20% modulated ($m = 0.2$) tone, and the right panel shows a fully (100%) modulated ($m = 1$) tone. In Figure 5–10, the fine structure is represented in the rapid pressure fluctuations and the envelope in the slow fluctuations. Notably, the fine structure is the same across panels, but the degree of fluctuation in the envelope is reduced in the 20% modulated stimulus compared with the fully modulated stimulus. Note that even the unmodulated sound has an envelope, but it is flat over time, reflecting the steady nature of this sound.

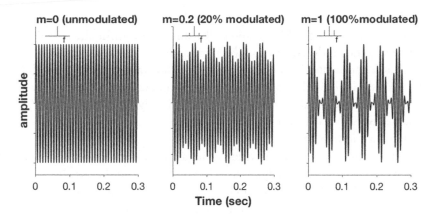

FIGURE 5–10. Waveforms of three different SAM tones at different modulation depths. Going from left to right, the stimuli progress from no modulation ($m = 0$), 20% modulation ($m = 0.2$) and fully modulated ($m = 1$). The small insets in the upper left hand corners represent the spectra of the SAM tones.

Not surprisingly, modulating sounds has an impact on the spectra of those sounds, which are plotted in the upper left-hand corners along with the waveforms in Figure 5–10. The spectra clearly demonstrate differences in comparison to that of the unmodulated sound, in the form of *side bands*. The modulation rate (f_m) determines the frequency of these side bands and the modulation depth (m) determines the size of the side bands. The higher the modulation rate, the farther the sidebands occur from the carrier. Each sideband is exactly f_m Hz away from the carrier. The modulation depth determines the size of the side bands—the larger the modulation depth, the greater the amplitude of the side bands. A 100% modulated stimulus will have both sidebands at 6 dB below the level of the carrier. Decreasing the modulation depth will decrease the size of the side bands. In many instances, the ear is very capable of hearing these frequency components as being separate from the carrier, particularly when they fall outside of the critical band. These stimuli can be heard as a "chord" or complex tone, rather than as a temporal pattern. Consequently, as with gap detection, these acoustic conse-

quences can make it quite difficult to obtain frequency-specific measures of temporal processing using modulation detection. Noise stimuli have an amplitude spectrum that is the same, regardless of whether the noise is modulated or not. Thus, it is common to use amplitude-modulated noise in amplitude-modulation detection experiments.

Modulation Detection: Psychoacoustics

Amplitude modulation detection experiments provide a more comprehensive view of the temporal resolution of the auditory system than gap detection. Viemeister (1979) was one of the first to use modulation detection and apply it to measure temporal resolution. Viemeister's listeners detected the presence of amplitude modulation on an otherwise steady stimulus, and Viemeister measured the ability to detect amplitude modulation as a function of the modulation rate. The modulation was sinusoidal in nature, and the carrier was a white noise. He measured the *just detectable modulation depth* (m), which ranges between

0 (no modulation) and 1 (100% modulation). In essence, Viemeister asked, "How much does a sound need to be modulated before the listener can tell it is modulated?" For illustration, Figure 5–11 shows how this task would be implemented using a 2I–2AFC paradigm. Here, a listener is presented with two intervals: one that contains a modulated stimulus and one that does not. The listener selects which of the two intervals contains the modulation.

Listeners having difficulty detecting modulation will need more modulation to detect it, therefore requiring a larger modulation depth (m) at threshold. Higher modulation detection thresholds would indicate difficulties following the changes in amplitude over time, compared with lower modulation detection thresholds. We could also interpret this result to indicate that the modulation rates associated with high modulation detection thresholds are not well represented in the auditory system.

Viemeister dubbed the plot that relates modulation detection threshold (y-axis; 20log$m$) to modulation rate (x-axis; f_m) the **temporal modulation transfer function**, or the **TMTF**. Figure 5–12 illustrates the TMTF and plots better thresholds at the top (low modulation detection thresholds) so that the function has the appearance of a low-pass filter. In Viemeister's experiment, listeners most easily detected modulation at relatively low modulation rates (<30 Hz). In these cases, very little modulation was needed for detection—about 0.5%!

As the modulation rate was increased, the task became more difficult, and listeners needed more modulation to detect it. The poorest threshold was reached at a modulation rate of approximately 1000 Hz, but even here listeners still only needed about 20% of modulation to detect it. If one considers the TMTF to be similar to a low-pass filter, the TMTF has a cut-off frequency of 55 to 65 Hz. Thus, modulation rates below about 55 Hz are well represented by the auditory system, and rates higher than that become more poorly represented. Across the board, however, the ability to detect the presence of modulation is quite excellent.

These different ways of characterizing the features of the TMTF are illustrated on Figure 5–11, and each of these features describes a different characteristic of temporal resolution. (1) The *best threshold* achieved reflects a listener's overall ability to follow amplitude changes in the stimulus. (2) The *cutoff frequency* is related to the bandwidth of modulation rates represented well in the auditory system (e.g., the TMTF "bandwidth"). (3) The *slope* of the function indicates how much change in ability occurs across the different modulation rates. A low best threshold, a higher cutoff frequency, and a shallower filter slope would all be associated with superior temporal processing measures.

The TMTF has been measured at different stimulus presentation levels, for differ-

Interval 1   Interval 2   Response

Amplitude-modulated stimulus   Unmodulated stimulus   Which interval has the modulated stimulus?

Time (s) ⟶

FIGURE 5–11. Illustration of an experimental trial for a modulation detection task. Here, the modulated stimulus has 50% amplitude modulation (a modulation depth of 0.5).

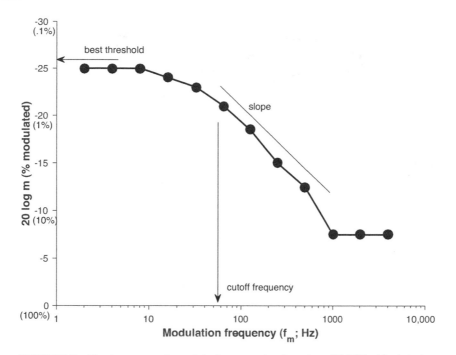

FIGURE 5–12. A temporal modulation transfer function (TMTF). Modulation detection thresholds in 20log(m), where *m* is the modulation depth, are plotted as a function of modulation frequency in Hz. The amount of modulation in percent is also shown. Better thresholds are shown at the top of the figure so that the function has the appearance of a low-pass filter. Different features of the TMTF are highlighted on the figure. Adapted from Viemeister (1979).

ent frequencies, and for different bandwidths, with the following results:

- *Little influence of stimulus level.* The TMTF was generally unaffected by stimulus level, except at the very low levels where portions of the stimulus may be inaudible (Viemeister, 1979). As with gap detection, this result indicates that stimulus levels need to be high enough to support good access to temporal information present in sounds.
- *Limited effects of stimulus frequency.* Although very few studies have measured TMTFs for frequency-specific stimuli, Kohlrausch, Fassel, and Dau (2000) measured TMTFs for sinusoidal carriers. Frequency effects of temporal resolution were only interpretable at high frequencies due to the acoustic

constraints discussed previously. At least for these high frequencies, they found no effect of frequency on the TMTF.

- *Large effects of stimulus bandwidth.* Generally speaking, TMTF measurements are highly dependent on the bandwidth of the stimulus. Bacon and Viemeister (1985) showed this when they measured TMTFs for low-pass noises. Data adapted from their study are illustrated in Figure 5–13. We observe that the best threshold was poorer (worse) and the cutoff frequency was lower for the TMTF measured for the low-pass noise compared with the TMTF measured for the unfiltered noise. These results suggest that reducing the stimulus bandwidth limits the ability of the ear to use temporal information. Consequently, the bandwidth of the

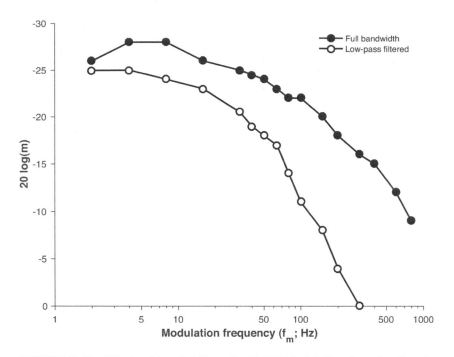

FIGURE 5–13. Effects of bandwidth on the TMTF. Modulation detection thresholds in 20log(m) are plotted as a function of modulation frequency in Hz for unfiltered (*filled circles*) and low-pass filtered (*unfilled circles*) stimuli. Adapted from Bacon and Viemeister (1985).

stimulus must be considered when interpreting TMTF data. As with gap detection, these effects demonstrate that the ear uses information across the frequency range of the stimulus to detect the presence of modulation. In contrast, having a wide bandwidth facilitates our perception of temporal information, and devices, like the telephone, that low-pass filter sounds, also limit the ear's access to that temporal information.

TEMPORAL MASKING

Another class of experiments that are influenced by the temporal resolution of the ear is that of *temporal masking.* This approach to measuring temporal resolution is also sometimes referred to as *forward masking.* Although we discussed forward masking

in Chapter 4, here we look at the way this technique allows a measurement of temporal processing. Recall that in a forward masking experiment, the signal and masker <u>do not</u> overlap in time. Typically, the signal is presented very close in time to the masker, and always is presented after the masker has been turned off. The first stimulus to arrive at the ear is the masker, which can be a noise or a tone or really any other stimulus. The second stimulus to arrive at the ear is usually a tone and has a short duration compared with the masker. In temporal masking experiments, the threshold of the signal in the presence of the masker is measured as a function of the time delay between the signal and the masker.

To refresh our memory, the stimulus sequence for a forward-masking experiment is illustrated in Figure 5–14, which shows a typical 2I–2AFC experiment in which one of two observation intervals contains a signal and both observation intervals contain a masker.

To illustrate how two stimuli that do not overlap in time might be related to temporal processing, Figure 5–15 illustrates how the perceptual representation of the masker might decay and provide masking of a signal. This decay is illustrated by the dashed line. As the two stimuli are separated farther in time, the effect of the masker on the signal should decrease, and the signal will become easier to detect. In a forward masking experiment, the level of the signal needed for detection is typically measured as the dependent variable. The experimental, independent variable is the time between the masker and the signal. Thus, the signal threshold is measured as a function of the time delay between the masker and signal. In some ways, this paradigm is very similar to Plomp's gap detection paradigm. However, rather than measuring the size of the just noticeable gap, we measure the threshold of a signal following a gap of a specified duration.

Forward masking occurs when the masker is high in intensity and has frequency components similar to the signal. In order to produce masking, forward maskers must have similar frequency ranges to the stimulus they are masking. The temporal relationship between the two sounds is also relevant, and forward masking decreases as the signal is moved farther away from the masker in time. The decrease in detection threshold as the signal and masker are increasingly separated is ***the release from forward masking***. Figure 5–16 shows data taken from Plack and Oxenham (1998), who measured the signal detection threshold as a function of the delay between the masker and the signal. In their experiment, the signal and masker were both tones, and they measured forward masking at different stimulus levels. Figure 5–16, then, illustrates the effects that the temporal separation masker level and the delay between the signal and masker have on forward masking.

Figure 5–16 illustrates two major factors that are relevant to the amount of forward masking:

- *Temporal effects: The amount of masking decayed as signal and masker became farther apart.* The closer the two sounds were

FIGURE 5–14. Schematic of the stimulus presentation sequence used in a 2I–2AFC task for forward masking.

FIGURE 5–15. Schematic of forward masking. Temporal effects of masking are illustrated by a masker (*gray rectangle*) and a signal presented after a certain time delay. The dotted line shows the decay of the internal representation of the masker.

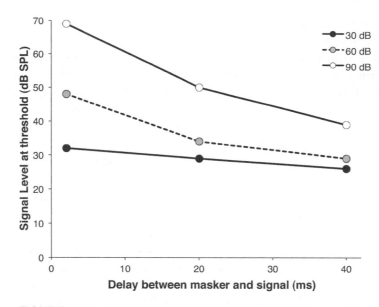

FIGURE 5–16. Forward masked thresholds in (dB SPL) are plotted as a function of the delay in ms between the masker (a 2-kHz tone) and signal (also a 2-kHz tone) for three different masker levels (30, 60, and 90 dB SPL). Adapted from Plack and Oxenham (1998).

in time, the greater the signal detection threshold and therefore, more masking. In all cases, we observe a release from forward masking as the masker and signal were increasingly separated in time.

- *Level effects: The release from forward masking was higher for high-intensity signals than for low.* First, the greater the intensity of the forward masker, the more forward masking. Note that thresholds were higher across the board for the more intense maskers. Second, increasing the level of the forward masker also led to greater release from masking. This is observed in the greater decrease in thresholds with time for the higher masker levels than for the lower masker levels.
  - This finding has some interesting implications and suggests that the ear has mechanisms that support release from masking, particularly in situations where masking effects are large. Although a more intense masker produces more masking than low-level sounds, the ear

provides some added release through nonlinear auditory processes.

Results from forward-masking experiments demonstrate that sounds that precede other sounds in time impact the perception of those occurring sounds. Given that many everyday sounds contain informative components that unfold over time (e.g., like speech), forward masking has strong implications for everyday listening. A listener who is very susceptible to forward masking, or who has an ear that does not release from forward masking quickly, is likely to experience difficulties understanding rapid speech, due to the temporal smearing of auditory representations.

COMPARISON OF TEMPORAL PROCESSING MEASURES

A variety of different techniques have been used to assess temporal resolution in the auditory system: gap detection, amplitude modulation detection, and forward masking. Because each technique has strengths and weaknesses, an experimenter or clinician can choose the method that best suits the particular application. Gap detection is an intuitive task, relatively easy to implement, and yields a single number to describe temporal acuity. Gap detection experiments can also be executed relatively quickly compared with more comprehensive methods of assessing temporal resolution because they generally yield a single number representing temporal resolution. Yet, gap detection experiments are fairly limited in their ability to broadly characterize temporal processing performance, as they only measure the ability to detect when a sound is interrupted.

On the other hand, the TMTF is comprehensive and results in multiple parameters that describe temporal acuity. Because temporal resolution is measured at multiple modulation rates, the TMTF provides a more complete picture of the temporal resolution of the ear. Further, the TMTF can be used to better pinpoint any sources of temporal processing difficulties because it contains more comprehensive information about temporal resolution than gap detection. However, measuring the TMTF is relatively time consuming and requires modulation detection thresholds to be measured at multiple modulation rates.

Finally, forward-masking experiments specifically evaluate the effects of one sound on another and provide a measure of temporal processing rather different from gap and amplitude-modulation detection. Such measures can be used to assess temporal representations between sounds, rather than within the same stimulus.

Despite the differences in these techniques, they effectively converge on the same conclusions:

- Measurement of temporal acuity is poorer at low levels versus high. The implication

is that sufficient audibility is necessary to provide the ear access to the temporal information in sounds.

- Measurement of temporal acuity depends on stimulus bandwidth. The wider the bandwidth, the better access the ear has to the temporal information in sound. Thus, filtering sounds will negatively impact the ear's ability to use temporal information.

Both findings have implications for listeners with hearing loss who experience reduced audibility, and therefore an impoverished representation of sound level, and often a restricted audible bandwidth, particularly if they have a sloping or rising hearing loss. These issues are discussed in the hearing loss section of this chapter.

TEMPORAL INTEGRATION

The previous sections of this chapter focused on temporal resolution, or the ability of the auditory system to follow amplitude changes in a stimulus. Another well-known aspect of auditory temporal processing is that absolute thresholds of sounds depend on their duration. This process is referred to as *temporal integration* or *temporal summation*, defined as the ability of the ear to accumulate information over time to improve detection threshold.

The Critical Duration

Temporal integration measures changes in auditory abilities as a function of the duration of a stimulus. Temporal integration has been demonstrated using a variety of experimental paradigms, including loudness (e.g., Zwislocki, 1969), intensity discrimination (e.g., Garner & Miller, 1944), and frequency discrimination (e.g., Moore, 1973). Broadly speaking, temporal integration follows a similar pattern for all tasks. Because detecting pure tones is so important, we review those data here as representative for temporal integration.

Here we review temporal integration for detecting pure tones. Watson and Gengel (1969) measured the threshold for detecting a pure tone as a function of its duration and frequency. Data adapted from their study are illustrated in Figure 5–17. To understand this figure, we first note that Watson and Gengel (1969) calculated thresholds relative to the average threshold obtained for durations of 512 and 1024 ms, which they defined to be 0 dB. In this way, they could easily observe the difference in thresholds for the shorter- versus longer-duration stimuli. Figure 5–17 shows the relative threshold as a function of the stimulus duration. Each curve represents data from a different signal frequency. In general, Figure 5–17 demonstrates a robust decrease in threshold as duration increases. Although

the improvement of threshold with duration varied somewhat for the different signal frequencies, all frequencies demonstrated a clear pattern of improvement. Additionally, once the stimulus duration exceeded about 250 ms, large changes in threshold were not evident. The duration at which thresholds no longer increase has been referred to as the ***critical duration***. For a variety of psychophysical experiments, the critical duration has been estimated to be approximately 200 to 300 ms. The slopes of temporal integration also depended on frequency, and were shallower for low-frequency tones. Thus, listeners benefit more from increased duration of sounds at high frequencies compared with low frequencies.

We should keep in mind that temporal integration does not imply that short-duration sounds are inaudible. Rather temporal integration indicates that thresholds for short-dura-

FIGURE 5–17. Temporal Integration. Normalized thresholds of pure-tone signals are plotted as a function of the stimulus duration. Thresholds are normalized to the 512- and 1024-ms thresholds averaged together. Adapted from Watson and Gengel (1969).

tion sounds are elevated with respect to long-duration sounds. Indeed, we have the ability to discriminate between sounds that are short in duration, although any discrimination task will be more difficult if the sounds are short in duration. Essentially, our perception is at its optimal performance when perceiving stimuli with durations that exceed the critical duration.

Mechanisms of Temporal Integration

Two major hypotheses have been proposed that explain temporal integration, and they differ primarily in their assumptions about the time frame over which integration occurs (i.e., the *time constant*). The first class of models assumes a long time constant (on the order of hundreds of milliseconds). These models were developed in an attempt to explain a critical duration between 200 and 300 ms. However, a second class of models assumes a short time constant (on the order of 5 or 10 milliseconds). Both models can predict that performance improves with increasing duration and that beyond a certain duration, improvements are so small as to be negligible. They do, however, make different predictions under certain circumstances, as will be discussed here.

Energy Detection

A few variants of the long time constant integration models exist, which all propose some form of integration or accumulation process over time. A common implementation of this model is an *energy detector* (Green, 1960), which posits that the ear integrates the intensity over time up to the critical duration. This model follows the equation:

$$I \times t = k, \qquad \text{Eq. 5–2}$$

where I is the intensity of the stimulus at threshold, t, is the time of the stimulus in seconds, and k is a constant. Following Equa-

tion 5–2, a stimulus with a short duration will require a high intensity at threshold to maintain the constant, k, whereas a stimulus with a longer duration will require a lower intensity at threshold. Because temporal integration varies with frequency, the constant would also be different for different frequencies, and integration would only occur up to the critical duration.

The Multiple Looks Hypothesis

Viemeister and Wakefield (1991) questioned the energy detector model and suggested that perhaps temporal integration is not based on long-term intensity integration. They noted that the energy detector is not a "smart" model, as it integrates energy rather than information. They noted that any type of stimulus energy, even if it comes from an interfering sound, would be accumulated into the energy detector. Rather, they proposed that over time, the ear conducts a series of short "snapshots" which provide more opportunities to detect the stimulus. In this way, snapshots that do not contain information could be discarded.

They describe the *multiple looks hypothesis*, which essentially states that increasing the duration of the stimulus provides multiple opportunities to detect the stimulus. This model is based on a signal-detection integration model, in which information from the observations (the "looks" at the stimulus) is combined, so that detection ability is improved. If we consider that the ear takes a series of snapshots of a stimulus over time, the ear can combine information from each of those snapshots together to enhance detection. Thus, detection could occur for a long-duration sound presented at a much lower stimulus level than a brief sound, which would require a higher stimulus level. In contrast, if the ear has only one or a few looks at a stimulus, the ear has a limited ability to combine information across the looks. In this way, the more snapshots provided to the auditory system via increased duration, the better the threshold (up to a point).

In developing the multiple looks hypothesis, Viemeister and Wakefield (1991) argued that if a stimulus contained uninformative snapshots, the energy detector would integrate them and degrade performance. However, the multiple looks mechanism would discard those uninformative pieces and use only the informative snapshots for detection. Their clever experiment is illustrated in Figure 5–18, which illustrates two tone pulses temporally embedded within a noise stimulus, which is indicated by the gray areas.

In three different conditions, the level of the noise between the two pulses was incremented, left alone, or decremented. The arrow on the noise stimulus between the two tone pulses illustrates the level changes. Thresholds were measured for pulse 1 plus the noises, for pulse 2 plus the noises, and for both pulses together with the noises. The energy detector predicts that the noise would be integrated into the perception, leading to a *higher* threshold for the two pulses than for one pulse. The level of the noise should also be important, with a higher noise leading to higher detection thresholds. On the other hand, the multiple looks model predicts that thresholds for the two pulses should be *lower* than threshold for one pulse, as the intervening noise is not informative. Here, the level of the noise should not affect thresholds. Figure 5–19 plots the

thresholds obtained for pulse 1 (filled, black circles), pulse 2 (filled, gray circles), and both tone pulses (open circles) as a function of the level increment in the noise. First, thresholds were better for two tone pulses than for one. Second, the intervening noise had little effect on the detection threshold, regardless of whether it was incremented or not. Both pieces of evidence are compelling in support of the multiple looks model.

The multiple looks experiment is consistent with the idea that a signal can be sampled and stored in memory so that only the informative temporal looks can be used for the task at hand. One interpretation is that the auditory system conducts a form of intelligent processing in the way it integrates information over time. Such a mechanism would be very useful for everyday listening. In certain circumstances, the auditory system may be capable of discarding extraneous information.

Implications of Temporal Integration for Audiology

The concept of temporal integration is extremely important for psychoacoustic experimentation and audiological testing. From pure-tone testing in the clinic to presenting sounds in the research lab, both professionals must consider the impact of stimulus duration on test results. For the psychoacoustician, the

time ⟶

FIGURE 5–18. Illustration of stimuli for the multiple-looks experiment. Schematics of the stimuli used by Viemeister and Wakefield (1991) are shown. Two tone pulses are presented in a sequence with a noise stimulus, which is shown as the gray rectangles. The arrow illustrates that the center of the noise was incremented by 6 dB, decremented by 6 dB, or left unchanged.

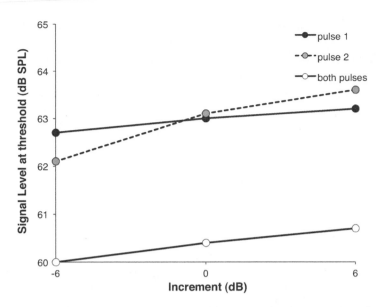

FIGURE 5–19. Multiple looks data. Thresholds for the detection of one tone pulse (*filled circles*) or two tone pulses (*unfilled circles*) plotted as a function of the noise increment. Adapted from Viemeister and Wakefield (1991).

concept of temporal integration is important for stimulus design and interpreting experimental results. For clinical applications, the idea is also extremely important. When testing absolute thresholds in the audiogram, the audiologist is interested in obtaining the "lowest level sound the listener can hear." Under this goal, the audiologist is tasked with obtaining the best threshold possible. Thus, the audiologist must present sounds at a duration that is sufficient to achieve that best threshold.

The ASHA standards for audiometric assessment provide two possible stimulus presentation modes that are both based on the concept of temporal integration. Steady tones for threshold testing are expected to be between 1 and 2 seconds (ASHA, 2005), a duration that far exceeds the critical duration. The long duration allows for differences in temporal integration that may be evident across individuals with hearing impairment who have large differences in thresholds and potentially degraded temporal integration

abilities. Pulsed tones used in obtaining the audiogram are also standardized at 200 ms (ASHA, 2005), a value very similar to the critical duration. Three pulsed tones are sufficient for testing, which gives the listener multiple opportunities to detect the tone.

EFFECTS OF HEARING LOSS ON TEMPORAL PROCESSING

It would be easy, but incorrect in many cases, to assume that sensorineural hearing loss degrades all auditory abilities, including temporal processing. An example that is often given in support of degraded temporal processing is that listeners with hearing loss need speech to be slowed so that they can fully understand it. However, slowing speech may simply allow a listener time to process a poorly represented signal that has a degraded spectral and amplitude representation. Consequently, we must measure temporal processing directly before making inferences about temporal processing using speech stimuli.

Ultimately, though, the prevailing consensus is that when temporal processing is measured by gap detections and amplitude modulation detection, many listeners with sensorineural hearing loss do not have degraded temporal processing. In other cases, such as forward masking and temporal integration, hearing loss indeed disrupts the temporal representation of sounds. The studies discussed in this section also have demonstrated huge variability in abilities within the group of listeners with hearing loss. Thus, we should avoid making general, sweeping statements about the temporal processing abilities of listeners with sensorineural hearing loss. Such variability stresses the importance of making measurements in individual listeners.

Temporal Resolution in SNHL

The hallmark of hearing loss is elevated thresholds, which lead to a reduction in stimulus audibility in a frequency-dependent way. Hearing loss decreases the representation of sound level in the auditory system and in many cases alters the internal representation of stimulus bandwidth, particularly for sloping or rising losses. Thus, care must be taken when interpreting the results of temporal processing experiments, as experiments on temporal resolution (gap detection, TMTF, and forward masking) all, to some degree, illustrate level and bandwidth effects.

Recall that low stimulus levels and restricted stimulus bandwidths lead to elevated gap detection thresholds (e.g., Plomp, 1964) and poorer modulation detection thresholds (e.g., Bacon & Viemeister, 1985; Viemeister, 1979). Stimulus level also impacts forward masking, and lower stimulus levels are associated with less release from forward masking (Plack & Oxenham, 1998). In order to interpret temporal processing measurements in listeners with hearing loss, then, we must consider stimulus audibility and the effective internal bandwidth. The experiments discussed here have gone to great lengths to address these two issues. Approaches include presenting stimuli at supra-threshold levels, equating sensation levels between two groups of listeners, and simulating hearing loss by presenting a threshold-equalizing noise to normal-hearing listeners while they perform the tasks at hand.

Temporal Resolution and SNHL: Steady Sounds

A number of studies have measured both gap detection and TMTFs in listeners with hearing loss for steady sounds, such as white or narrowband noise. Fitzgibbons and Wightman (1982) measured gap detection thresholds within band-pass sounds presented at similar sensation levels (SLs) to two groups. They found a large range of performance across the listeners in their study, and on average, gap detection thresholds were slightly elevated for listeners with hearing loss. Florentine and Buus (1984) controlled for audibility and internal bandwidth differences in a different way by simulating hearing loss by presenting a masking noise to the normal-hearing listeners during the task. They measured gap detection thresholds within noise stimuli presented at the same SPL to their two groups. They found that the listeners with true hearing loss and those with simulated hearing loss had higher gap detection thresholds than the normal-hearing listeners. From this result, Florentine and Buus concluded that it was the increase in thresholds that caused the higher gap detection thresholds, not a true temporal processing pathology. Yet, Florentine and Buus also noted that some listeners with hearing loss performed worse than the normal-hearing listeners with the simulated hearing loss at the highest presentation levels. These listeners likely experienced true temporal processing deficits.

We can conclude from these studies that while many listeners with SNHL do not experience deficits in temporal processing when measured using gap detection, some listeners likely experience temporal processing deficits associated with SNHL. The audiogram has not been a reliable indicator of who may or may not experience such deficits.

Equating the stimuli used in studies that compare performance between groups of listeners with different hearing levels can be very difficult. Presenting sounds at equal sensation level sounds appealing, but the internal representations of the sounds likely differ between two groups due to loss of cochlear nonlinearity. As a result, we may not be comparing "apples to apples." Studies also frequently use noise-masking to elevate thresholds in listeners with normal hearing in an attempt to deal with this problem. This experimental manipulation is considered to yield more valid comparisons between the two groups of listeners than equating sensation level, but also has limitations. Listeners with normal hearing must conduct the perceptual measurements in the presence of an audible noise masker.

Bacon and Viemeister (1985) measured TMTFs in listeners with normal and impaired hearing. When stimuli were broadband noises, the listeners with impaired hearing had higher modulation detection thresholds and a lower TMTF cutoff frequency than listeners with normal hearing. However, when Bacon and Viemeister low-pass filtered the stimuli, the TMTFs measured in normal-hearing listeners demonstrated the same trend—higher modulation detection thresholds and a lower TMTF cutoff frequency, suggesting that this result may have occurred due to portions of the broadband noise being inaudible to the listeners for SNHL. Other well-controlled studies have confirmed that TMTFs are generally similar for listeners with normal-hearing and those with hearing loss (Bacon & Gleitman, 1992; Moore, Shailer, & Schooneveldt, 1992). Although most studies come to this conclusion, there are others that document small deficits in the ability to detect amplitude modulation in listeners with SNHL (e.g., Lamore, Verweij, & Brocaar, 1984).

Taken together, it is thought that sensorineural hearing loss does not yield large deficits in either gap detection or amplitude modulation detection when audibility and bandwidth are taken into account. Across the studies conducted, however, one hallmark is a wide range of performance by listeners with hearing loss (Hall, Grose, Buss, & Hatch, 1998). Gap detection thresholds can be very elevated in some listeners with hearing loss, suggesting that a small subset of listeners may have true deficits in temporal processing. Because these deficits can exist, we should not treat listeners with hearing loss as a homogenous group in their perceptual abilities. We must consider that some listeners with hearing loss experience temporal processing deficits, even if many do not.

Temporal Resolution and SNHL: Fluctuating Sounds

When stimuli contain slow fluctuations, such as narrowband noise, listeners with hearing loss demonstrate significant deficits in gap detection compared with those with normal hearing (Glasberg & Moore, 1992; Glasberg, Moore, & Bacon, 1987). These differences can be attributed to a loss of compression in the impaired auditory system, which greatly alters the internal representation of fluctuating sounds for listeners with hearing loss and leads to an elevated gap detection threshold.

Consider that sensorineural hearing loss is almost always associated with a loss of outer hair cells. Absent or damaged outer hair cells cause low-level sounds to be inaudible and contribute to a loss of the compressive non-linearity within the cochlea. Loss of the compressive nonlinearity changes the cochlear response and has a particularly profound effect on the representation of sounds that fluctuate over time. To illustrate these effects, Figure 5–20 provides a schematic of how loss of the compressive nonlinearity alters the shape of the internal psychological representation

of a fluctuating waveform. The top panel of Figure 5–20 illustrates the representation of a fluctuating sound in an ear with the compressive nonlinearity intact (a normal ear), and the bottom panel depicts the same sound without the compressive nonlinearity (the impaired ear). By comparing the two panels, we observe that the waveform that has been passed through the compressive nonlinearity has reduced fluctuations compared with the waveform that has not been processed.

Applying this illustration to gap detection tasks, we observe that compressed sound also has fewer temporal valleys in the waveform than the uncompressed sound. If we consider that when listeners are asked to detect a gap, they may be confused between the naturally occurring valleys in the waveform and a gap placed into a sound by the experimenter. Thus, listeners who do not have the compres-

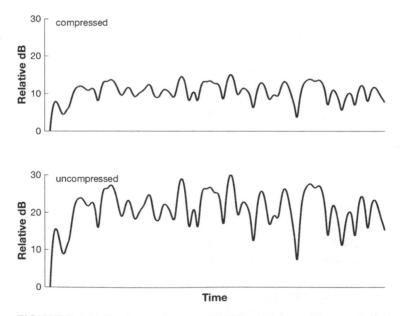

FIGURE 5–20. Two internal representations of a fluctuating envelope. The top panel illustrates the envelope of waveform representative of an ear with a functioning compressive nonlinearity. The bottom panel illustrates the same envelope, but for an ear that has lost compressive nonlinearity.

sive nonlinearity may have greater difficulty determining if a gap is present, resulting in an elevated (larger) gap detection threshold.

In some way, we can think about this as an indication that an impaired ear provides a more faithful representation of the fluctuations present in sounds. This more faithful representation leads to an internal representation in which the stimulus envelope is exaggerated compared with someone with normal hearing. In fact, when audibility is carefully controlled for and sounds are presented at the same sensation levels, listeners with hearing impairment sometimes demonstrate better amplitude modulation detection thresholds than listeners with normal hearing, in certain circumstances (Bacon & Gleitman, 1992). This finding suggests that the representation of the envelope is indeed exaggerated in listeners with SNHL. We can envision that the exaggeration of stimulus envelope could alter the perception of envelope in everyday sounds and is not necessarily advantageous.

Forward Masking

Forward masking is highly impacted by the presence of hearing loss. Regarding masking in general, listeners with hearing loss experience greater effects of masking and poorer frequency selectivity in both forward and simultaneous masking paradigms. Applied to temporal processing measures, we observe that listeners with SNHL experience a reduced release from forward masking—that is, the decay of a forward masker persists for a longer period of time than for normal-hearing listeners. Figure 5–21 illustrates this result by plotting Glasberg, Moore, and Bacon's (1987)

FIGURE 5–21. Forward masking effects for listeners with SNHL. Masked thresholds (dB SPL) are plotted as a function of the time delay between a 200-ms masker onset and signal onset. Thresholds from listeners with hearing impairment are plotted with unfilled squares. Data from normal-hearing listeners measured at the same SPL (*filled circles*) and same SL (*gray circles*) are also shown. Adapted from Glasberg et al. (1987).

data obtained from a forward-masking experiment. Glasberg et al. (1987) measured the detection threshold of a brief 10-ms tone pulse presented at various temporal locations within and after a 200-ms band-limited noise masker. They measured performance for the hearing-impaired listeners at a high and audible level. They measured performance for listeners with normal hearing at two levels: the same sound pressure level (SPL) and the same sensation level (SL) as the hearing-impaired listeners.

Examining the data obtained at the same SPL (black, filled circles versus unfilled squares), we observe that detection thresholds were very similar for the two groups of listeners as long as the tone pulse was presented within the masker. However, for the presentations occurring after cessation of the masker, we see a marked difference in thresholds between the two groups, where thresholds decreased much more rapidly with signal delay for the listeners with normal hearing than for those with sensorineural hearing loss. Thus, these listeners with sensorineural hearing loss experienced: (a) more forward masking and (b) less of a release from forward masking than those with normal hearing. The reduced release from forward masking suggests that the maskers and signals need to be separated farther in time from one another in order for the listener with hearing loss to experience a return to absolute threshold.

Next, evaluating the data from the listeners with normal hearing, we see that thresholds were much lower for the same-SL conditions than the same-SPL conditions. Here, the release from forward masking over time was greatly diminished compared with the same-SPL data measured in the same listeners. However, when we compare these data with the data from the listeners with SNHL, the masking release was still faster but only slightly. Presenting stimuli at the same sensation levels illustrates that forward-masking effects can be similar between two groups of listeners, although hearing loss is still associated with a reduced release from forward masking.

The reduced release from forward masking has substantial implications for listeners with sensorineural hearing loss. Even when target stimuli are presented in a quiet environment, components of the target stimulus that precede other components can drastically influence the ability to extract information present throughout the duration of the target. For example, within a speech signal, a high-intensity vowel could, in theory, forward-mask a low-intensity consonant, causing difficulty for the listener with hearing loss to identify that consonant. Slowing speech can also help with forward masking effects, but is not always easily achievable.

Temporal Integration and SNHL

Recall that temporal integration is the ability to take advantage of increases in stimulus duration to improve perception. Not surprisingly, temporal integration is also impacted by SNHL. Hall and Fernandes (1983) and Carlyon, Buus, and Florentine (1990) measured temporal integration in listeners with normal hearing and with SNHL and found that the benefit afforded by increasing the duration of the stimulus was about 1/2 or less for listeners with SNHL.

Florentine, Fastl, and Buus (1998) measured thresholds for pure tones at a variety of stimulus durations and attempted to control for audibility and bandwidth using a noise masker to simulate hearing loss. Figure 5–22 plots their average data from normal-hearing listeners (solid line) and individual data from their listeners with the listeners with hearing loss. Because of the different degrees of hearing loss across these listeners, they normalized thresholds to the threshold for a 500-ms stimulus (which was set to 0 dB). For reference, functions with steeper slopes indicate greater

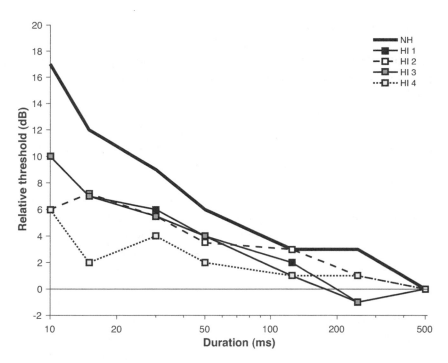

FIGURE 5–22. Temporal integration in listeners with SNHL. The threshold difference in dB between the measured signal threshold and the signal threshold for a 500-ms stimulus is plotted as a function of the signal duration. Data from individual listeners with SNHL are shown as squares with different shading, whereas average data from listeners with normal hearing are shown as the solid line. Adapted from Florentine et al. (1998).

amounts of temporal integration. All of the listeners with sensorineural loss demonstrated thresholds that change less with increasing duration (shallower slopes), indicative of a temporal integration deficit in listeners with hearing loss.

As we observe in Figure 5–22, listeners with hearing loss achieved their lowest threshold at a duration somewhere between 200 and 500 ms. This value is very similar to the critical duration that was observed for listeners with normal hearing. However, a similar critical duration does not automatically imply healthy temporal integration abilities, as we also observe that these listeners did not benefit from increasing the duration of the stimulus to the same degree as listeners with normal hearing. One conclusion, then, is that the

duration of the stimulus matters much less for those with sensorineural hearing loss than it does for listeners with normal hearing. In general, these listeners do not benefit from the increased duration to the same degree as those with normal hearing.

Summary of Temporal Processing in SNHL

Generally speaking, listeners with SNHL experience a variety of deficits in temporal processing, but not all measures of temporal processing demonstrate these deficits. For gap detection and amplitude modulation, listeners with hearing loss in general do not experience deficits. Only a small subset of listeners with SNHL experience true temporal resolution deficits. Nevertheless, poor audibility and a reduced audible bandwidth prevent all of these listeners from fully perceiving the temporal fluctuations in sound. On the other hand, forward-masking experiments illustrate poorer temporal processing in listeners with SNHL. Listeners experience a reduced release from forward masking, in which the representation of the masker persists for a greater period of time than for normal-hearing listeners. Finally, these listeners also experience a reduction in temporal integration. Listeners with SNHL receive only very small benefits in detection ability from increasing stimulus duration.

SUMMARY AND TAKE-HOME POINTS

Temporal processing measures relate to the ability of the ear to perceive a variety of temporal events in sound and fall into distinct categories: temporal resolution, temporal masking, and temporal integration. Temporal resolution experiments, such as gap detection and amplitude modulation detection, reflect the ability of the ear to represent the envelope of a stimulus. Temporal masking experiments are also used to measure the amount and duration of internal decay produced by a masker. Temporal integration experiments measure the ability of the ear to benefit from increasing the duration of the stimulus.

Sensorineural hearing loss impacts temporal masking and temporal integration, but many listeners with SNHL do not demonstrate deficits in temporal resolution when measured using gap detection or amplitude modulation detection. Some listeners, however, may experience true temporal resolution deficits, and there is considerable variability in temporal resolution measures in this group of listeners. Overall, the audiogram provides insufficient information to determine whether these deficits are present and the degree to which listeners experience temporal processing difficulties.

The following points are key take-home messages of this chapter:

- Gap detection and the temporal modulation transfer function (TMTF) provide estimates of temporal resolution. The best thresholds require audible stimuli and broad bandwidth.
- Forward masking is commonly used to measure temporal masking. Listeners experience a release from forward masking as a signal is moved later in time from a masker.
- Temporal integration experiments demonstrate an improvement in detection thresholds with stimulus duration up to about 200 to 300 ms.
- For many listeners with hearing loss, gap detection and TMTF measures are similar to those for normal hearing, as long as audibility is taken into account.
- Hearing loss leads to less of a release from forward masking and a decrease in temporal integration.

EXERCISES

1. Gap detection is often a component of an auditory processing disorder test battery, and one indicator of auditory processing disorder may be an elevated gap detection threshold. What considerations must be taken into account in order to interpret whether this threshold is related to poor temporal processing?

2. Consider the following TMTFs measured in two listeners (Figure 5–23). Which listener has the best modulation detection threshold? Which one has the highest cutoff frequency? Can you conclude which listener has better or worse temporal processing? Discuss.

3. Studies have demonstrated that amplitude modulation rates below 16 Hz are

FIGURE 5–23. Exercise 5–2.

the most important for speech intelligibility. Given this information, which listener in Exercise 5–2 will have the easiest time understanding speech? Explain.

4. Discuss the advantages and disadvantages of measuring temporal processing using gap detection versus the TMTF. In your answer include which of these methods might be more appropriate in a clinical setting?

5. Loudness is subject to temporal integration. Sketch data for loudness as a function of stimulus duration that you predict would be consistent with temporal integration.

6. The multiple looks experiment showed that thresholds decreased by 3 dB for the detection of two tone pulses compared with one. If the threshold for one tone pulse was 50 dB SPL, sketch predicted thresholds for 1, 2, 4, and 8 tone pulses (all separated by the same amount, perhaps 20 ms).

7. Discuss how a reduced release from forward masking by listeners with hearing

loss might make speech more difficult to understand, even if presented in quiet.

8. ASHA suggests that three 200-ms tone pulses can be used to test thresholds. If your patient has normal hearing, would using more tone pulses improve his threshold? Discuss. What if your patient had a hearing loss?

9. ASHA suggests that three 200-ms tone pulses can be used to test threshold. Using your knowledge of temporal integration, would using three 100-ms tone pulses provide poorer thresholds? Discuss. Consider, in particular, whether the frequency of the test tone makes a difference and whether any changes in threshold are within test-retest reliability of the clinical adaptive procedure.

10. Using your knowledge of temporal integration, is there any benefit of presenting a steady tone of three seconds instead of one second when measuring an audiogram in a listener with sensorineural hearing loss?

REFERENCES

American Speech-Language-Hearing Association. (2005). *Guidelines for manual pure-tone threshold audiometry* [Guidelines]. Available from http:www.asha.org/policy

Bacon, S. P., & Gleitman, R. M. (1992). Modulation detection in subjects with relatively flat hearing loss. *Journal of Speech and Hearing Research, 35*(3), 642–653.

Bacon, S. P., & Viemeister, N. F. (1985). Temporal modulation transfer functions in normal-hearing and hearing-impaired listeners. *Audiology, 24*(2), 117–134.

Carlyon, R. P., Buus, S. R., & Florentine, M. (1990). Temporal integration of trains of tone pulses by normal and by cochlearly impaired listeners. *Journal of the Acoustical Society of America, 87*(1), 260–268.

Eddins, D. A., Hall, J. W., & Grose, J. H. (1992). The detection of temporal gaps as a function of frequency region and absolute noise bandwidth. *Journal of the Acoustical Society of America, 91*(2), 1069–1077.

Fitzgibbons, P. J., & Wightman, F. L. (1982). Gap detection in normal and hearing-impaired listeners. *Journal of the Acoustical Society of America, 72*(3), 761–765.

Florentine, M., & Buus, S. (1984). Temporal gap detection in sensorineural and simulated hearing impairments. *Journal of Speech and Hearing Research, 27*(3), 449–455.

Florentine, M., Fastl, H., & Buus, S. (1988). Temporal integration in normal hearing, cochlear impairment, and impairment simulated by masking. *Journal of the Acoustical Society of America, 84*(1), 195–203.

Garner, W. R., & Miller, G. A. (1947). The masked threshold of pure tones as a function of duration. *Journal of Experimental Psychology, 37*(4), 293.

Garner, W. R., & Miller, G. A. (1944). Differential sensitivity to intensity as a function of the duration of the comparison tone. *Journal of Experimental Psychology, 34*(6), 450–463.

Glasberg, B. R., & Moore, B. C. J. (1992). Effects of envelope fluctuations on gap detection. *Hearing Research, 64*(1), 81–92.

Glasberg, B. R., Moore, B. C., & Bacon, S. P. (1987). Gap detection and masking in hearing-impaired and normal-hearing subjects. *Journal of the Acoustical Society of America, 81*(5), 1546–1556.

Green, D. M. (1960). Auditory detection of a noise signal. *Journal of the Acoustical Society of America 32*(1), 121–131.

Hall, J. W.,,.& Fernandes, M. A. (1983). Temporal integration, frequency resolution, and off-frequency listening in normal-hearing and cochlear-impaired listeners. *Journal of the Acoustical Society of America, 74*(4), 1172–1177.

Hall, J. W., Grose, J. H., Buss, E., & Hatch, D. R. (1998). Temporal analysis and stimulus fluctuation in listeners with normal and impaired hearing. *Journal of Speech, Language, and Hearing Research, 41*(2), 340–354.

Kohlrausch, A., Fassel, R., & Dau, T. (2000). The influence of carrier level and frequency on modulation and beat-detection thresholds for sinusoidal carriers. *Journal of the Acoustical Society of America, 108*(2), 723–734.

Lamore, P. J. J., Verweij, C., & Brocaar, M. P. (1984). Reliability of auditory function tests in severely hearing-impaired and deaf subjects. *Audiology, 23*(5), 453–466.

Moore, B. C. (1973). Frequency difference limens for short-duration tones. *Journal of the Acoustical Society of America, 54*(3), 610–619.

Moore, B. C. J., Shailer, M. J., & Schooneveldt, G. P. (1992). Temporal modulation transfer functions for band-limited noise in subjects with cochlear hearing loss. *British Journal of Audiology, 26*(4), 229–237.

Plack, C. J., & Oxenham, A. J. (1998). Basilar-membrane nonlinearity and the grown of forward masking. *Journal of the Acoustical Society of America, 103*(3), 1598–1608.

Plomp, R. (1964). The rate of decay of auditory sensation. *Journal of the Acoustical Society of America, 36*(2), 277–282.

Pumplin, J. (1985). Low-noise noise. *Journal of the Acoustical Society of America, 78*(1), 100–104.

Shailer, M. J., & Moore, B. C. (1985). Detection of temporal gaps in bandlimited noise: Effects of variations in bandwidth and signal-to-masker ratio. *Journal of the Acoustical Society of America, 77*(2), 635–639.

Viemeister, N. F. (1979). Temporal modulation transfer functions based upon modulation thresholds. *Journal of the Acoustical Society of America, 66*(5), 1364–1380.

Viemeister, N. F., & Wakefield, G. H. (1991). Temporal integration and multiple looks. *Journal of the Acoustical Society of America, 90*(2), 858–865.

Watson, C. S., & Gengel, R. W. (1969). Signal duration and signal frequency in relation to auditory sensitivity. *Journal of the Acoustical Society of America, 46*(4B), 989–997.

Zwislocki, J. J. (1969). Temporal summation of loudness: An analysis. *Journal of the Acoustical Society of America, 46*(2B), 431–441.

6

Pitch Perception

LEARNING OBJECTIVES

Upon completion of this chapter, students will be able to:

- Understand the differences between waveform and spectral representations of harmonic sounds
- Describe the two different models of pitch perception
- Connect physiological representations to the perception of pitch
- Assess the perceptual mechanisms that underlie pitch perception of pure tones and complex sounds
- Discuss the role of pitch perception in everyday listening
- Characterize the effects of hearing loss on pitch

INTRODUCTION

The perception of pitch is an important part of everyday sound perception: from identifying a person's voice in a background to following the melody of a musical passage, perceiving pitch facilitates our communication and allows us to enjoy the sounds around us. Pitch is defined as the "attribute of auditory sensation in terms of which sounds may be ordered on a musical scale" (ANSI S1.1, 2013). This definition may appear somewhat vague, and it may be easier to think of pitch as the perceptual property of sounds that allows them to be ordered from "low" to "high."

In many cases, pitch can be considered a perceptual correlate of frequency: Increases in frequency are often associated with increases in the perceived pitch. Yet, the terms frequency and pitch are not interchangeable—pitch is a perceptual attribute, whereas frequency is an acoustic property. It is misleading to substitute the word pitch when one means frequency and vice versa. Notably, as we will see in this chapter, factors other than frequency influence the pitch of sounds. Even more importantly, not all sounds have a pitch, even though all sounds have frequency content. This reason alone is compelling enough to avoid the common mistake of interchanging these two, rather different, terms.

Because pitch is a psychological perception (like loudness), we also cannot measure it directly. Consequently, experiments employ measurement techniques similar to those used for loudness assessment. Matching and rating have historically often been used to quantify pitch. However, as we will see in this chapter, subjective assessments of pitch, particularly those adopting rating techniques, have been much less successful than when those same techniques are applied to loudness. Perhaps this is because pitch is different from loudness, as pitch does not really have a magnitude—a high pitch is not really bigger than a low pitch. Further,more the pitch of sounds contains more dimensions than just "high" or "low." Rather, sounds have pitch strengths—they can be clear, strong pitches or they can be weak.

Over the years, many techniques have been used to study pitch perception and this chapter will focus on the following aspects:

- *The codes for pitch perception.* This section reviews the two possible codes for pitch perception—the place model, a spectral code for pitch, and the temporal model, a code for pitch based on temporal periodicities.
- *Pitch of pure tones.* Here, we review the experiments that have led to our understanding of whether the place model or temporal model codes for the pitch of pure tones.
- *Pitch of complex sounds.* Here, we review the experiments that have led to our understanding of whether the place model or temporal model codes for the pitch of complex sounds.

The perception of pitch has been of great interest to auditory scientists and musicians for centuries, so it may not be surprising that the study of pitch has historically been a central question for the field of psychoacoustics. This chapter will review how experiments have contributed to our understanding of

pitch and how hearing impairment affects pitch perception.

In this chapter, we will discuss the following concepts, as they apply to pitch perception:

- Acoustics: Complex tones
- Theories of pitch perception
  - The place code
  - The temporal code
- Pitch perception of pure tones
- Pitch perception of complex sounds
- Effects of sensorineural hearing loss

ACOUSTICS: HARMONIC COMPLEX TONES

Many types of sounds in our environment have a pitch, including both pure tones and complex sounds. Pure tones are typically considered to have the purest and the strongest pitch, and we have extensively reviewed the acoustic characteristics of pure tones in Chapter 2. Complex sounds can also have pitch; the pitch of those sounds and the strength of their pitches depend on certain acoustic characteristics that are important to our understanding of pitch perception. Complex sounds can be noisy in nature, or they can be harmonic. Here, we focus specifically on harmonic stimuli, although it is worth noting that in certain circumstances, noises can also evoke a pitch, as is discussed later in this chapter. In order to fully understand how sounds evoke a pitch, we must first review the acoustics of those sounds.

Whereas a pure tone can be characterized by its amplitude and frequency, with the period (T) being easily determined by $1/f$, where f is the frequency of the pure tone, *complex tones*, on the other hand, consist of multiple tones. Complex tones containing frequencies that are related to each other by integer multiples are called *harmonic* sounds or *harmonic* tones. The lowest frequency of a complex tone is the *fundamental frequency (f_0)*, and the harmonics occur at integer multiples of the fundamental frequency. There are numerous examples of harmonic sounds in our daily lives, such as vowels and sounds typically generated by stringed, woodwind, and brass musical instruments.

The following equation characterizes the waveform of harmonic tones:

$$y = \sum_{n=1}^{N} a_n \sin(2\pi n f_0 t + \theta_n),$$

where a_n refers to the amplitude of the nth tone or *harmonic*, f_0 refers to the **fundamental frequency** (in this type of sound, the lowest frequency in the stimulus), t refers to time, θ_n indicates the phase of the nth tone, and N indicates the total number of harmonics in the complex tone. Note that the Σ denotes a sum, and therefore this equation represents the sum of harmonics 1 to N.

All harmonic sounds contain certain common acoustic characteristics:

- *They are periodic.* Periodic sounds repeat over time. A pure, synthesized sound will repeat exactly; however, most natural sounds contain some variability such that each cycle of the period appears slightly different from the others.
- *The repetition rate is determined by the f_0.* The rate at which the stimulus repeats (the *repetition rate*) is determined by the fundamental frequency and can be calculated by $1/f_0$. We can also quantify the repetition rate in terms of the period (T) of the complex sound.

In order to illustrate the nature of complex tones, the acoustics of a natural complex sound produced by a trumpet ("middle-C"; C4) are illustrated in Figure 6–1. The waveform shown in the left panel is a short snapshot of the full note. It is clear that this waveform is not that of a pure tone because the overall characteristic does not appear to be sinusoidal. Yet, we see a very consistent structure in

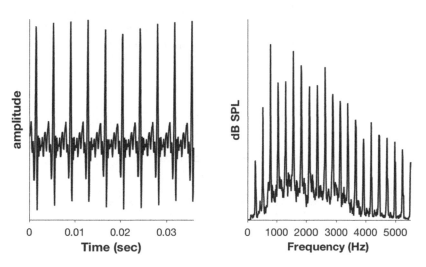

FIGURE 6–1. Waveform (*left panel*) and spectrum (*right panel*) of the musical note C4 (f_0 = 261 Hz) played by a trumpet.

the waveform, and this consistent structure repeats over time: The repetition rate of the stimulus is 3.83 ms, as we can observe a peak in the waveform occurring every 3.83 ms. Because the period of this sound is 3.83 ms, we can calculate the fundamental frequency of the stimulus to be 261 Hz.

We also easily see the representation of the fundamental frequency in the spectrum, plotted in the right panel of Figure 6–1. The peaks in the spectrum occur every 261 Hz. For example, the first four peaks occur at frequencies of 261, 522, 783, and 1044 Hz. The spectral representation contains information about the fundamental frequency in two different ways. The first is that the fundamental frequency is represented as the lowest frequency component in the spectrum. We see this in Figure 6–1 as a harmonic at the 261-Hz frequency. It is extremely common for natural sounds to contain a spectral peak that corresponds exactly to the f_0. However, the fundamental frequency is also represented by the relationship between the various harmonics. Note that the spectral peaks occur at multiples of the fundamental frequency (e.g., 261, 522, 783, and 1044 Hz), and as a result they all have a common frequency of 261 Hz. More generally, an easy way to determine the f_0 of any sound from its spectrum is to calculate the *greatest common frequency (GCF)* from the harmonics.

When we use the GCF to calculate the fundamental frequency, we notice that removing the lowest frequency of the stimulus does not alter the fundamental frequency. For example, the harmonics of 522, 783, and 1044 still have a GCF of 261 Hz. The effects of removing low-frequency components from a complex tone are illustrated in Figure 6–2. This complex tone has a fundamental frequency of 200 Hz. The top panels illustrate the effects of removing low-frequency harmonics from the sound spectrum. The bottom panels show the waveforms of each of the corresponding sound spectra. As the top panels illustrate, removing the low-frequency harmonics does not alter the spacing between the other spectral components, keeping the GCF and, therefore, the f_0 intact. The bottom panels indicate that removing the harmonics does not change the repetition rate of the stimulus, although some of the waveform characteristics do change. For any stimulus, we can remove subsequent harmonics (e.g., the 1st and 2nd and 3rd and 4th and so on) with the same results: The fundamental frequency will remain at 261 Hz until all harmonics are removed except the very last one. Note also that removing the odd harmonics will yield a different result: if 261,

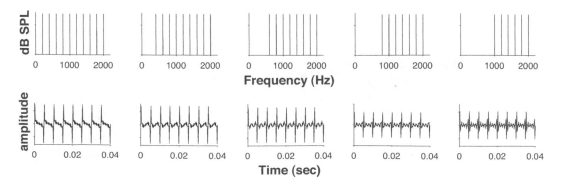

FIGURE 6–2. Illustration of the acoustic effect of removing low-frequency harmonics. Spectra (*top panels*) and waveforms (*bottom panels*) are shown. Low-frequency harmonics are progressively removed from a complex tone, illustrated by moving from the left panels to the right panels.

783, 1305 Hz, etc. are removed, the remaining components will be 522, 1044, 1566 Hz, etc. This stimulus would have a fundamental frequency of 522 Hz.

This section has primarily focused on the representation of the fundamental frequency, as that is a primary determinant of the pitch of complex tones (Helmholtz, 1863). However, as we observed in Figure 6–1, each harmonic can have a different amplitude. Although the amplitudes of those harmonics have little to do with the pitch of the sound, they contribute to different attributes of the stimulus, primarily its loudness and timbre (the quality). The characteristics of the sound source (e.g., voice source at the glottis) and the filtering of that source (e.g., resonant cavities of the vocal tract) determine the amplitudes of the harmonics.

THEORIES OF PITCH PERCEPTION

There are two main theories underlying perception of pitch in the auditory system: the *place code* and the *temporal code*. Both models were originally developed to describe the phenomena that the frequency of a pure tone determines its pitch and that the fundamental frequency of a complex tone determines its pitch. Each code has its roots in the acoustics of stimuli: the place code is based on a spectral representation, whereas the temporal code is based on a temporal representation of the sound. These theories come about because of the interchangeability between the frequency, or fundamental frequency, and the period of both simple and complex sounds. Essentially, the period and the f_0 are two different ways of describing the same acoustic property. Physiological evidence also supports these two codes, as we now know that the auditory system contains place and temporal representations of the frequency and fundamental frequency in the auditory periphery. Yet, a physiological representation does not automatically infer a

psychological representation. Thus, we must discuss psychoacoustic data in light of the physiological data in order to fully understand the perception of pitch. This section reviews the physiological evidence for the two codes and then places them in a psychoacoustic context. Subsequent sections will then present evidence to support or refute these two codes in the formation of pitch.

The Place Code

The *place code* is effectively a spectral model that posits that frequency of a sound is coded in terms of the place of stimulation in the auditory pathway. This code is rooted in the idea that the ear functions as a Fourier analyzer, with different locations on the basilar membrane (or different neurons) responding to different frequencies. In its simplest form, the place of maximum stimulation determines the pitch (Helmholtz, 1863). In more complex versions, the pattern of excitation determines the pitch in terms of the multiple locations maximally stimulated by harmonics (e.g., Goldstein, 1973).

Helmholtz's version of the place code is elegant, simple, and straightforward to understand. He believed that the pitch of a stimulus was determined from the place of maximum excitation in the cochlea. A pure tone evoked a pitch because there was a location on the basilar membrane that coded for the frequency of that pure tone. Thus, because tones of different frequencies stimulated different basilar membrane locations, different pitches were perceived. In addition, he argued that a complex tone evoked a pitch at the fundamental frequency because the harmonic component corresponding to the fundamental frequency was associated with maximal stimulation of the basilar membrane. Any manipulation that shifted the location of maximum excitation would be expected to alter the pitch of a stimulus.

For years, Helmholtz's place theory of pitch perception was the dominant theory of pitch perception. However, modern experimentation has demonstrated that Helmholtz's ideas, while elegant, have not been able to explain all pitch phenomena. These failings will be discussed in subsequent sections in this chapter. Because of failures of his model, more complex variants of the place model have been developed to explain the pitch of complex sounds.

These complex variants of the place model have been referred to as **harmonic template models**, and are based on the principles that the fundamental frequency of a sound is coded on the basilar membrane and can be derived from the locations of the traveling wave peaks distributed along the length of the cochlea. The excitation peaks occur at locations that correspond to the harmonics, and, as we discussed in the section on acoustics,

those peaks occur at a spacing determined by the fundamental frequency. In this case, then, the pitch of a stimulus is determined by a pattern analyzer, which determines the frequencies from the locations of maximum vibration and searches for the common frequency.

The two versions of the place code are illustrated in Figure 6–3, which shows a schematic of the envelope of the cochlear traveling wave for a pure tone (top panel) and for a complex tone (bottom panel). The frequency of the tone in the top panel can be coded from the place of maximum excitation à la Helmholtz (a simple place model). This model can effectively explain why pitch increases with increasing stimulus frequency. Changing the frequency causes different basilar membrane locations to be associated with different peak excitation. The pitch of the complex stimulus, however, can be coded in multiple ways: (1) the location of the lowest-frequency (api-

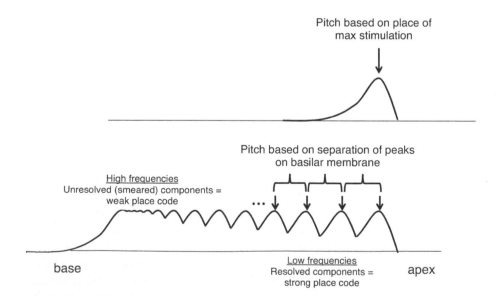

FIGURE 6–3. Schematic of the traveling wave envelope for a single tone (*top panel*) and a complex tone (*bottom panel*). The top panel illustrates a single place of maximum vibration. The bottom panel illustrates multiple places of high vibration and shows that low-frequency harmonics are resolved at the apex and high-frequency harmonics are unresolved at the base of the cochlea.

cal) component, as in Helmholtz's variant, and (2) the spacing between the places of maximum basilar membrane excitation, as in harmonic template models. Because the spacing between components decreases as frequency increases (as the place representation moves toward the base of the cochlea), the place code is a poor representation of the fundamental frequency at high fundamental frequencies. When the excitation peaks associated with individual harmonics are not **resolved** (that is, they are smeared together), the place code indicates that the pitch of the stimulus should be difficult to determine or should be very weak. Although the place code is illustrated here using a cochlear representation, excitation patterns are commonly used to make psychoacoustic predictions.

The Temporal Code

Unlike the place code, which is a spectral representation, the **temporal code** postulates that the pitch of a stimulus is based on the temporal patterns of neural impulses evoked by that stimulus. Wever and Bray (1937) first proposed a physiological temporal code explanation for frequency coding, and called their code the **volley theory**. Their theory stated that individual fibers could be synchronized to a waveform, even if they did not fire on every cycle. A group of fibers could then code for the frequency of sound via their pooled response. Through modern measurements, the volley theory has been refined and we now know that a temporal code for frequency is present in the auditory system (Tasaki, 1954), but is only available for frequencies below approximately 3000 to 5000 Hz in the mammalian ear. The temporal code begins at the level of the auditory nerve and requires responses of multiple auditory nerve fibers. The mechanism by which the period of a stimulus is coded is

called **phase locking**, which is defined as the propensity for auditory nerve fibers to fire at a particular phase of a low-frequency tone.

Phase locking is demonstrated in Figure 6–4, which illustrates the pattern of firing for multiple auditory nerve fibers in response to a single tone. The top panel of Figure 6–4 illustrates a periodic stimulating wave, whereas each of the bottom panels represents a potential firing pattern for a single auditory nerve fiber. Each of these fibers generates an action potential coincident with the peaks of the stimulus. However, due to refractory periods and other limiting factors, a single auditory nerve fiber cannot always fire at every peak in the waveform. For example, fiber 1 in Figure 6–4 fires during cycles 2, 4, 7, and 11. Other fibers, however, may fire during other cycles of the waveform. Perhaps a different fiber (fiber 2) fires during cycles 1, 4, 6, and 10. Another fiber might fire during cycles 1, 5, 8, and 11 and so on. Taken collectively, the firing pattern of multiple auditory nerve fibers provides a code for the period of a stimulus, as the temporal separation between spikes is always a multiple of the stimulus period. The temporal separation between the pooled spikes corresponds to the period.

A common way to represent the behavior of an auditory nerve fiber is to describe the firing patterns in the form of a period histogram. A period histogram represents the number of spikes (summed over many stimulus presentations) plotted as a function of the phase within a single period. To illustrate phase locking abilities measured physiologically, Figure 6–5 shows a period histogram measured in the auditory nerve of a squirrel monkey measured by Rose, Hind, Anderson, and Brugge (1971). Figure 6–5 illustrates the number of spikes generated for an auditory nerve fiber tuned to 1100 Hz and a stimulating tone of 50 dB SPL. We observe that this fiber tends to generate the most spikes at the peak of the stimulus cycle.

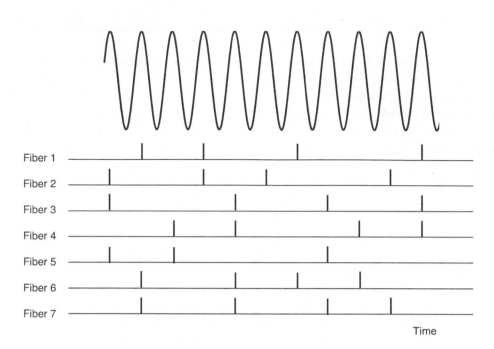

FIGURE 6–4. Illustration of phase locking to a pure tone. The top panel illustrates sine wave stimulation. The bottom panels illustrate firing of individual neurons, where each line represents an action potential (a spike). Note that neurons tend to fire at the peak of the sine wave, but not necessarily every cycle. Collectively, the nerve fibers code for the stimulus period.

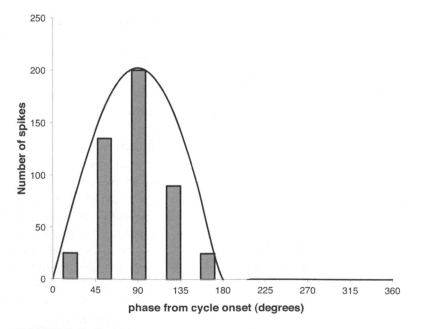

FIGURE 6–5. Period histogram of the squirrel monkey auditory nerve for an 1100-Hz tone. Adapted from Rose et al. (1971).

Numerous other investigators have measured phase locking abilities in the auditory nerve, and have made the following observations.

- *Dependence on frequency.* Phase locking to pure tones has been demonstrated to occur up to frequencies of approximately 3 to 5 kHz (Johnson, 1980) and depends on the species. The limiting factor in this case is the frequency of stimulation, and not the center frequency of the auditory nerve fibers themselves, as auditory nerve fibers are homogeneous—their properties do not vary based on the location of cochlear innervation.
- *Small, but measurable, dependence on intensity.* Phase locking to pure tones can be dependent on the intensity of the stimulus. The interval between spikes varies little with changing intensity (Rose et al., 1971). However, other measurements, such as those by Young and Sachs (1979), demonstrated that the synchronization of phase locking across fibers increases with stimulus level. Young and Sachs (1979) demonstrated that the degree of neural synchrony could be used to code the spectral represen-

tation of a vowel, for at least the first two formants.

The auditory nerve has also been demonstrated to phase lock to the envelope of a stimulus. Although high-frequency auditory nerve fibers may not be able to phase lock to an individual harmonic within a complex stimulus, it can phase lock to the period of that complex stimulus (Joris & Yin, 1992). Figure 6–6 illustrates how this might work. The top panel illustrates a complex waveform with slow envelope fluctuations. Schematics of firing by two fibers are shown in the bottom panels. Here, the fibers fire in response to the peaks of the stimulus envelope, and not to the fast fluctuations of the stimulus. In this way, high-frequency auditory nerve fibers can code the fluctuation rate.

Taking these results together, we note that auditory nerve fibers may phase lock to pure tones, as long at their characteristic frequencies are below 3 to 5 kHz. For pure tones, then, the temporal code is a *low-frequency* phenomenon. For complex tones, however, the temporal code is present in both high- and low-frequency fibers. Although high-

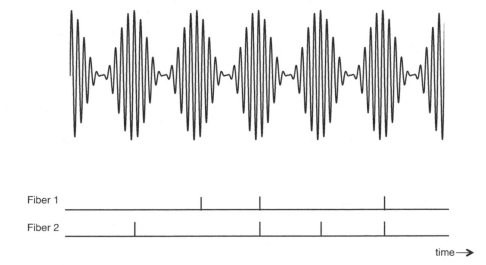

FIGURE 6–6. Illustration of phase locking to a complex stimulus.

frequency fibers will not phase lock to pure tones, they can and do phase lock to slow fluctuations of complex stimuli. Given that fundamental frequency is represented as individual harmonics but also in the repetition rate, both high- and low-frequency auditory nerve fibers can code for the fundamental frequency. Low-frequency fibers will phase lock to individual harmonic components, whereas high-frequency fibers will phase lock to the fluctuation rate of the envelope. Psychophysically, this temporal code is implemented as an autocorrelation function, which is discussed in the next section.

A focus of the field has been to determine which code best describes pitch perception, but both codes might work in concert. One possibility is a combination of the place and temporal codes. This *spectral-temporal* code posits that the temporal patterns in the auditory nerve form the code for the pitch, but these temporal patterns must align with the appropriate place in the cochlea (Loeb, White, & Merzenich, 1983). This particular version of the codes requires both place and temporal information to be appropriately aligned and synchronized. Distortions to either cochlear representation could lead to altered pitch.

In summary, auditory physiology provides two potential codes for representing the frequency and the fundamental frequency of a stimulus—the place and the temporal code. The place code is based on extracting stimulus frequencies from the place(s) of maximum basilar membrane vibration. The temporal code is based on the ability of the auditory nerve to phase lock as a representation of temporal patterns present in sounds.

Psychophysical Representations

As we have just discussed the physiological representation of stimulus frequency, we now turn to psychoacoustical representations. To demonstrate how the ear provides multiple representations for complex sounds from a psychoacoustical perspective, Figures 6–7 and 6–8 depict how the pitch of a stimulus might be generated for a 100-Hz harmonic tone. Figure 6–7 represents the place code in the form of the excitation pattern, whereas Figure 6–8 illustrates the temporal code by showing waveforms at the output of different auditory filters across the range of frequencies in the stimulus.

In the place model, the excitation pattern is used, which is a representation of the power at the output of the auditory filter bank. The excitation pattern in Figure 6–7 reveals the two possible place models: an excitation pattern peak at 100 Hz, and a representation of the integer-multiple harmonics in the low frequencies. Note that the low-frequency harmonics are *resolved*, meaning that their peaks are represented in the excitation pattern. We can see the peaks at 100, 200, and 300 Hz and so on. However, these peaks reduce in size as the frequency of the harmonics increase, due to the broadening of frequency selectivity with increasing frequency. At some point, around the 10th harmonic, we observe that the high frequency components are no longer resolved. The frequencies within the stimulus are so close together that their representations are smeared together. A complex place model that recognizes patterns would be capable of extracting the resolved frequencies present in the stimulus using the low-frequency filters. Using this information, the auditory system could calculate the greatest common frequency and determine the pitch.

The temporal model also uses the auditory filter bank, but is based on the waveform output from those filters. Figure 6–8 illustrates how the temporal code might work. Each of these waveforms represents the output of a different auditory filter. Note that the outputs of the 100-Hz and 200-Hz filters look nearly sinusoidal, illustrating that these filters pass a

FIGURE 6–7. Excitation pattern of a harmonic tone with a 100-Hz fundamental frequency. Large peaks associated with the harmonics are visible for the first to about the 10th harmonic.

FIGURE 6–8. Illustration of the temporal representation of a harmonic tone with a 100-Hz fundamental frequency. Each channel represents the output of a single auditory filter, and the 10-ms consistent periodicity is illustrated on each output waveform.

single harmonic. A temporal code based on consistent periodicities could represent these two frequencies easily—the auditory nerve can phase lock to these low frequencies. As the auditory filter frequency increases, however, interactions between components begin to occur and the output waveforms no longer appear sinusoidal. The waveform outputs of the 1300- and 3000-Hz auditory filters contain multiple frequencies leading to a modulated waveform having slow and fast fluctuations. A temporal code would have the ability to represent the slow fluctuations, as the auditory nerve would phase lock to the fundamental frequency. Note that these filtered waveforms repeat at the same rate as the 100-Hz tone, and their 10-ms periods are illustrated in Figure 6–8. Synchrony in the output waveforms across multiple auditory filters could provide a very robust code for the period (and therefore the pitch) of a sound. Psychophysical models capture the temporal synchrony across frequency bands in the form of across-frequency *autocorrelation*, which determines the periodicities present in the stimulus and captures whether those periodicities are coherent across frequency.

As we have discussed, a physiological representation of frequency does not automatically imply that this information is used at higher levels of the auditory system to create the pitch of a stimulus, although it is probable. Coupling behavioral measurements with physiological provides more powerful (and perhaps necessary) arguments to support of one model over the other for pitch perception, or perhaps the operation of both. After all, physiological measures do not assess hearing and must be interpreted under measurements of perception.

The primary questions addressed by the studies on pitch perception are, "Which mechanism is responsible for pitch perception?" and "Is that mechanism the same for pure and complex tones?" So far, it has not been straightforward to deduce which mechanism is dominant, and all mechanisms likely work together to varied degrees. The codes can operate simultaneously and in parallel, and it can be very difficult to determine whether one code dominates over another. Furthermore, if one code is disrupted, say through hearing loss or another factor, another code may remain to provide a pitch perception.

PITCH OF PURE TONES: SUBJECTIVE MEASURES

The earliest work on pitch perception consisted of connecting scientific observations with acoustics. Musicians, physicists, and otologists understood that there was a strong relationship between the acoustic quantity of frequency and the psychological quantity of pitch and that increases in frequency were associated with increases in pitch. This knowledge formed the beginning of our understanding of the relationship between pitch and stimulus frequency and led to models of pitch perception that are still accepted by modern scientists.

However, the early observations did not allow the measurement of pitch for two reasons. First, as with loudness, we cannot measure the pitch of a pure tone—we can only measure the pitch of that tone relative to another tone. Second, in order to measure the relationship between the pitch of one tone and that of another tone, we need a reference stimulus and a measurement scale. In the 1930s, S. S. Stevens, a pioneer in the study of loudness perception, also paved the way for measurement of pitch. He applied his methodologies to pitch, although, as we will see, with less success. Although we can be rather critical of many of Stevens' methodologies and assumptions, there is no doubt that his investigations laid the groundwork for our understanding of pitch perception.

Effects of Frequency

In 1937, Stevens, Volkmann, and Newman (1937) employed a *magnitude production* technique to determine the relationship between the pitch of a pure tone and its frequency. In this seminal study, Stevens et al. presented a reference tone to listeners and asked them to adjust the frequency of another tone so that its pitch was estimated to be 1/2 that of the reference. In this way, they measured the relationship between the pitch of one sound and another. Stevens et al. then assigned the number of 1000 to the 1000-Hz tone, and called the unit of pitch the ***mel***, where 1000 mels is defined as the pitch associated with a 1000-Hz tone. The mel scale can be interpreted in the following way: 500 mels corresponds to a pitch ½ that of 1000 Hz and 2000 mels would be a pitch twice that of the pitch at 1000 Hz. Stevens et al. constructed a function relating the pitch of a sound (in mels) to the frequency of that sound. Figure 6–9

illustrates data obtained from Beranek (1949), which shows even greater discrepancy between pitch and frequency than originally measured by Stevens et al.

The data in Figure 6–9 show a number of important findings:

- *Increases in frequency were associated with increases in pitch.* There was a clear, monotonic relationship between frequency and pitch, in which increasing the frequency also increased the pitch.
- *The relationship between frequency and pitch was not linear.* The relationship between the pitch of the sound in mels and frequency was different above and below 1000 Hz. For frequencies below 1000 Hz, there was a mostly linear relationship between the pitch in mels and frequency: A 500-Hz tone had a pitch of approximately 500 mels and a 100-Hz tone had a pitch of approximately 100 mels. On the other hand, for frequencies above 1000 Hz, the pitch in mels

FIGURE 6–9. Mels versus frequency (Hz). Adapted from Beranek (1949).

tended to be lower than the frequency of the test tone, and the higher the frequency the greater this discrepancy.

Criticisms of the mel scale are many, ranging from bias in experimental techniques to wide variability within and across listeners with normal hearing to the fact that it does not correspond to the musical scale and its associated perceptions. In fact, if we conceptually consider the implications of applying subjective scaling procedures to a perception like pitch, further questions arise. Unlike loudness, pitch does not have a "magnitude," and the mel scale ignores pitch strength (the degree to which a pitch is clear and strong) and pitch chroma (the perception of similarities of octaves), which are also important aspects of the pitch percept. The data relating the mel to frequency are suspect and potentially problematic. As a consequence, the mel is rarely used in the psychophysical literature, although it is still used in the field of speech perception and by acoustic engineers. However, the experimental result that increasing frequency leads to increasing pitch is important and has been replicated numerous times. The difference in the shape of this function at low vs. high frequencies is also repeatable, and suggests different physiological mechanisms responsible for the perception of pitch of sounds of low versus high frequencies.

Pitch Strength

Although the mel scale was an attempt at quantifying the pitch of a stimulus, it does not provide a description of the clearness of the pitch, or whether the sound can be used in a melody. We have all heard sounds with very clear pitches—like those generated by a clarinet or a trombone—and weak pitches—like noises or a whisper. In particular, high-frequency pure tones do not evoke a clear,

strong pitch. Illustrating this very compelling result, Ward (1954) asked listeners to adjust the frequency of a higher-frequency tone so that it was an octave above a reference tone. When the higher-frequency tones were greater than about 4000 Hz, the matches became highly variable. Later, Attneave and Olson (1971) demonstrated that pure tones at frequencies above 5 kHz do not produce a clear sense of melody, even when their frequencies are organized in a way that one would expect a melody. Attneave and Olson state particularly: "Something changes rather dramatically at this level [5000 Hz]; phenomenally it is identifiable as a loss of musical quality, whatever that may be." Semal and Demany (1990) measured the upper limit of "musical pitch" and found that it was approximately 4.7 kHz, consistent with the studies of Ward, Attneave, and Olson. Thus, it is likely not a coincidence that the highest note on a piano has a fundamental frequency of 4186 Hz. As a whole, these observations support the idea that pure tones at high frequencies do not evoke a clear, strong pitch, unlike pure tones at low frequencies. High-frequency pure tones can even be perceived as unpleasant, rather than melodic.

The data described here point to an aspect of pitch that is not present in the perception of loudness—sounds can also have a weak or a strong pitch. This dimension is referred to as ***pitch strength***. Pitch strength is typically quantified using magnitude estimation techniques, in which the listener rates the pitch strength of a sound. We consider high-frequency pure tones to have low pitch strength, whereas low-frequency pure tones have a high pitch strength.

Effects of Intensity

The pitch of a stimulus is dependent not only on its frequency, but also on its intensity, though pitch shifts with intensity are not nearly as large as pitch shifts with frequency. Stevens (1935) made some of the earliest measurements of pitch under conditions of various intensities and demonstrated large changes in pitch with changes in intensity (as high as shifts of 15–20%). Using some modifications to Stevens' method, Morgan, Garner, and Galambos (1951) found much smaller changes in pitch with intensity than Stevens. They employed a matching procedure in which listeners adjusted the frequency of a test tone so that its pitch matched that of a reference tone. The reference stimulus was always set at 100 dB SPL, and the test tones were set to levels lower than that. They conducted their experiment at many different frequencies, three of which are shown in Figure 6–10. Their median data are plotted as the percent change in frequency between the test tone (the lower level stimulus) and the reference tone (the higher level stimulus) for the two sounds to have the same pitch.

Morgan et al.'s data illustrate that the relationship between the pitch of a tone and its intensity depends on the frequency of the sound being tested:

- *Low frequency*—as the intensity of a stimulus increased, the pitch of a low-frequency tone (shown as the black, filled circles) *decreased.*
- *Mid frequency*—as the intensity of a stimulus increased, the pitch of a mid-frequency pure tone (e.g., 500–2000 Hz; shown as the unfilled circles)) *changed very little.*
- *High frequency*—as the intensity of a stimulus increased, the pitch of a high-frequency pure tone (shown as the gray, filled circles) *increased.*

Thus, although pitch changes with increasing intensity, it does so in a fairly complex way. We generally assume that pitch shifts with intensity are fairly small, though the variability across listeners can be rather large.

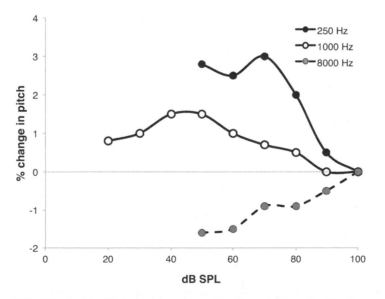

FIGURE 6–10. Pitch matches as a function of intensity. Median percent change in pitch is plotted as a function of stimulus intensity for pure tones presented at three frequencies. Adapted from Morgan et al. (1951).

Pitch of Pure Tones: Frequency Discrimination

Subjective measures of pitch can be valuable and inform our understanding of how sounds are assigned a pitch and the factors that affect that perception. Accompanying measures, such as just noticeable differences, can complement the subjective measures of pitch described previously. Due to the problematic nature of subjective pitch measurements, most modern experimental evaluations of pitch perception involve discrimination experiments. Techniques adopted in frequency discrimination experiments usually involve standard psychophysical procedures, such as 2-interval, 2-alternative-forced choice (2I–2AFC) and adaptive staircase threshold estimating procedures. A typical *frequency discrimination* task requires a listener to hear two (or more) sounds with differing frequencies and to select the sound with the (often) higher (or different) frequency. To illustrate how this might be implemented in an experiment, Figure 6–11 shows an experimental trial for a frequency-discrimination experiment, where the experimenters ask, "What is the smallest frequency difference necessary to tell that two sounds have a different pitch?" Although the frequency of the stimulus is manipulated, listeners are asked which of the two intervals contains the stimulus with the higher pitch.

A number of investigators have evaluated frequency discrimination, but Wier, Jesteadt, and Green (1977) conducted one of the most comprehensive studies. They evaluated frequency discrimination for many different frequencies and many different stimulus levels. In their experiments, they measured the *frequency difference limen* (**the FDL**), otherwise known as the *just noticeable frequency difference* (Δf in Hz) between two tones. Data adapted from their study are illustrated in Figure 6–12, which plots the FDL in hertz as a function of frequency for three different stimulus levels.

Taken together, the data illustrate three primary findings:

- *Exceptional sensitivity.* The frequency-discrimination data shown in this figure indicate that humans have an exquisite ability to tell when two tones have different frequencies. At a moderate stimulus level (e.g., 40 dB sensation level), the FDL at 1000 Hz was roughly 2 Hz. Thus, we can hear a change in frequency approximately 2/1000ths of the reference frequency, or 0.2%!

- *Increasing FDL with frequency.* Most strikingly, the FDL increased as the frequency of the reference tone increased. Thus, in absolute frequency, it was more difficult for the listeners to discriminate between pure tones of different frequencies when the frequency was high. In relative terms, however, the relationship is more complicated. To illustrate this, Figure 6–13 plots the data in terms of the Weber fraction, which is

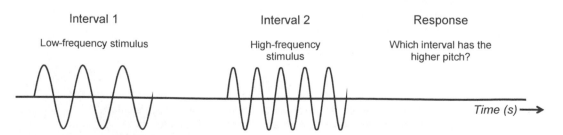

FIGURE 6–11. Illustration of an experimental trial in a frequency-discrimination experiment.

FIGURE 6–12. Frequency difference limens (Δf) plotted as a function of frequency in Hz. Different functions represent data collected from different stimulus levels. Adapted from Wier et al. (1977).

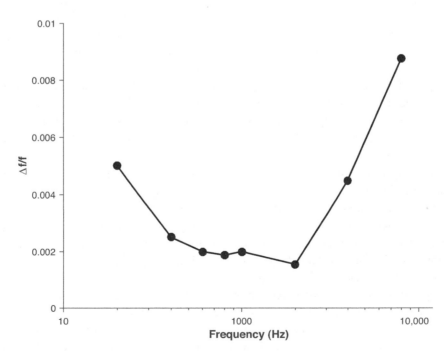

FIGURE 6–13. Weber fractions for frequency discrimination (Δf/f) plotted as a function of tone frequency measured at 40 dB SL. Adapted from Wier et al. (1977).

Δf/f when applied to a frequency discrimination task. Plotting the data in this way indicates that for frequencies below 1500 Hz, the Weber fraction decreases with increasing frequency. For frequencies above 2000 Hz, the ratio increases with increasing frequency.

- *Better FDLs at higher intensities.* Referring back to Figure 6–12, we observe that thresholds decreased as the intensity of the stimulus is increased. The task became easier at higher and higher stimulus levels. Notably, the change in the FDL with frequency was also much larger for the low frequencies than the high ones. For example, between the 10 and 80 dB levels, thresholds decreased by about a factor of 4 at 800 Hz but only by a factor of 1.25 at 8000 Hz.

MECHANISMS FOR CODING THE PITCH OF PURE TONES

Thus, we return to the primary question: Which mechanism is responsible for pitch perception of pure tones? Wier et al. had hoped to find strong evidence in support of either the temporal or the place model. However, their data, by themselves, did not provide strong support for either the place or the temporal model, but they too identified different trends for low versus high frequencies in the form of the frequency and level effects just mentioned. Thus, their data do implicate two models at work for pitch perception.

We can look to another frequency discrimination experiment, conducted by Henning in 1966, to provide additional input into this question as it relates to frequency discrimination. Henning measured frequency discrimination for multiple frequencies, just like Wier et al. However, on every trial, Henning randomly varied the intensity of the sound presented in each observation interval. Henning's manipulation would keep the temporal code intact, because random variations in intensity do not affect the degree of phase locking. However, random variations would disrupt the place model, because increasing the intensity of a tone changes the pitch of the tone. Henning found that at low frequencies, the intensity variation did not affect the FDL. However, at high frequencies, the FDL was much worse under the intensity variation. Henning concluded that the place code was supported at the high frequencies and the temporal code was supported at the low frequencies.

Across the studies we have discussed, we see a major trend: Pitch perception seems to follow a different pattern at low frequencies versus high frequencies. It follows, then, that a different mechanism is responsible for coding pitch at high frequencies, above about 3 kHz, vs. low frequencies, below about 3 kHz. Let us first consider the evidence in this vein:

- Mels and frequency are in rough correspondence below 1000 Hz but not above.
- The pitch strength of high-frequency tones is much weaker than for low-frequency tones.
- Morgan et al.'s intensity data indicate a lowering of pitch with increasing intensity at low frequencies but an increasing pitch with increasing intensity at high frequencies.
- The increasingly poor proportion ($\Delta f/f$) needed for frequency discrimination at high frequencies
- The greater effects of level on the FDL at low frequencies compared with high frequencies
- An influence of intensity variation on the FDL at high frequencies but not low

Recall that the place code is a spectrally based code and is based on the place/s of excitation represented in the cochlea. On the other hand, the temporal code is based on the pattern/s of neural firing and is related to the representation of the period of a stimulus via neural synchrony. Generally speaking, these two codes should lead to different patterns of pitch perception, particularly with respect to behavior and high and low frequencies.

Evidence in Support of the Place Code

We first consider the place code. The place code is likely the only code available for pitch perception of pure tones at high frequencies: Physiological data indicate that the temporal model is not in operation at high frequencies due to the lack of auditory nerve phase locking to high-frequency pure tones. Although we can argue that the place code is the only code in operation for high frequencies, evidence across a variety of studies supports the place code in general. First, the place code is consistent with the increasing pitch with increasing intensity. Recall that increasing the intensity of a stimulus leads to a basal shift in the peak of the traveling wave. This peak shift could lead to an increase in pitch with increasing intensity. However, it should be noted that the perceived shift in pitch is generally much less than that predicted by the shift in the traveling wave peak that occurs when the intensity of a tone is increased (McFadden, 1986). Excitation pattern modeling of frequency discrimination data also supports the place code (Wier et al., 1977), as does the effects of intensity variation on the FDLs as measured by Henning. On the whole, the place code is supported as coding pitch perception at frequencies above 4 to 5 kHz.

Evidence in Support of the Temporal Code

Next, we consider the temporal code as a potential mechanism for pitch perception of pure tones at low frequencies. Some data sets are encouraging for the temporal code, but not all data are in robust support. The strong perceptions of pitch of low-frequency tones, in contrast to the weak perceptions at high frequencies, suggest that the same code is not responsible for pitch perception in both low and high frequencies. Given that we just concluded that the place model is supported for the pitch of high-frequency tones, perhaps the temporal code is more active for low-frequency tones. Notably, FDLs are not correlated with measures of frequency selectivity, providing an indication of a failure of the place model (Moore & Peters, 1992). However, there are some issues with a temporal account of pitch perception at low frequencies. The finding that FDLs depend on stimulus level appear to contradict a purely temporal code, and the lowering of pitch with increasing intensity also poses some problems for a purely temporal interpretation. The degree or rate of phase locking does not depend on intensity; rather it is the synchrony across channels.

Summary: Place Versus Temporal Code

On the whole, it seems clear that the place code is responsible for coding the pitch percept of pure tones at high frequencies. For low frequencies, however, the conclusions are less clear. The temporal code explains some of the findings, but not all experimental data are consistent with a pure temporal code. Given that the patterns of data are so different for pitch perception between high and low frequencies, we are driven to conclude that the place code is not exclusively responsible for both. Thus, we typically believe that the temporal code has a role to play in the perception of pitch of pure tones in the low frequencies, although further investigations are clearly necessary to fully flesh out the two possibilities. However, it is likely that both codes are in operation for low-frequency sounds to some degree and that the pitch of sounds is determined by a combination of both models, or the model which provides the most robust representation for the task at hand. As Chris Plack states in his 2016 book, "After all, if both sets of information are available to the auditory system, why not use both?"

PITCH OF COMPLEX SOUNDS

Observations of the pitch of complex sounds have been conducted over many centuries. Helmholtz, though not the first to make these observations, had a clear impact on the theories of pitch perception. A particularly notable observation from his time is that a complex tone produced a pitch that was similar to a tone with a frequency that matched the fundamental frequency of the complex tone. Consider the trumpet note (C4) illustrated in Figure 6–1. In general, someone would hear the pitch of this note as corresponding to middle C. Any instrument playing a note with the same fundamental frequency (261 Hz in this case), would also be perceived as having the same pitch. From observations such as these, we know that the pitch of a complex, harmonic sound is determined by the fundamental frequency.

Using observations like this one, Helmholtz theorized that the pitch of the sound was determined by the place of maximum excitation within the cochlea, and that location must be stimulated by the component corresponding to the fundamental frequency. The simple version of place model was a reasonable explanation for this perception at the time, as his complex tones all contained energy at the fundamental frequency. However, in 1843, Seebeck constructed a siren that produced a harmonic complex that was missing the component corresponding to the fundamental frequency. He observed that the pitch of this sound also matched to the fundamental frequency, despite the absence of that particular component in the stimulus. At the time, Helmholtz discounted Seebeck's observations, and while other investigators did continue to investigate Seebeck's result, little traction was gained on alternate theories of pitch perception until 1940 when Schouten revisited Seebeck's observations (Plomp, 1967).

So, if Helmholtz's model wasn't correct, what model was? Could a temporal explanation explain the pitch of complex sounds? Over the years, a number of explanations have emerged. Given that both place and temporal codes are present in the auditory system and that both of these codes are present at a single frequency and across frequency (see Figures 6–7 and 6–8), it has been difficult to establish the main code responsible for the perception of pitch of complex sounds.

Pitch of the Missing Fundamental

In 1940, Schouten observed that Helmholtz's version of the place model could not account for the pitch of a complex sound when the harmonic associated with the fundamental frequency was removed (Schouten, 1940). Schouten dubbed this phenomenon the *residue pitch*, also sometimes called the *pitch of the missing fundamental*. One hypothesis explaining the residue pitch was related to Helmholtz's theory: The residue pitch occurred because distortion in the cochlea yielded a traveling wave representation at the location corresponding to the fundamental frequency. However, in 1954, Licklider demonstrated that a residue pitch still was perceivable even when a low-frequency noise was added that would have masked any representation of that component (Licklider, 1954). This put the nail in the coffin on the distortion hypothesis and confirmed that Helmholtz's theory of pitch perception was incomplete and insufficient.

To address the mechanisms responsible for pitch perception, let us examine experiments that have followed those of Seebeck and Schouten to determine whether place or temporal models provide the best explanation for the perception of the missing fundamental. Given the presence of phase locking in the auditory nerve, it seemed distinctly possible that a temporal code for pitch might provide an explanation for the pitch of the missing fundamental.

Ritsma's (1967) seminal findings expanded on Shouten's work and showed that the residue pitch occurs even when <u>many low-frequency harmonics are removed!</u> This work took the pitch of the missing fundamental to another level and demonstrated that many components could be absent from the stimulus and still produce a residue pitch. Over a series of systematic investigations, Ritsma demonstrated that the residue pitch generally only occurs up to removal of about the 10th harmonic. Removing more harmonics than that causes the pitch of the stimulus to change. The frequency region over which the pitch does not change when harmonics are removed is called the ***existence region*** of the residue pitch. Data from Houtsma and Smurzynski (1990) are shown in Figure 6–14 to illustrate the existence region. They generated a series of complex sounds and asked listeners to identify the melodic interval (e.g., a musical third or a fifth). They then progressively removed the low-frequency harmonics and measured the percent correct identification as a function of lowest harmonic present in the stimulus. Figure 6–14 illustrates, very strongly, that listeners began to have difficulty identifying the melodic intervals once about 9 or 10 harmonics were removed. However, even when many harmonics were missing, the scores obtained by Houtsma and Smurzynski were above guessing.

The residue pitch is an astonishing phenomenon, and we probably experience it every day without being aware of it. The telephone does not represent frequencies below about 300 Hz, yet we do not notice difficulties in

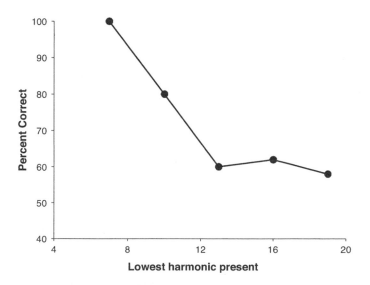

FIGURE 6–14. Data illustrating the existence region for pitch perception. Percent correct melodic interval identification is plotted as a function of the lowest harmonic present in the stimulus. Adapted from Houtsma and Smurzynski (1990).

perceiving the pitch of adult voices that have fundamental frequencies below 300 Hz. Certain musical instruments also do not represent the fundamental well, but we still perceive melodies and notes produced by those instruments. Audio engineers have been able to capitalize on the pitch of missing fundamental to generate low-frequency fundamental frequencies that are beyond the capability of their equipment, and we benefit from this when we listen to music over our mobile devices.

The Code for the Residue Pitch

The residue pitch effectively renders Helmholtz's view of pitch perception for complex tones obsolete, and leaves two possibilities for pitch perception of complex tones. The variant of the place model, the harmonic template model, would require stimulus components to be *resolved* in order to extract the pitch of a sound. The existence region of the residue pitch supports this model. Recall that when a complex stimulus is presented, only the low-numbered harmonics have a robust representation in the excitation pattern (see Figure 6–7). Note, in particular, that Figure 6–7 shows that only harmonics 1 to 8 or 1 to 10 have visible peaks in the excitation pattern, and this number does not vary much with fundamental frequency. When harmonics 1 to 10 are removed from the excitation pattern, only the high-frequency smeared portion of the excitation pattern remains. This stimulus, then, would not evoke a pitch based on the place code, and the findings on the residue pitch are consistent with this interpretation.

However, Houtsma and Smurzynski noted that performance on their melodic interval identification task was never at the level of guessing, even when about 20 harmonics were removed from the stimulus! Thus, these sounds must evoke a pitch, albeit a weak one. Thus, there must be some other code for pitch

that allowed people to perform that task. The temporal code is a distinct possibility.

A Temporal Code for Complex Pitch Perception

Burns and Viemeister (1976) demonstrated strong support for a temporal code by using noises to evoke a pitch. They measured whether amplitude modulated noises, with modulation rates selected to correspond to musical notes, could be put together to form a melody. These stimuli contained no spectral cues, ensuring that the mechanism for coding pitch was temporally based. They then constructed a number of common melodies using these stimuli and found that all of their listeners were able to identify the melodies 100% of the time, using only temporal information present in the sounds.

However, data from Fastl and Stoll (1979) indicate that even though a temporal code is present in the auditory system, it does not yield strong pitches like the place code. Fastl and Stoll (1979) measured the pitch strength of a variety of different sounds and used a pure tone as the reference. All stimuli were designed to evoke a pitch matching a 250-Hz pure tone, which was assigned a pitch strength of 100. Their listeners rated the strength of the pitch of the test sounds in comparison to the pitch strength of that tone. A subset of their data are shown here in Figure 6–15 for illustration, which shows the pitch strengths of various sounds plotted in order from high to low. The spectra associated with each sound are also shown, except for the amplitude modulated noise, for which the waveform is plotted. The pure tone had the strongest pitch of all, the complex tones all had pitch strength ratings greater than 60, and the noisy stimuli were assigned pitch strengths close to zero. The amplitude modulated noises

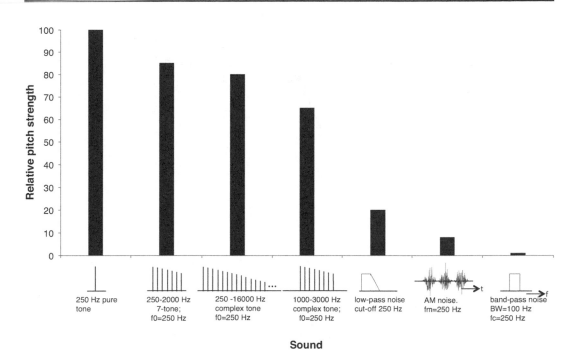

FIGURE 6–15. Pitch strength measured for different stimuli. Spectra or waveforms illustrated below the chart. Adapted from Fastl and Stoll (1979).

were assigned very low pitch strengths, despite their fluctuating nature. Their results demonstrate that low-frequency pure tones are generally associated with the highest pitch strength and that the pitch strength decreases as the acoustics of the stimulus become more like a noise and less like a tone. Note that white noise was assigned a rating of 0, suggesting that it did not evoke a pitch. Together, there is evidence for a temporal code in pitch perception, but the temporal code likely yields very weak pitches.

f_0 Discrimination

As with pitch perception of pure tones, discrimination experiments can allow additional, rigorous tests of the place and temporal models. Discrimination experiments have provided considerable information about the perception of pitch of pure tones, and this is no different for complex tones. Rather than evaluating frequency discrimination, however, these experiments focus on the ability to discriminate between two sounds with different fundamental frequencies (f_0s) and they measure the ***fundamental frequency difference limen*** (**F_0DL**). The harmonics of the sound can all be present, or can be removed like Ritsma did in his experiments on the subjective experience of pitch.

In one test of pitch perception models, Houstma and Smurzynski (1990) measured the F_0DL as a function of the lowest harmonic number present in the stimulus for a complex stimulus with a 200-Hz f_0. Their data are shown in Figure 6–16, which shows that as long as the low-frequency harmonics were present, fundamental frequency discrimination was excellent: the F_0DL was less than 1% of the fundamental frequency (Houtsma

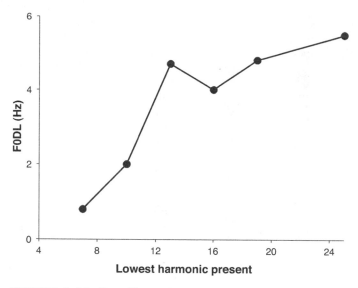

FIGURE 6–16. Data illustrating the existence region for pitch perception. The JND for f_0 (F_0DL) in Hz is plotted as a function of lowest harmonic present in the stimulus. Adapted from Houtsma and Smurzynski (1990).

& Smurzynski, 1990). Removing the low-frequency harmonics led to greater and greater difficulties discriminating between two sounds with different f_0s. A general trend is that as long as the harmonic stimuli contained harmonics 1 to 10, f_0 discrimination was very good, but became worse off after more harmonics were removed. Although the F_0DL was larger when some of the harmonics are removed, it was still very low at about 2.5% of the fundamental frequency.

Houstma and Smurzynski's data again provide support for the two models working in concert. When low frequency harmonics are resolved, f_0 discrimination is very good, suggesting a place mechanism. Here, the pitch is extracted from the resolved components. Once harmonics are no longer resolved, f_0 discrimination becomes more difficult, and the pitch is extracted from the temporal waveform. There would be no possible way for the ear to represent the pitch on a place-based frequency-extraction process when harmonics are not resolved.

Comparison with Pitch Perception of Pure Tones

Taking the results for both pure tones and complex tones as a whole, there is compelling evidence in support of both place and temporal mechanisms of pitch perception in the human auditory system. For pure tones, the place code is predominant for high frequencies and the temporal code dominates for low frequencies, but the place code is also likely in operation for low frequencies as well. These two codes are also working in concert for pitch perception of complex sounds. Across-frequency representations and resolvability of harmonic components are important to yield clear and strong pitches. We also see support for both place and temporal codes when low-frequency harmonics are available, whereas the temporal code operates when harmonic components are not resolved. It should not be surprising, then, that models of pitch perception that use both place and temporal codes are the most successful (de Cheveigne, 2005).

IMPORTANCE OF PITCH PERCEPTION IN EVERYDAY LISTENING

Pitch plays a very important role for the perception of speech and music—we use pitch to identify voices, perceive emotion and intonation in speech, and hear melodies in music. Pitch perception also is important for our ability to represent and understand speech in the presence of background sounds. The ability to represent and follow a melody is important for perceiving music and allows a trained ear to listen in on a single instrument playing within an orchestra. This same process also likely influences our ability to focus on a single talker in a room, essentially inhibiting the other talkers to improve understanding.

The ability to use differences in fundamental frequency to improve understanding of speech has been conducted using a number of studies, ranging from sentences and words to "synthetic vowel" stimuli. Brokx and Nooteboom (1982) demonstrated that speech intelligibility for sentences improves with an increasing f_0 difference between speech and a speech interferer. These benefits generalize to benefits from perceiving speech from different talkers, and are particularly beneficial at low signal-to-noise ratios (SNRs). Data from Brungart (2001) illustrate this robust benefit in Figure 6–17. In this study, listeners were presented with a speech signal having the following framework: "Ready <call-sign> go to <color> <number> now." There were eight possible call signs, four colors, and eight numbers. A listener was presented with two sentences, from either the same talker, or different talkers of the same sex, or different talkers of different sex. The target sentence always had the call sign "baron," whereas the masker sentence had a different call sign. Listeners identified the color and number spoken in the target sentence. Figure 6–17 illustrates the

FIGURE 6–17. Percent correct for color and number plotted as a function the SNR in dB for different target + masker configurations. Target and maskers sentences were spoken from the same talker, different talkers but the same sex, and different talkers with different sexes. Adapted from Brungart (2001).

percent correct for identifying both the color and number, plotted as a function of SNR for the three different talker configurations.

Figure 6–17 shows a robust benefit from two primary factors: increasing the SNR and increasing the difference between the target and masker voice characteristics. The benefits of presenting the talker with a background a voice of a different sex were huge—at low SNRs performance increased by 40 percentage points! The largest effects were evident at the low SNRs, where performance was worst. The lack of benefit at the highest SNRs either may be due to ceiling effects, as performance cannot be better than 100%, or may reflect that the mechanism responsible for the release from masking is no longer necessary due to the ease of the task.

Using speech as the experimental stimulus has high ecological validity, as these are sounds that humans use and hear on a daily basis. However, natural speech stimuli can carry many other variations that might contribute to the benefits measured in this experiment. For example, while female voices have

different fundamental frequencies than male voices, their speech has different formant frequencies and may also have temporal differences that facilitate the ability to separate sounds of interest from background sounds. Thus, interpreting data across multiple and different approaches allows better assessment of the mechanisms responsible for perception of natural stimuli.

In an experiment that bridges speech perception and auditory perception, a double-vowel task has also illustrated that listeners benefit from f_0 differences in speech-like stimuli. In this type of experiment, a listener is presented with two simultaneous harmonic sounds, which each has formants modeled after natural vowel sounds. The two synthetic vowels can have the same or different fundamental frequencies, and a listener identifies the two vowels in the double-vowel pair. Data obtained from Summerfield and Assmann (1991) are shown in Figure 6–18, to illustrate the benefits to speech understanding that can be provided by a simple difference in f_0 between two sounds. Summerfield and Ass-

FIGURE 6–18. Percent correct double vowel identification plotted as a function of the f_0 difference between the two vowels in semitones. Adapted from Summerfield and Assmann (1991).

mann manipulated their frequency differences in the form of semitones, which are twelfths of an octave, the equivalent of two adjacent keys on the piano. They showed that small differences in fundamental frequency were associated with improvements of 20 to 30 percentage points on the double-vowel task. Figure 6–18 shows that performance improved drastically for f_0 differences less than a one half of a semitone.

Thus, we observe that this trend of benefits afforded by f_0 differences is also present for vowel perception. Even double-vowel experiments have their limitations, however. In some cases, the f_0 benefits may be attributed to a representation of the temporal interactions between the vowel sounds, which is why using all forms of stimuli (speech, synthetic speech, and complex sounds) are important to fully understand the mechanisms responsible for the representation of pitch and its use in everyday listening.

The studies described here both illustrate the importance of pitch perception in our ability to separate a target sound from a background. Given that much of everyday communication occurs in complex environments with many competing signals, robust pitch perception mechanisms are important to facilitate effective communication. Deficits in pitch perception are likely to lead to deficits in the ability to understand speech in the presence of background noise, particularly when that background noise is also speech. As we discuss next, sensorineural hearing loss damages pitch perception and therefore contributes to difficulty communicating in complex environments.

PITCH PERCEPTION IN LISTENERS WITH SNHL

Generally speaking, listeners with sensorineural hearing loss experience disruptions in their perception of pitch. These disruptions come from alterations to both the place and temporal codes. We know that listeners with SNHL have disruptions to the place code, particularly in the form of reduced frequency selectivity. Consequently, to the extent that the place code is responsible for the pitch of sounds, disruptions to pitch perception are expected. Further, we can measure the amount of disruption to the place code in listeners with hearing loss, using our tools to measure frequency selectivity. Broadening of frequency selectivity would impact the ability of listeners with hearing loss to select resolved harmonic peaks, thereby impacting pitch perception. Psychophysical experiments also have demonstrated disruption to the temporal code in listeners with hearing loss (Hopkins & Moore, 2011), suggesting that hearing impairment may alter both the place and temporal codes for pitch.

Subjective Measures

Pitch perception in listeners with sensorineural hearing loss is often poorer than for listeners with normal hearing, but as with other auditory phenomena, considerable variability exists across listeners. Because hearing loss influences the perception of pitch, it can lead to ***diplacusis***, or the perception of hearing the same tone at a different pitch in each ear. Another way to think of diplacusis is that a single tone is heard as two tones with different pitches, one in each ear. Diplacusis can be measured by asking a listener to adjust the frequency of a tone in one ear so that its pitch matches a tone in the other ear. Normal-hearing listeners have also been demonstrated to have diplacusis, with pitch discrepancies of about 1% to 2% across the ears (e.g., Albers & Wilson, 1968). Yet, the magnitude and prevalence of diplacusis is higher in listeners with sensorineural hearing loss. Diplacusis can be quite pronounced in listeners with asymmetrical and severe-to-profound hearing losses.

In general, subjective studies of pitch perception, especially those that have used pitch-matching techniques, find that most listeners with SNHL do not experience vastly different pitches than listeners with normal hearing. That is, when a pure tone is presented to them, most listeners do not hear the "wrong pitch." However, studies do demonstrate greater variability in the perception and weaker pitch perceptions in general (Leek & Summers, 2001). Burns and Turner (1986) measured pitch shifts with intensity, using an approach similar to Morgan, Garner, and Galambos (1951) and found that some of their listeners with hearing loss also experienced greater pitch shifts with intensity than listeners with normal hearing.

Frequency and f_0 Discrimination

Evaluating models of pitch perception, as mentioned earlier, is often conducted using discrimination experiments. Many studies have demonstrated that listeners with hearing loss experience abnormally large frequency discrimination thresholds for pure tones (FDLs; e.g., Moore & Peters, 1992; Tyler, Wood, & Fernandes, 1983). However, these studies also document a wide range of performance abilities when it comes to frequency discrimination. FDLs can be nearly normal in some listeners, but severely elevated in others. Notably, the audiogram does not correlate with the alterations in pitch perception experienced by these listeners. Further, when frequency selectivity is measured (as was done by both Tyler et al., who measured psychophysical tuning curves, and Moore and Peters, who measured auditory filters using the notched-noise method), FDLs were not correlated with frequency selectivity measures. The lack of correlation is particularly problematic for place models of pitch perception, which would predict that poor frequency selectivity should elevate FDLs. The results from this

work provide support for the involvement of the temporal code in the pitch perception of pure tones.

Numerous studies have also evaluated f_0 discrimination in listeners with SNHL. In one of these experiments, Moore and Peters (1992) tested a fairly comprehensive set of conditions to broadly characterize f_0 discrimination abilities in this population, and they used particular stimulus constructions designed to address the place code only, the temporal code only, and both the place and temporal codes. Moore and Peters found that, on average, hearing loss elevated the F_0DL for *all* of their experimental conditions. Given that they selected stimuli to address both place and temporal codes, they concluded that deficits to both pitch codes are present in this population.

However, as we have seen before, Moore and Peters also noted considerable variability across the listeners in the study, with some SNHL listeners performing near normal and others performing much worse than the normal-hearing listeners. They argued that some listeners may lose place cues to pitch, requiring them to rely more on the temporal code, and other listeners may lose temporal cues, requiring them to rely more on the place code. Taken as a whole, they suggested that both place and temporal cues can be important for pitch perception and that either code for pitch can be impacted by hearing loss.

Historically, the effects of SNHL on pitch perception have often been attributed to deficits in the place model of pitch perception. This interpretation has been widely influenced by the view that phase locking does not depend strongly on level or with hearing loss (Harrison & Evans; 1979). However, modern psychophysical research suggests that there must be some deficit in the temporal code for listeners with hearing loss. Behavioral experimental evidence strongly supports the idea that listeners with SNHL have an altered representation of the temporal code (Hopkins &

Moore, 2011). Modern physiological experiments, such as that by Heinz, Swaminathan, Boley, and Kale (2010), also find that across-frequency representations of neural synchrony are disrupted in the impaired auditory nerve. Consequently, the poor pitch perception of listeners with hearing loss may be due to disruptions to the temporal code, although further investigations are needed.

Summary of Pitch Perception in Listeners with SNHL

Regardless, we see that pitch perception in listeners with hearing loss can be disrupted in a variety of ways. Disruptions to the place code can occur because of poor frequency selectivity or an altered representation of the place of maximal stimulation on the basilar membrane. Distortions to the temporal code may also contribute to poor perception of pitch by listeners with hearing loss. Asymmetries in pitch representations across the ears can also be problematic, leading to diplacusis, and sloping or rising hearing loss could cause the pitch code to be contradictory at high versus low frequencies. In all, these deficits can have a great impact on the appreciation of music and in the perception of speech.

SUMMARY AND TAKE-HOME POINTS

Two distinct models have been proposed to explain the perception of pitch: the place model and the temporal model. These two codes likely work in concert to produce the perception of pitch. For pure tones, the temporal model is likely the strongest for low-frequency sounds and the place model for high-frequency sounds. On the other hand, the temporal code likely operates in high-frequency regions when representing the pitch of complex sounds, and both codes code for sounds when harmonics are resolved. The perception of pitch is of great importance to facilitate listening in complex environments. Unfortunately for listeners with SNHL, disruptions to pitch perception are commonly associated with cochlear hearing loss.

The following points are key take-home messages of this chapter:

- The auditory system contains two codes of pitch perception: the place code and the temporal code:
  - The place code of pitch perception states that a pitch of a stimulus is determined from the locations stimulated by the frequencies contained in a sound on the basilar membrane.
  - The temporal code of pitch perception states that the pitch of a stimulus is calculated from the pattern of neural firing.
- Pitch perception of pure tones is determined primarily by the temporal code for frequencies below about 3 kHz and by the place code for frequencies above about 3 kHz.
- Pitch perception of complex sounds is determined primarily by both codes when harmonics are resolved and by the temporal code when harmonics are not resolved.
- Pitch perception plays a key role in the ability to separate a target sound from a background, particularly when both target and background are speech.
- Sensorineural hearing loss disrupts both the place and the temporal code, leading to poor pitch perception in listeners with sensorineural hearing loss.

EXERCISES

1. Determine the frequency of a pitch match for the following sounds. Also indicate whether the pitch is strong, weak, or non-existent.

a. A harmonic stimulus with components at 200, 400, 600, 800, 1000, and 1200 Hz

b. A harmonic stimulus with components at 600, 800, 1000, and 1200 Hz

c. A noise modulated at 150 Hz

d. White noise

2. Describe how the place code works for pure tones. Can the place code work at high frequencies, low frequencies, or both?

3. Describe how the temporal code works for pure tones. Can the temporal code work at high frequencies, low frequencies, or both?

4. Using a sketch of traveling waves on the basilar membrane, illustrate how the place model can account for the pitch perception of a harmonic complex with a fundamental frequency of 100 Hz.

5. Using the same sketch in #4 as a baseline, illustrate how the place model can code for a residue pitch if the first three harmonics are missing. You may sketch a new illustration if necessary.

6. In your own words, explain the temporal theory for encoding the pitch of a harmonic complex with a fundamental frequency of 100 Hz. How might this theory explain the pitch of a harmonic complex that does not contain energy at 100 Hz but has a 100-Hz fundamental frequency?

7. You have a patient with a 50 dB hearing loss at 1000 Hz and above. If the place model accounted wholly for pitch perception, what should happen to his pitch perception at 2000 Hz? If the temporal model accounted wholly for pitch perception, what should happen to his pitch perception at 2000 Hz? In your answer, discuss the pitch of the sound as well as the pitch strength of the sound. Assume that a 2000-Hz pure tone is presented at an audible level.

8. Tinnitus evaluation often includes pitch matching as a part of the procedures. Given everything that you have learned about pitch so far, consider the following:

a. If your patient pitch matched his tinnitus to 1000 Hz, do you think that this is a valid measure? Discuss.

b. Would your answer in (a) change if your patient had a sensorineural hearing loss at 1000 Hz?

c. If your patient pitch matched his tinnitus to 8000 Hz, do you think that this is a valid measure? Discuss.

9. Steph comes to your clinic complaining about difficulty understanding speech in the presence of other background talkers. You measure her hearing and find that her hearing levels are within normal limits. Given that she also complains about some deficits in her music perception, you suspect that she might have a deficit in her pitch perception. Consider the methodologies discussed in this chapter and discuss which method might be the best to measure whether poor pitch perception is the source of her difficulty. Discuss.

10. A variety of hearing aid algorithms have been developed to help listeners with hearing loss better understand speech. One of these technologies is a frequency-lowering hearing aid, which essentially takes high-frequency sounds that are inaudible and transposes (lowers) the frequencies so that they can be presented in a region of usable hearing. Considering what you have learned about pitch perception, what are your predictions on the <u>pitch</u> of sounds if they are processed by a frequency-lowering aid? Using the information you have just provided, address whether you would recommend a frequency-lowering aid to a musician. Consider:

a. if pitch is based on a place code

b. if pitch is based on a temporal code

REFERENCES

Albers, G. D., & Wilson, W. H. (1968). Diplacusis: III. Clinical Diplacusimetry. *Archives of Otolaryngology, 87*(6), 607–614.

ANSI American National Standards Institute. SI.1-2013. (2013). *USA standard acoustic terminology.*

Arehart, K. H., King, C. A., & McLean-Mudgett, K. S. (1997). Role of fundamental frequency differences in the perceptual separation of competing vowel sounds by listeners with normal hearing and listeners with hearing loss. *Journal of Speech, Language, and Hearing Research, 40*(6), 1434–1444.

Attneave, F., & Olson, R. K. (1971). Pitch as a medium: A new approach to psychophysical scaling. *American Journal of Psychology,* 147–166.

Beranek, L. L. (1949). *Acoustic measurements.* New York, NY: McGraw-Hill.

Brokx, J. P. L., & Nooteboom, S. G. (1982). Intonation and the perceptual separation of simultaneous voices. *Journal of Phonetics, 10*(1), 23–36.

Brungart, D. S. (2001). Informational and energetic masking effects in the perception of two simultaneous talkers. *Journal of the Acoustical Society of America, 109*(3), 1101–1109.

Burns, E. M., & Turner, C. (1986). Pure-tone pitch anomalies. II. Pitch-intensity effects and diplacusis in impaired ears. *Journal of the Acoustical Society of America, 79*(5), 1530–1540.

Burns, E. M., & Viemeister, N. F. (1976). Nonspectral pitch. *Journal of the Acoustical Society of America, 60*(4), 863–869.

de Cheveigne, A. (2005). Pitch perception models. In *Pitch* (pp. 169–233). New York, NY: Springer.

Fastl, H., & Stoll, G. (1979). Scaling of pitch strength. *Hearing Research, 1*(4), 293–301.

Goldstein, J. L. (1973). An optimum processor theory for the central formation of the pitch of complex tones. *Journal of the Acoustical Society of America,* 54, 1496–1516.

Harrison, R. V., & Evans, E. F. (1979). Some aspects of temporal coding by single cochlear fibres from regions of cochlear hair cell degeneration in the guinea pig. *European Archives of Oto-Rhino-Laryngology, 224*(1), 71–78.

Heinz, M. G., Swaminathan, J., Boley, J. D., & Kale, S. (2010). Across-fiber coding of temporal fine-structure: Effects of noise-induced hearing loss on auditory-nerve responses. In *The neurophysiological bases of auditory perception* (pp. 621–630). New York, NY: Springer.

Helmholtz, H. (1863/1954). On the Sensation of Tone. English translation published in 1954 by Dover Publications, New York. (First German edition, On the Sensation of Tone as a Physiological Basis for the Theory of Music, published in 1863.)

Henning, G. B. (1966). Frequency discrimination of random-amplitude tones. *Journal of the Acoustical Society of America, 39*(2), 336–339.

Hopkins, K., & Moore, B. C. (2011). The effects of age and cochlear hearing loss on temporal fine structure sensitivity, frequency selectivity, and speech reception in noise. *Journal of the Acoustical Society of America, 130*(1), 334–349.

Houtsma, A. J., & Smurzynski, J. (1990). Pitch identification and discrimination for complex tones with many harmonics. *Journal of the Acoustical Society of America, 87*(1), 304–310.

Johnson, D. H. (1980). The relationship between spike rate and synchrony in responses of auditory-nerve fibers to single tones. *Journal of the Acoustical Society of America, 68*(4), 1115–1122.

Joris, P. X., & Yin, T. C. (1992). Responses to amplitude-modulated tones in the auditory nerve of the cat. *Journal of the Acoustical Society of America, 91*(1), 215–232.

Kaernbach, C., & Bering, C. (2001). Exploring the temporal mechanism involved in the pitch of unresolved harmonics. *Journal of the Acoustical Society of America, 110*(2), 1039–1048.

Leek, M. R., & Summers, V. (2001). Pitch strength and pitch dominance of iterated rippled noises in hearing-impaired listeners. *Journal of the Acoustical Society of America, 109*(6), 2944–2954.

Licklider, J. C. R. (1954). "Periodicity" pitch and "place" pitch. *Journal of the Acoustical Society of America, 26*(5), 945–945.

Loeb, G. E., White, M. W., & Merzenich, M. M. (1983). Spatial cross-correlation. *Biological Cybernetics, 47*(3), 149–163.

Lorenzi, C., Gilbert, G., Carn, H., Garnier, S., & Moore, B. C. (2006). Speech perception problems of the hearing impaired reflect inability to use temporal fine structure. *Proceedings of the National Academy of Sciences, 103*(49), 18866–18869.

McFadden, D. (1986). The curious half-octave shift: Evidence for a basalward migration of the traveling-wave envelope with increasing intensity. In *Basic and applied aspects of noise-induced hearing loss* (pp. 295–312). New York, NY: Springer.

Moore, B. C., & Peters, R. W. (1992). Pitch discrimination and phase sensitivity in young and elderly subjects and its relationship to frequency selectivity. *Journal of the Acoustical Society of America, 91*(5), 2881–2893.

Morgan, C. T., Garner, W. R., & Galambos, R. (1951). Pitch and intensity. *Journal of the Acoustical Society of America, 23*(6), 658–663.

Oxenham, A. J. (2008). Pitch perception and auditory stream segregation: Implications for hearing loss and cochlear implants. *Trends in Amplification, 12*(4), 316–331.

Plack, C. J. (2016). *The sense of hearing* (2nd ed.). New York, NY: Routledge.

Plomp, R. (1967). Pitch of complex tones. *Journal of the Acoustical Society of America, 41*(6), 1526–1533.

Ritsma, R. J. (1967). Frequencies dominant in the perception of the pitch of complex sounds. *Journal of the Acoustical Society of America, 42*(1), 191–198.

Rose, J. E., Hind, J. E., Anderson, D. J., & Brugge, J. F. (1971). Some effects of stimulus intensity on response of auditory nerve fibers in the squirrel monkey. *Journal of Neurophysiology, 34*(4), 685–699.

Schouten, J. F. (1940). The residue, a new component in subjective sound analysis. *Proc. Konikl. Ned. Akad. Wetensehap. 43*, 356–365.

Seebeck, A. (1843). Ueber die Sirene. *Annals of Physics and Chemistry, 60*, 449–481.

Semal, C., & Demany, L. (1990). The upper limit of "musical" pitch. *Music Perception: An Interdisciplinary Journal, 8*(2), 165–175.

Stevens, S. S. (1935). The relation of pitch to intensity. *Journal of the Acoustical Society of America, 6*(3), 150–154.

Stevens, S. S., Volkmann, J., & Newman, E. B. (1937). A scale for the measurement of the psychological magnitude pitch. *Journal of the Acoustical Society of America, 8*(3), 185–190.

Summerfield, Q., & Assmann, P. F. (1991). Perception of concurrent vowels: Effects of harmonic misalignment and pitch-period asynchrony. *Journal of the Acoustical Society of America, 89*(3), 1364–1377.

Summers, V., & Leek, M. R. (1998). f0 processing and the separation of competing speech signals by listeners with normal hearing and with hearing loss. *Journal of Speech, Language, and Hearing Research, 41*(6), 1294–1306.

Tasaki, I. (1954). *Nerve impulses in individual auditory nerve fibers of the guinea pig.* St. Louis, MO: Central Institute for the Deaf.

Tyler, R. S., Wood, E. J., & Fernandes, M. (1983). Frequency resolution and discrimination of constant and dynamic tones in normal and hearing-impaired listeners. *Journal of the Acoustical Society of America, 74*(4), 1190–1199.

Ward, W. D. (1954). Subjective musical pitch. *Journal of the Acoustical Society of America, 26*(3), 369–380.

Wever, E. G., & Bray, C. W. (1937). The perception of low tones and the resonance-volley theory. *Journal of Psychology, 3*(1), 101–114.

Wier, C. C., Jesteadt, W., & Green, D. M. (1977). Frequency discrimination as a function of frequency and sensation level. *Journal of the Acoustical Society of America, 61*(1), 178–184.

Young, E. D., & Sachs, M. B. (1979). Representation of steady-state vowels in the temporal aspects of the discharge patterns of populations of auditory-nerve fibers. *Journal of the Acoustical Society of America, 66*(5), 1381–1403.

7

Hearing with Two Ears

INTRODUCTION

Up to this point, we have discussed the perception of acoustic information that is represented by a single ear. In fact, many of the experiments discussed presented sounds to a single ear of the listener, and they therefore tested *monaural hearing*. Yet, a critical component of everyday listening is using two ears—our experiences in the natural environment would be drastically altered if we had only one ear. We also know that people who have monaural hearing loss experience great difficulties in communication compared with those who have *binaural hearing* (hearing with two ears). Further, the location of our ears, which are separated in space on the hori-zontal plane, causes each of our ears to receive different signals in natural environments.

Binaural hearing provides advantages in a multitude of ways, and this chapter is organized in a way that allows us to discuss the advantages of binaural hearing from multiple perspectives. We will discuss the following aspects of binaural hearing:

- *Binaural summation.* In this section, we review the literature on the advantages of having two ears on sound detection, sound discrimination, and speech understanding.
- *Localization and lateralization.* Acoustic cues and neural mechanisms both have roles in our ability to find the location of sound sources in a three-dimensional (3D)

space. In this section, we discuss the roles of time delays between the two ears, level differences between the two ears, and the function of the pinnae to facilitate sound localization.

- *Binaural unmasking.* Both acoustic and neural mechanisms work to cancel background noise from our auditory perception. In this section, we will review the variety of experiments that have led to our understanding of the role that two ears play in the reduction of the effects of masking noise on perception.

We have already reviewed some of the basic data on hearing with two ears in Chapter 2 in the threshold differences observed between the MAP and MAF functions. MAF thresholds can be 10 to 15 dB better than MAP thresholds. However, these data do not allow a definitive assessment on the hearing advantages that are specific to having two ears. In particular, free-field measurements cannot easily disambiguate the contributions of true binaural phenomena from acoustic interactions between the sound field and the body. Thus, this chapter will review both free-field experiments as well as experiments conducted over headphones.

This chapter will cover the following topics:

- Binaural advantages in detecting and discriminating between sounds
- Sound localization
  - Acoustics
  - Physiology
  - Perception
- Binaural unmasking
- Effects of hearing loss on binaural abilities

BINAURAL ADVANTAGES TO DETECTION AND DISCRIMINATION

If asked whether two ears are better than one, most people would answer with an emphatic *yes!* Almost a century of psychoacoustical work has demonstrated small, but consistent, benefits on detection, discrimination, and identification for the same sounds presented to one (monaural) versus two (binaural) ears. These psychoacoustic experiments require presenting sounds over headphones, as free-field measures do not allow presenting *identical* stimuli to each ear. This is the only way to quantify the benefit provided by having a second, but independent, sample of the same stimulus. Note that these conditions are commonly referred to as **monotic** (one ear) and **diotic** (each ear receives an identical stimulus), respectively, and any time the ears receive different sounds, a **dichotic** stimulus results.

Psychoacoustic experiments that use headphones provide a unique opportunity to test the advantages of having two ears over one, as each ear can be stimulated independently from the other. Investigators have used this approach to assess whether detection and discrimination thresholds are better when tested using two ears vs. one ear. These experiments all test **binaural summation** abilities, or the ability to utilize information from both ears as a means of improving performance.

Many of the early psychoacoustic studies demonstrated small benefits of binaural hearing on the threshold for detection or discrimination sounds across various tasks. Results across the various types of studies that have been conducted are listed in Table 7–1. The table is not an exhaustive review of the extensive work that has been conducted on this subject, but is intended to provide a broad overview of the advantages of the binaural system on detection, discrimination, and identification. Roughly speaking, Table 7–1 illustrates that the binaural advantage is small, consistent, and very similar across the different tasks. We also note that reaction time experiments to pure tones have demonstrated a small and consistent binaural advantage (about 4 ms; Simon, 1967).

TABLE 7–1. Amount of Binaural Advantage Measured in a Variety of Tasks

Task	Binaural Advantage	Investigators
Loudness summation of tones	Almost doubling of loudness	Algom, Rubin, and Cohen-Raz (1989)
Loudness summation of noise	Doubling of loudness	Marks (1980)
Absolute threshold of noise	2–3 dB	Pollack (1948)
Absolute threshold of tones	2–3 dB	Shaw, Newman, and Hirsh (1947)
Threshold in noise	0–2 dB	Hirsh (1948)
Intensity discrimination	~60%	Jesteadt and Wier (1977)
Frequency discrimination	~60%	Jesteadt and Wier (1977)
Speech (speech recognition threshold)	~2.5 dB	Shaw et al. (1947)

Although variability across listeners can also be present, and can range from less than 1 dB to over 10 dB depending on the task and listener, no matter the approach (detection, discrimination, or identification), there is a consistent benefit afforded to the listener who is listening with two ears versus one. Binaural summation does depend strongly on symmetrical hearing between the ears (e.g., Shaw, Newman, & Hirsh, 1947). Even small asymmetries in absolute threshold between the ears reduce the amount of binaural summation observed.

That being said, a small improvement in detection threshold can be amplified at higher levels in the auditory system, particularly when we consider Erber's (1982) four different levels of perception. A small difference in detection threshold can manifest into a large change in performance at the identification level. For example, a change of 1 dB in the speech recognition threshold can be associated with a change of 15 to 20 percentage points on a speech identification task (Duquesnoy, 1983). Thus, we should not underestimate the potential benefit of binaural summation on our ability to communicate.

LOCALIZATION IN THE HORIZONTAL PLANE: ACOUSTICS

A primary function of having two ears is the ability to determine a sound's location in space, a process called *localization*. Humans are best at localizing in the horizontal plane (e.g., left versus right), primarily because that is where the acoustic cues are strongest due to the separation of our ears. Here, we discuss the acoustic cues that are present in this environment.

The binaural representation of sound is generated by the interaction between the head and the acoustic field. The signal received by each ear is determined by the characteristics of the acoustic field, the size of the head, and the location of the sound of interest with respect to the head. We also listen in a three-dimensional space, and so we characterize the location of sounds in terms of their azimuth and elevation. The azimuth of sound is represented by the angle on a spherical coordinate system representing the horizontal plane. For reference, 0° is the azimuth of the center of the head (i.e., the nose), 90° is the azimuth of the right ear, and –90° is the azimuth of the left ear. The elevation of sound is represented by the angle on the median plane (the plane that divides the body into left and right halves). In this way, a sound directly to the right has 90° azimuth and 0° elevation, whereas a sound directly above has 0° azimuth and 90° elevation.

The most relevant binaural cues to the human listener lie in the horizontal plane and differ only in their azimuth (e.g., whether a sound is closer to the left or right side of the body). This is true as our ears are only separated from each other on the horizontal dimension: They are in the same location with respect to elevation (neither ear is higher than the other) and they are in the same location with respect to the front/back plane (neither ear is closer to the front of our bodies than the other). If we assume that the head is a sphere and has no pinnae, the acoustic cues across the ears would provide information about only azimuthal location. However, we should note that our pinnae are asymmetric in both of those planes, and they (along with our bodies) alter sound in subtle ways that influence our binaural auditory perception. The effects of the pinnae are discussed in another section of this chapter, and localization on the horizontal plane is addressed here.

In order to fully understand the mechanisms responsible for hearing with two ears, we must first discuss the relationship between the **wavelength** of sound (the distance sound travels in a single cycle) and the size of the human head. Any object within a sound field will disrupt that sound field; however, the relationship between the wavelength of sound and the size of that object is of critical importance.

When a sound wave encounters an object, one of three events will occur:

1. The sound wave may reflect off the object,
2. The sound wave may diffract around the object, or
3. The sound may be absorbed by the object.

For the purposes of this course, we assume that the sound absorption by the head is negligible. Thus, we need only be concerned with whether sound reflects off the head or diffracts about the head. The degree by which these two events occur will determine the characteristics of the signals that are received by each ear.

Whether a sound is reflected or diffracted is determined by its wavelength and the size of the object encountered. The smaller the ratio between wavelength and object size, the greater the reflected sound energy. The wavelength of sound (λ) is determined by the frequency of sound and the speed of sound, $\lambda = c/f$, where c is the speed of sound and f is the frequency of sound in Hz. The speed of sound is roughly a constant, and is approximately 340 m/s. Thus, we observe that the wavelength of sound is *inversely proportional* to its frequency: Low-frequency sounds have long wavelengths and high-frequency sounds have short wavelengths. Thus, high-frequency sounds are more likely to reflect from objects whereas low-frequency sounds are more likely to diffract around objects.

Duplex Theory of Sound Localization

Lord Rayleigh (aka John William Strutt [1877]) first proposed the idea that the ability to localize sound was driven by two primary acoustic cues: difference in level between the two ears (*interaural level difference; ILD*) and the difference in arrival time of a sound between two ears (***interaural time difference; ITD***). Rayleigh suggested that ILDs were used for high-frequency sound localization and ITDs were used for low-frequency sound localization. The two acoustic effects are illustrated in Figure 7–1, which shows how reflection and diffraction alter the acoustic signal received by each ear. The top panel of Figure 7–1 shows a sound with a short wavelength, whereas the bottom panel shows a sound with a long wavelength with respect to the size of the head. In these two examples, the sound source is located to one side of the body.

Interaural Level Differences (ILDs)

In the top panel of Figure 7–1, the sound source is a tone with a wavelength much smaller than the diameter of the human head (e.g., 5000 Hz, which has a wavelength of about 0.07 m, or 2.6 inches). Because the wavelength is smaller than the head, some portion of this sound reflects off the head.

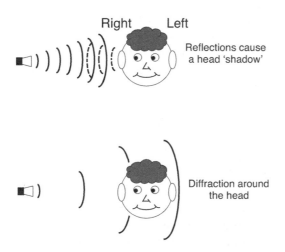

FIGURE 7–1. Illustration of the effects of a spherical body (e.g., a head) on a sound field. The top panel illustrates a high-frequency sound and the bottom panel illustrates a low-frequency sound. In both cases, the sound is depicted as being to the right of the listener.

When a sound is to the right of a listener, the reflection reduces the sound energy that arrives at the left ear. Consequently, the intensity of the sound reaching the right ear will be much higher than the intensity of the sound reaching the left ear. The reduction in intensity at the ear distant from the source is called ***head shadow***. Note also that the head shadow is greatest when the sound is to one side of the head. As a sound moves around the head from the left ear to the center of the head, the degree of head shadow will decrease. A sound directly in front of a listener will not yield a head shadow, and sound intensity at both ears will be the same.

As a result, the level difference (in dB) between the two ears, the *interaural level difference (ILD)* varies as a function of frequency and location of the sound source. Feddersen, Sandel, Teas, and Jeffress (1957) measured ILDs as a function of the azimuthal angle and frequency using human listeners. They placed a small microphone in their ears and measured the sound levels for a variety of sounds. Their measurements are shown in Figure 7–2, which plots the ILD in dB as a function of the angle between the center of the head and the sound. A sound directly in front is presented at 0°, whereas a sound directly to the side is presented at 90°. The different functions indicate measurements made for different tone frequencies. Figure 7–2 illustrates the following trends:

- For all frequencies tested, the ILD was 0 dB when the sound source was directly in front or in back of the listener.
- The ILD was greatest when the sound source was 90° to the side of the listener.
- The size of the ILD increased as frequency increased. The ILD can be as large as 20 dB for high frequencies (>4000 Hz), particularly for sounds located to one side of the body.

FIGURE 7–2. ILDs (in dB) are plotted a function of sound location with respect to a human listener, where 0° is front and center. Each function represents an ILD measurement for a different frequency. Adapted from Feddersen et al. (1957).

Feddersen's results demonstrate that ILDs become increasingly available to the ear as the frequency increases and as the sound approaches one side of the body.

Interaural Time Differences (ITDs)

In contrast to high-frequency sounds, low-frequency sounds, such as those with wavelengths longer than the diameter of the head, do not produce a head shadow. The bottom panel of Figure 7–1 illustrates this case where the sound source is a low-frequency tone (for example, 200 Hz, which has a wavelength of 1.7 m, or 66.3 inches). Here, reflections of the sound from the head do not occur. Rather, sound diffracts about the head, and the intensity of the sound received by both ears is equal. In this case, there is no head shadow. In a sense, the head is invisible to the sound field. However, because the two ears are separated in space, there is a delay between the time the sound arrives at the right ear compared with the left.

Feddersen et al. also measured the time delay between the two ears as a function of the location between the listener and the speaker. Figure 7–3, which is adapted from Feddersen et al.'s data, shows the general pattern of time delay versus azimuthal angle. As with the head shadow effect, the time delay between the two ears was greatest for a sound source to the left or the right of the body. These *interaural time differences* (*ITDs*) were very small, even at the maximum ITD; the maximum ITD was about 0.63 ms or 630 μs.

Because the speed of sound does not vary with frequency, the time for a sound to travel from one ear to another does not depend on frequency. Consequently, both high-frequency and low-frequency sounds will produce an ITD of a fixed amount. However, the *availability* of this information to the ear does depend on frequency. A fixed delay corresponds to a different number of cycles for a low-frequency sound than for a high-frequency sound. For example, a 200-Hz tone presented directly to the right side of the body

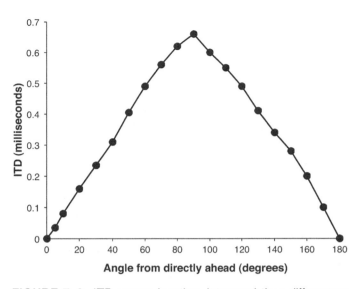

FIGURE 7–3. ITD versus location. Interaural time differences in milliseconds are plotted a function of sound's location with respect to a human listener, where 0° is front and center. Adapted from Feddersen et al. (1957).

does not complete a full cycle in the 630 µs needed to reach the left ear, as its period is 5 ms. On the other hand, a 5000-Hz tone has a period of 200 µs, and when presented to the right side of the body, cycles more than three times in 630 µs. Because of this phenomenon, we must consider the relationship between the ITD (which does not depend on frequency) and the ***interaural phase difference*** (IPD, which does vary with frequency). We can calculate the IPD for any given frequency from the following equation: 360° * (630 µs/T), where T is the period of the stimulus.

Consider our two frequencies again and a sound presented to one side of the body. This location is associated with the largest ITD possible: 630 µs. For a 200-Hz tone, which has a period of 5 ms, the IPD = (.630 ms/5 ms) * 360° = 45°, about 1/8th of a single cycle. Here, both ears receive a different phase of the *same cycle* of the sinusoid, and therefore there is <u>unambiguous</u> information about the phase of the sound across the ears. This is the largest potential IPD for any sound of this frequency.

More specifically, there is no other location on the horizontal plane that can produce that same IPD—all other azimuthal angles will yield phase differences that are smaller than 45°. On the other hand, a 5000-Hz tone, which has a period of .2 ms (200 µs), will cycle about 3.15 times in 630 µs (5000 Hz * 630 * 10^{-6} s). Because this tone cycles many times over 630 µs, there are multiple sound source locations that result in the same IPD. For a 5000-Hz tone presented to the left ear, the IPD is equal to 1134° [(630 µs/200 µs) * 360°], but this value is equivalent to 774°, 414°, and 54°. In this case, the sound could be originating from one of four azimuthal locations. In this way, phase differences across the ears provide <u>ambiguous</u> information about location on the horizontal plane. As a prime example, consider that when a tone of 1587 Hz (which has a period of 630 µs) is presented to the left ear, the IPD is 0°, (630 µs/630 µs * 360° = 0°). In this case, one would not be able differentiate whether the sound is presented to the left side or to the front of the body.

As a general rule, frequencies below about 1500 Hz will have unambiguous phase differences across the ears, whereas frequencies above 1500 Hz will not. As a result, the ITD is realistically only available at frequencies below about 1500 Hz.

In summary, the duplex theory of sound localization is primarily based on the availability of acoustic cues to sound location. For high frequencies, the ILD is dominant and for low frequencies, the ITD is dominant.

The Cone of Confusion

Again assuming a spherical, pinnae-less head, there would be a 3D conical surface extending out of each ear that represents the same ITD on the surface (Mills, 1972). Figure 7–4 illustrates this surface, which is called the ***cone of confusion***, and it should be thought of as extending infinitely into space. The ITD is a relative feature of sound (i.e., it is a difference, not an absolute), and sounds originating from a variety of locations could be perceived as being in the same location. The location of any sound on the cone of confusion could be confused with all other sound locations on that surface.

Note that within the cone of confusion, listeners cannot determine whether sounds are above or below them or whether they are in the front or in the back. Listeners would be able to tell if a sound were on the left or the

FIGURE 7–4. Illustration of the cone of confusion for a specific ITD. All points on that conical surface have the same ITD.

right. However, the cone of confusion only exists as long as the head is held stationary. Head movements can resolve ambiguities and allow for improved localization (Wallach, 1940). The asymmetrical and curved shape of the pinnae also assists with resolving the cone of confusion.

SOUND LOCALIZATION IN THE HORIZONTAL PLANE: PHYSIOLOGICAL BASIS

To give a sense of the complex circuitry involved in the binaural processing that underlies sound localization, a brief overview of binaural auditory physiology is provided here. A schematic illustrating the binaural connections in the brainstem is shown in Figure 7–5. Binaural auditory interactions begin at the level of the brainstem, in the superior olivary complex (SOC), a collection of brainstem nuclei. The left and right portions of the brain each contain components of the SOC, with the left and right SOCs receiving input from both ipsilateral and contralateral cochlear nuclei. Within each SOC are two nuclei with primary roles in binaural hearing: the lateral superior olive (LSO) and the medial superior olive (MSO). The LSO provides codes for ILDs, whereas the MSO codes for ITDs.

Coding for ILDs consists of both excitatory and inhibitory connections (Brownell, Manis, & Ritz; 1979), and the neural connections to the LSO are illustrated in Figure 7–5. An excitatory neural connection, shown by the solid line, exists between the cochlear nucleus and the ipsilateral (same side) LSO, whereas an inhibitory connection, shown by the dashed line, exists between the cochlear nucleus and the contralateral (opposite side) LSO. To illustrate how this might work, consider a sound located in the left side of the body with a large ILD. Because of head shadow, this sound has a high intensity

FIGURE 7–5. Schematic of the binaural connections in the superior olivary complex for a sound presented to one side of the body. AN—auditory nerve; CN—cochlear nucleus; LSO—lateral superior olive; MSO—medial superior olive. ILD processing in the LSO is illustrated with solid lines indicating excitatory connections and dashed lines indicating inhibitory connections. The weight of the line indicates the strength of the connection. Within the MSO, the cells receiving coincident input are illustrated by the black ovals.

on the left side of the body and a low intensity on the right and will produce the following pattern:

- The high-intensity sound on the left side will be associated with a large degree of excitation to the left LSO and a large degree of inhibition to the right LSO. This is illustrated by the thick solid lines for the excitatory connections and thick dashed lines for the inhibitory connections.
- The low-intensity sound on the right side will be associated with a small degree of excitation to the right LSO and a small degree of inhibition to the left LSO. This is illustrated by the thin solid lines for the excitatory connections and thin dashed lines for the inhibitory connections.

Together, the left LSO will have net excitation and the right LSO will have net inhibition, providing a physiological cue that a sound is on the left side of the body.

These connections for the MSO are also shown in Figure 7–5. The MSO also receives input from the cochlear nucleus, but it functions as a delay line and coincidence detector (Jeffress, 1948), which is a mechanism for aligning and detecting the neural temporal patterns across the ears. In this example, the left MSO will receive signals from the left cochlear nucleus sooner than it receives signals from the right cochlear nucleus. This effect is illustrated by the black cells responding in the MSO. For example, because the sound arrived at the left ear before it arrived at the right ear, the neural signal from the left ear will take longer to travel within the left MSO before it is coincident with the neural signal coming from the right ear. The reverse is true for the cells active in the right MSO. Specific cells located within the MSO respond to specific time delays between the right and left ears.

Together, the LSO and MSO code for ILDs and ITDs, respectively, in the auditory system. They must receive appropriate level and temporal cues to properly represent spatial cues. Consequently, disruptions to auditory nerve input can lead to difficulties representing the appropriate environmental ILD or ITDs. Note also that the LSO and MSO are the first auditory nuclei to receive input from the two ears, but they are not the only binaural nuclei in the auditory system, and other auditory centers also contain binaural representations.

SOUND LOCALIZATION IN THE HORIZONTAL PLANE: PERCEPTION

Stevens and Newman (1936) made some of the earliest measurements of the localization of pure tones. As we have discussed, interac-

tions between the head and the sound field are frequency dependent, and their study was among the first to test sound localization abilities in a frequency-specific manner. Stevens and Newman (1936) measured sound localization abilities in the free field with a speaker placed 6 feet away from the listeners. The speaker was located in one of 13 different positions on the right side of the listener, ranging from 0° (directly in front) to 180° (directly behind). A pure-tone sound was played from the speaker, and the listener indicated where the speaker was located. Stevens and Newman measured the errors (in degrees) in sound localization and obtained the results plotted in Figure 7–6.

Interestingly, the size of the errors was roughly constant for frequencies up to about 1000 Hz, but in the range of 2000 to 4000 Hz, the size of the errors increased considerably. The errors then decreased again for

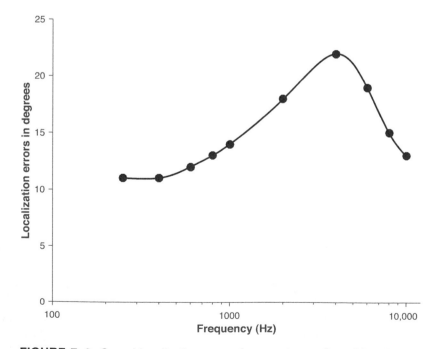

FIGURE 7–6. Sound localization errors for pure tones. Sound localization errors in degrees are plotted as a function of tone frequency (Hz) measured in the free field. Adapted from Stevens and Newman (1936).

the very high frequencies. These data support Rayleigh's duplex theory that ITDs and ILDs operate in different frequency regions, with low-frequency localization driven by ITDs and high-frequency localization driven by ILDs. Neither acoustic cue is particularly strong in the mid frequencies, which explains the greater errors between 2000 and 4000 Hz.

Stevens and Newman also calculated the errors in degrees as a function of the location of the speaker. Figure 7–7 shows that they found the lowest error rates when the speaker was located in the front of the body (0°). Performance was considerably poorer and was fairly equal when the speaker was located at all other positions tested (between 15° and 90°). Their work indicates that good sound localization abilities are only achievable when our face is pointed toward the sound.

Mills (1958) took a somewhat different approach to measuring the ability to localize sounds and measured the just detectable angle between two sounds. This quantity is commonly called the ***minimum audible angle (MAA)*** today. Mills placed a speaker at a specific location (e.g., 0° in front or 90° to the side) and measured how far the speaker must be moved (in degrees) before the listener was able to determine that the speaker was in a different location. Mills measured the MAA as a function of frequency and location of the sound source, and data adapted from his experiment are plotted in Figure 7–8. This figure illustrates the MAA plotted as a function of frequency for three different reference speaker locations (in front, 0°, and 30° and 60° to the right side).

The curve obtained at 0° (in front of the listener) demonstrates that for low-frequency sounds the MAA was incredibly small, and is about 1°. However, the outstanding sound localization abilities only occurred for the low-frequency tones. Once the signal frequency exceeded about 1000 Hz, sound localization

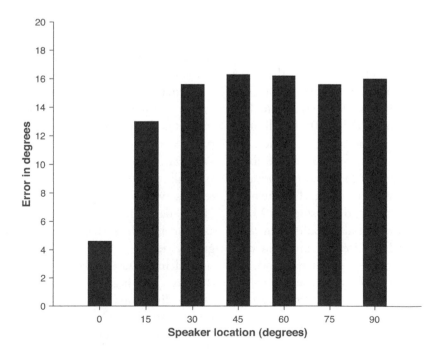

FIGURE 7–7. Sound localization errors as a function of speaker location. Adapted from Stevens and Newman (1936).

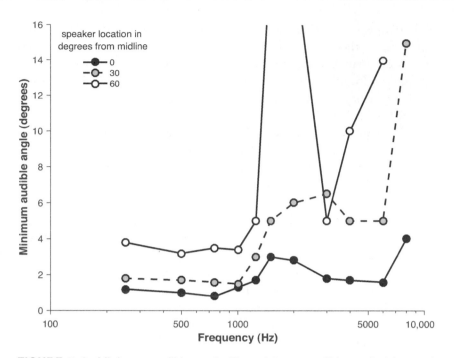

FIGURE 7–8. Minimum audible angle. The minimum audible angle (degrees) is plotted as a function of tone frequency. Each function represents a different reference spatial location with respect to the head, where 0° is front and center. Adapted from Mills (1958).

became relatively poor, being two to four times worse at about 2000 Hz. As Mills moved the reference location of the speaker, the MAA also increased. At the 30° reference location, localization for all frequencies was poorer by a factor of two or more than at 0°. Localization again degraded with increasing frequency, and was very poor for all frequencies above about 1000 Hz. For the 60° location, performance actually was so poor at the mid frequencies that Mills was unable to measure the MAA. In summary, we see similar results from Mills as we observed from Stevens and Newman: Sound localization is best when sounds are in front of the body. Further, sound localization abilities are very good at low and high frequencies.

The results of Mills and of Stevens and Newman can also be explained using the duplex theory of sound localization. First, sound localization is best for low and high frequencies, suggesting that the acoustic cue to a sound's location is not robust in the mid-frequencies. These results provide supporting evidence that a different cue is used to localize sounds in the low frequencies (the ITD) compared with the high frequencies (the ILD). Localization performance also degrades substantially when listeners are asked to localize sounds away from midline. Feddersen et al.'s (1957) data illustrate why this might happen, as their data show that ILD does not change greatly between 45° and 135°. These functions demonstrate a plateau in this range. In this case, moving the speaker does not produce a different ILD, making it difficult for listeners to use ILDs alone to perceive sound location. As a result, orienting our heads to the sound source is necessary for good sound localization.

SOUND LOCALIZATION IN THE MEDIAN PLANE

Although the previous review has discussed how ITDs and ILDs provide information about sound localization in the horizontal plane, humans also have an ability to localize sounds in the median plane (e.g., elevation). These abilities are primarily influenced by the pinnae, which alter the characteristics of sound in a way that depends on the angle of incidence, thereby providing information about the elevation of a sound source and whether a sound is in the front or back. The pinnae contain ridges and cavities that modify incoming sound and ultimately alter the spectrum of the sound received by the ear. Depending on the angle between the sound source and the pinnae, the amplitude of specific frequencies is altered, producing spectral peaks and valleys that are unique to different angles of incidence in the median plane. In this way, the pinnae provide cues to a sound's location in 3D space, with the largest effects occurring for frequencies above 4 kHz (due to the small size of the cavities). Because it is the pattern of peaks and valleys across frequency that provide these cues, experimental evaluation of the role of the pinnae in sound localization is only possible using complex sounds, and specifically complex sounds that contain high frequencies.

The effects of pinnae have been known since as early as the mid-1800s, but Gardner and Gardner's (1973) experiment demonstrated the strong influence of the pinnae by covering the pinnae convolutions using a rubber mold. As they varied the amount of coverage, Gardner and Gardner found that localizing the elevation of wideband sounds became increasingly difficult and a greater number of errors were made. Their data, shown in Figure 7–9, illustrate the magnitude of errors for sound localization in elevation as the ridges and convolutions of the pinnae were covered.

They found that increasing amounts of pinnae occlusion led to poorer and poorer sound localization in elevation.

Gardner and Gardner also measured localization in elevation for noise bands with different cut-off frequencies and illustrated that pinnae influenced sound localization most in the high frequencies, but they had negligible effects at low frequencies. This result is consistent with the notion that pinnae cues are spectral in nature and result in a complex pattern of ILDs across the two ears.

Earlier, we discussed that the cone of confusion reflects an equal-ITD contour. However, ILDs are also very similar along the cone of confusion. Consequently, the pinnae can provide a mechanism to reduce the ambiguities associated with the cone of confusion, as the pinnae provide spectral cues that vary depending on the elevation of a sound source. However, the pinnae will not resolve the cone of confusion for low-frequency sounds, as their spectral alterations occur only in the high frequency regions. We should also note that the asymmetrical shape of the pinnae provides information about whether a sound is in the front or the back of a listener, although front-back errors are very common unless the sound source is moving or the head is able to move.

LATERALIZATION

Stevens and Newman (1936) and Mills (1958) both measured sound localization using the free field. While using the free field has some advantages over using headphones (such as having better real-world validity), some theories and ideas can only be tested using headphones for stimulation. Presenting sounds over headphones, however, does not always yield a perception of sounds being "outside" of the body, and the sounds are perceived instead as being 'inside' the head. We refer to these experiments as ***lateralization*** experi-

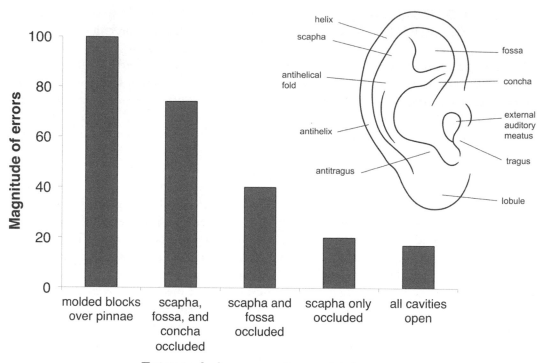

FIGURE 7–9. Magnitude of sound localization errors under different degrees of pinna occlusion. A schematic of the pinna is also illustrated for reference. Data adapted from Gardner and Gardner (1973), and image adapted from rendix_alextian/Shutterstock.com.

ments, as the experience of the listener is not one of sound localization.

However, presenting sounds over headphones does have benefits. For example, these methods provide the only way to manipulate one acoustic cue (such as ITD) without manipulating the other (ILD). Furthermore, the natural environment includes interactions between sound and the body, and these effects are eliminated with headphone presentation. Using headphones also allows psychophysical measurements in the absence of reverberation, which is a consequence of almost all natural environments except the anechoic chamber. Although one may argue that these experiments are artificial, they have greatly advanced our understanding of how the ear represents ITDs and ILDs. The discrimination experi-

ments that have evaluated the perception of these two important cues independently from one another are discussed here.

ITD/IPD Discrimination

One advantage of using headphones pertains particularly to the ability to represent the IPD separately from the ITD. Manipulating interaural phase without manipulating the interaural time delay is not easily done in the free field, but is very straightforward when testing over headphones. In one of these experiments, Yost (1974) measured the just noticeable *interaural phase difference* (**IPD**) as a function of stimulus frequency and reference IPD. He was able to manipulate the IPD of the stimulus, but he used a 0-ms ITD in which stimuli to the left and right ear were presented simultaneously. This allowed Yost to directly test whether the ear is able to access the phase difference across ears. Yost's data were also collected at a 0-dB ILD, and any perception of the ILD would have been constant across all experimental conditions. To simulate midline, listeners discriminated between a 0° reference IPD and an IPD of $\Delta\theta$ in degrees. To simulate other locations, he tested three other reference IPDs: 45°, 90°, and 180°. Figure 7–10 illustrates the just noticeable IPD as a function of frequency obtained from different reference IPDs. Yost's data showed small JNDs for IPD when the frequency was low and smaller JNDs for the reference angles closest to midline.

We see from this figure:

- *A constant just noticeable IPD at low frequencies.* The JND for IPD was about 3° when the sound was simulated to be at the front (the 0° condition). The JND for IPD was fairly constant for frequencies below 1000 Hz.

- *Poorer performance at reference IPDs different from 0°.* Simulating sounds at different spatial locations led to higher just noticeable IPDs. This finding follows the same results we obtained in the free-field sound localization experiments, with midline performance being the best.

Although Yost's experiment was conducted using headphones, his results are entirely consistent with those obtained in the free field. They support the conclusion that the auditory system does not have robust access to interaural phase differences at frequencies greater than about 1000 Hz. His results also indicate that best performance occurs when the head is pointed toward the sound source. Other IPD discrimination studies have also demonstrated that:

- *The JND for IPD varies with stimulus level.* Zwislocki and Feldman (1956) demonstrated that the sensitivity to IPDs was poor at low levels. However, for levels above

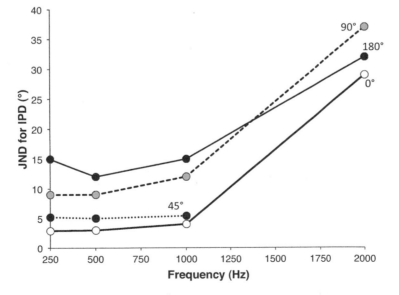

FIGURE 7–10. JND for IPD versus frequency. The just noticeable interaural phase difference (IPD) is plotted as a function of frequency. Each function indicates a different reference IPD. Adapted from Yost (1974).

about 30 dB SL or so, sensitivity was fairly constant.

- *ITDs and IPDs are available in high-frequency regions for complex sounds.* Although Yost measured the JND for IPDs to be difficult to detect at high frequencies, we must consider that Yost measured this for pure tones. If complex stimuli are used, and ITDs are imposed upon the stimulus envelope, then the ear is capable of using interaural time differences present in the envelope (e.g., Bernstein & Trahiotis, 2010; Henning, 1980).

ILD Discrimination

Yost and Dye (1988) conducted a similar experiment to that of Yost, but measured the just noticeable ILD in an ILD discrimination experiment. Yost and Dye conducted these

experiments with a fixed IPD of 0°, and they measured the just noticeable ILD (in dB) as a function of reference ILD: 0 dB (simulating midline), 9 dB, and 15 dB. Note that because of the dependency of ILD and frequency, the ILDs of 9 and 15 dB could be associated with a variety of locations. However, neither of these ILDs would occur for a sound near the front of the body; see Feddersen et al.'s data in Figure 7–2.

Figure 7–11 plots data adapted from Yost and Dye and shows the just noticeable ILD plotted as a function of stimulus frequency and for the three different reference ILDs. Yost and Dye's data illustrate some striking results:

- *ILD discrimination was good at both low and high frequencies.* Even though ILDs are not present in the environment at low frequencies, the ear possesses an ability to represent them. However, the elevation of the JND

FIGURE 7–11. JND for ILD versus frequency. The just noticeable interaural level difference (ILD) is plotted as a function of frequency. Each function indicates a different reference ILD. Adapted from Yost and Dye (1988).

at 1000 Hz is noteworthy and suggests a poorer representation of the ILD in the mid-frequency range.

- *ILD discrimination ability decreased as the reference ILD increased.* Following the same trends observed in all previous studies, the ability to detect changes in the ILD decreased as the reference ILD increased. Again, this is evidence that using interaural level cues is more difficult when sounds are at the side of the body.

These psychoacoustic experiments using headphones provide a strong complement to the results obtained in the free field. However, by "overriding" the natural acoustic cues, psychoacoustic experiments illustrate some important aspects of auditory processing of ITDs and ILDs. Yost illustrated that the ear can use interaural phase cues to lateralize sounds even when there is no environmental time delay. Further confirming the results conducted in the free field, these experiments illustrate that sound lateralization is the most robust for sounds presented at midline (i.e., to the front). Yost and Dye illustrated that the ear has the ability to perceive ILDs regardless of frequency. This finding could not have been easily revealed using free-field studies alone. Both results have implications for the development of technologies that may be used to improve binaural hearing for both hearing aid and cochlear implant users and provide a strong experimental supplement to free-field experiments.

Virtual Sound Representations

Although experiments using pure tones and headphones have advanced our understanding in binaural auditory processing, they do not test sound localization. The experiments discussed above led to perceptions of the sounds being inside the head. The reasons for

this are many, and they generally relate to the simplification of sounds that is common to psychoacoustic experiments. These sounds do not contain natural filtering produced by the pinnae or interactions between the sound field and the body. They also often contain incongruent cues to the true location of the sound source. For example, in the natural environment, a sound with a 0-ms ITD always has a 0-dB ILD, but headphone experiments can present ITD/ILD combinations that could never occur in the environment. Yet, if natural acoustic interactions are taken into account, sound manipulations can produce an externalized experience even when headphones are used. The applications for this work are in virtual reality and are currently being used for video gaming, military applications, and even medical rehabilitation.

Head-Related Transfer Functions

The pinnae and head are not the only aspect of human anatomy that influence the sound received by the two ears, and any component of the body in the sound field contributes to localization abilities. Without having to characterize the relative contributions of all potential obstacles to the sound source, the spectral and temporal changes can be captured by a ***head-related transfer function (HRTF)***, a three-dimensional function that codes for the acoustic changes that occur when sounds are presented at different locations with respect to the body.

Figure 7–12 illustrates how an HRTF might be measured using a sound source, S. The HRTF is essentially a response function that characterizes the changes that are imposed by the body interacting with a sound in space. The HRTF is typically recorded in an anechoic chamber from microphones placed at each ear (for either a human or a manikin), and the HRTF is measured by presenting S at multiple sound locations in the 3D space.

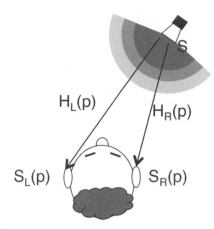

FIGURE 7–12. Illustration of an HRTF measurement. S represents the sound source, whereas $S_R(p)$ and $S_L(p)$ represent the stimulus recorded at the right and left ears, respectively, for each point in space, p. $H_R(p)$ and $H_L(p)$ represent the head-related transfer functions for each ear for that same spatial location.

$H_R(p)$ and $H_L(p)$ are the transfer functions for the right and left ears, respectively, at each point, p, in space.

Once an HRTF is recorded, sounds can be passed through the HRTF for presentation over headphones to a listener. Sound will then be perceived as external to the body, despite the headphone presentation. Interestingly, for localization in the horizontal plane, a listener-specific HRTF is not necessary. Wenzel, Arruda, Kistler, and Wightman (1993) compared sound localization abilities for people listening over headphones using their own HRTF and an HRTF measured using different people. They found that localization in the horizontal plane was generally unaffected by the specific HRTF. However, listeners performed better at localizing in the other two planes when they were presented sounds from their own HRTF. In particular, it appears that the pinnae cues were most relevant. Consequently, depending on the application, a specific HRTF may or may not be important. For example, listening to a concert over headphones may not require an individualized

HRTF. However, video games in which targets may come from above or below could be associated with a better immersive experiment using an individualized HRTF.

BINAURAL UNMASKING

Sound localization indeed is a primary function of the auditory system, but perhaps more important for the daily life of modern people is the ability of the binaural system to functionally reduce the effects of noise on listening. We saw earlier in this chapter that having two ears can assist a person when detecting sounds in noise, but the effect was an improvement of 3 dB or less. A characteristic of these binaural summation studies is the *diotic* presentation of sound. Essentially, these experiments mimicked a situation where a signal and noise are originating from the same location in front of the body (i.e., they had a 0-ms ITD and a 0-dB ILD). However, in the section on sound localization, we saw that the perception of different locations requires different signals presented to each ear. Such cases reflect *dichotic* presentation of sound. The diotic situation is rarely encountered in daily life, as each ear commonly receives different signals, even if only slightly different between the two ears. In these cases, our binaural system plays an important role in allowing us to better detect (or understand) a signal when it is <u>not</u> co-located with a noise. As described in the previous sections, experimenters have made measurements both in the free field and over headphones. Many of the experiments have also used speech, rather than tones or complex sounds.

Binaural Unmasking in the Free Field

Many investigators have been interested in the auditory mechanisms for understanding speech in noise. The ability to understand speech or detect a signal has been measured in free-field environments, with the signal and masker originating at different locations. Detection is much better when a masker and signal are in different locations. For free-field listening, aside from binaural summation, there are two primary binaural effects that reduce the effects of the masker: the better-ear advantage and binaural squelch. These effects are most commonly measured using speech, and are discussed here.

Better-ear advantage—In most environmental listening situations, one of the two ears receives a sound mixture with a higher signal-to-noise ratio (SNR) than the other. Acoustic head shadow causes the SNR at the two ears to be different, unless the rare condition occurs when the signal and masker are in the same location (e.g., like someone standing in front of a stereo speaker). In this way, typical everyday listening generates a "better ear" for listening. Consider a situation where a person is looking at a talker (the signal), but a noise source (such as a fan) is on their right side. Head shadow will attenuate the high-frequency components of the noise on the left side of the body, but the level of the talker will be the same at the two ears. In this way, the right ear will have a lower (poorer) SNR than the ear on the left. This effect is quantified by subtracting the threshold at the better ear from the threshold at the poorer ear.

Experiments that quantify the better-ear advantage are often conducted using headphones but with recordings obtained from the free-field environment, as ear-specific measures are necessary to quantify the better-ear advantage. Recordings are made at each ear and then played over the right and left earphones separately. Thresholds (or identification scores) for each ear are then obtained. The ***better-ear effect*** is then calculated by subtracting the performance scores between the two ears. Following this type of procedure, Bronkhorst and Plomp (1988) measured speech-recognition

thresholds (SRTs—the dB level at which words are identified 50% of the time) and found an 8 dB benefit from the better-ear advantage. For reference, an 8-dB improvement in SRT can correspond to an increase of 56 percentage points for word identification (e.g., Duquesnoy, 1983). For someone communicating in a noisy environment, this effect alone could be the difference between participating in a conversation or not. Because the better-ear effect is a purely acoustic effect, listeners can take direct advantage of it by strategic placement of their physical location with respect to people talking and the noise sources when listening in complicated environments.

Binaural squelch—Binaural squelch, first defined by Koenig (1950) is the advantage provided by the ability to supplement performance of the ear with the better SNR with the ear with the poorer SNR. This effect is contrasted with the better ear advantage in Figure 7–13 for illustration. Binaural squelch is determined by first measuring performance in the ear with the better SNR and then performance in the binaural hearing condition. Squelch is then calculated by subtracting the threshold obtained for the binaural condition from the threshold obtained for the ear with the better SNR. In this way, binaural squelch characterizes the benefits from including the ear with the poorer SNR. Generally speaking, the binaural squelch effect is considered to be fairly small for listeners with normal hearing, but does improve the SRT by about 3 to 5 dB (Bronkhorst & Plomp, 1988). The binaural squelch effect is not a purely acoustic phenomenon and demonstrates that the ear utilizes even the more poorly represented signal to improve perception.

Both types of experiments also illustrate the benefits of having two ears. In monaural hearing, the single ear is always "the better ear" regardless of the SNR at that ear. Importantly, however, binaural squelch illustrates how both ears function together to further reduce the effects of noise on speech perception.

FIGURE 7–13. Illustration of better ear advantage (*left panel*) versus binaural squelch (*right panel*).

The Binaural Masking Level Difference

Another set of compelling experiments demonstrating the strength of the binaural auditory system is the ***binaural masking level difference (BMLD or MLD)***. In 1948, Licklider measured speech intelligibility for a particular dichotic speech stimulus. In his experiment, the same speech signal was presented to the left and right ears. In one condition, the speech signal was *homophasic* (identical at the two ears) and in the other the speech signal was inverted at one of the ears (*antiphasic*). A homophasic noise stimulus was presented simultaneously with the speech in both of the conditions. An example of this type of experiment is illustrated using a pure tone in Figure 7–14, to allow better visualization of the phase inversion for the signal but not the noise in the antiphasic/dichotic case.

The top panel of Figure 7–14 illustrates the homophasic condition, in which the signal and noise are identical at both ears. The bottom panel represents the antiphasic condition, which has the signal inverted at one of the

ears. Notice the face in bottom panel is smiling—he is receiving a benefit in performance from this condition compared with his twin in the top panel. In particular, Licklider found that word identification was 20 percentage points better in the antiphasic condition compared with the homophasic condition. The difference in scores was most pronounced at low SNRs and essentially vanished at SNRs greater than 4 dB. Licklider noted that when the speech is out of phase compared with the noise (the antiphasic condition), "the speech literally jumps out of the noise-filled center of the head . . . and is immediately more intelligible." (Licklider, 1948). Such findings indicate a large *release from masking* by a simple inversion of the phase of the signal stimulus. These results were compelling, both in the amounts of benefits provided to a listener and in the perceptual experience provided by the experimental manipulations. It is clear that the binaural system provided robust benefits to communication, and functions best at low SNRs.

Psychophysical studies evaluating detection of pure tones have been able to more closely evaluate the frequency-specific nature

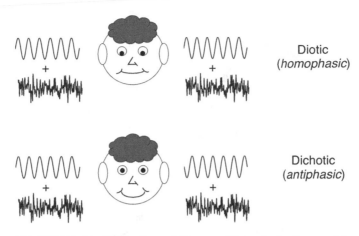

FIGURE 7–14. Illustration of the conditions typically used in an MLD experiment. The diotic homophasic condition (N_0S_0) is shown in the top panel, where the signal and noise are identical in the ears. In the dichotic antiphasic ($N_0S\pi$) condition shown in the bottom panel, the noise is identical between the ears but the signal phase is inverted in one ear compared with the other.

of the masking benefit. Because phase differences are manipulated, we expect benefits to be the most pronounced for low-frequency stimuli. The largest release from masking is obtained from the two conditions mentioned above: a *homophasic* condition (signal and noise are the same at both ears; also known as N_0S_0) and an *antiphasic* condition (the noise is the same at both ears, but signal is inverted at one ear compared with the other; commonly referred to as $N_0S\pi$). The subscripts refer to the phase relationships across the ears. Recall that π radians is the equivalent of a 180° phase shift (an inverted signal). In order to calculate the BMLD (which is sometimes shortened to MLD), the threshold obtained in the $N_0S\pi$– condition is subtracted from the threshold obtained in the N_0S_0 condition. This quantity reflects the amount of release from masking, in dB, provided by the phase shift.

Hirsh (1948) made the first measurements of the MLD using pure tones, and his data have been replicated and clarified in numerous studies. Summary MLD data obtained by Durlach and Colburn (1978) from a variety of MLD experiments are reported in Figure 7–15. Across these experiments, the MLD varied with frequency. It was largest for low frequencies, and as large as 15 to 20 dB for frequencies at or below 500 Hz. For frequencies greater than 500 Hz, the MLD gradually decreased with increasing frequency and then asymptoted at about 3 dB at 2000 Hz and above. Large MLDs at low frequencies have also been observed for homophasic signals and antiphasic noise ($N\pi S_0$ is about 13 dB) and monaural signals and homophasic noise (N_0S_m thresholds are about 9 dB lower than N_mS_m).

The N_0S_m configuration illustrates a striking binaural release from masking: A signal + noise in a single ear (monaural) yields a threshold that is 9 dB higher than a monaural signal presented with a binaural, diotic noise. Intuitively, we might expect that adding noise would increase the masking, but rather our binaural auditory system is able to take advantage of the correlated noise between the two ears and enhance performance.

Robust release from masking depends heavily on the amount of interaural correlation

FIGURE 7–15. Masking level difference (MLD). Masking level differences in dB are plotted as a function of tone frequency. Adapted from Durlach and Colburn (1978).

of the masking noise. Robinson and Jeffress (1963) demonstrated this by varying the amount of correlation of the noise between two ears. They found a systematic increase in the release from masking as the correlation of the noise between the ears progressively decreased. Noise highly correlated between the ears (e.g., identical noises to the two ears) led to the largest masking effects, whereas uncorrelated noise between the ears afforded the largest release from masking. Their results have formed the foundation for modern models of binaural hearing, which use interaural correlation as the basis for determining binaural benefit.

The Precedence Effect

The amazing aspects of binaural hearing do not end with binaural unmasking studies. The ear also contains mechanisms that work to reduce the influence of room reverberation. Rooms produce a complex acoustic field that consists of a direct path of sound from the source to the ear and multiple reflected paths because sound is reflected from surfaces and objects. These multiple sound paths produce a great deal of noise in the acoustic signal, yet we normally do not notice these sound reflections nor do they drastically affect our judgments of sound location. Wallach, Newman, and Rosenzweig (1949), who coined the term the ***precedence effect***, demonstrated that sound localization is based on the acoustic cues associated with the sound that arrives first at the ears. That the reflections do not alter the perceived sound location of the source implies that the first arriving sound takes *precedence* over the reflections of that sound in determining its location.

The precedence effect is responsible for a number of important binaural findings, including:

- *Localization dominance.* The perceived location is at or near the location of the actual sound source.
- *Fusion.* The originating sound and its reflections are fused into the perception of a single sound.
- *Echo suppression.* The precedence effect suppresses the perception of the echoes caused by reflections.

Wallach et al. developed a paradigm to evaluate the precedence effect that is still in use today. Wallach et al. measured the precedence under ITD manipulations, but ILDs have also been tested. Their general paradigm is illustrated in Figure 7–16, which also illustrates how these experiments can be conducted in the free field (anechoic chamber) or over headphones. In order to simulate reflections, the experimenter can manipulate the delay between a source sound and a reflection as well as the direction of the reflection. The left panel, which illustrates a free-field experiment, shows a simulated scenario in which a click originates from a speaker at the right side of the body and that click is reflected off a surface that is closer to the left ear than the right

ear. Here, the first set of clicks (one arriving at the right ear and one arriving at the left ear) is associated with a "direct" path of sound, and so the first set of clicks arrives at the right ear earlier than the left ear. The second set of clicks would be associated with a "reflected" path of sound, and so the reflection arrives at the left ear before the right. If headphones are used, an experimenter can independently manipulate the ITD and ILD, as shown in the right panel.

Using this technique, experimenters have measured sound localization abilities and the echo threshold [the delay at which the echo (the second set of clicks in an experiment) is just noticeable]. Localization based on the first set of clicks would indicate a sound to the right. Sound localization based on the echo would indicate a source near the left ear. Results indicate that location of the sound is associated with the direction of the first sound, not the reflection (*localization dominance*). Investigators have also shown that as long as the echo delay is short (on the order of milliseconds), the ear will fuse the two sets of clicks and hear only a single sound (*echo fusion*). Further, as long as the two sounds are fused, listeners are

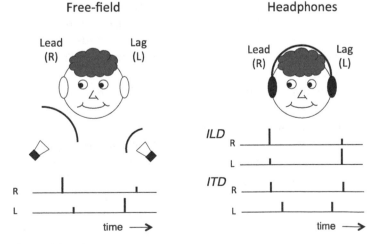

FIGURE 7–16. Schematics of the different stimulus configurations that can be used to measure the precedence effect.

unable to localize/lateralize the lagging sound (*echo suppression*; Zurek, 1980).

The precedence effect is a powerful process of the ear to reduce the impact that sound reflections have on perception, and is extremely important for our hearing in enclosed spaces. Without it, we likely would experience greater masking effects when communicating in rooms. The precedence effect can also be exploited in algorithms used to enhance signals presented across speakers.

IMPACT OF HEARING LOSS ON BINAURAL HEARING

Hearing impairment can have a drastic effect on binaural hearing, and a number of factors must be considered when evaluating the effects of hearing loss on binaural hearing. Here, we will only consider cases in which a listener has residual hearing in both ears, as a listener with unilateral hearing loss has no binaural hearing. Most studies have been conducted on bilateral, symmetrical sensorineural hearing loss, but even small asymmetries in hearing across the ears can disrupt binaural hearing abilities.

One important factor is the consideration of audibility. Even if listeners with hearing loss have symmetrical hearing impairment, or a slight asymmetry between the ears, acoustic effects can render certain components of sound inaudible. Head shadow effects are of particular concern, due to their importance at high frequencies and the common high-frequency sloping hearing loss configuration. Listeners with hearing loss are compromised in their abilities to use binaural intensity-based cues simply from the interaction between the acoustic environment and the hearing loss. Surely a listener cannot access a cue that he cannot hear. Thus, psychoacousticians must take great care when designing experiments to parse out the contributions of audibility and true binaural abilities.

Binaural Summation

Generally speaking, binaural summation is not greatly altered by sensorineural hearing loss. Hall and Harvey (1985) and Hawkins, Prosek, Walden, and Montgomery (1987) found that loudness summation was not altered by sensorineural hearing loss, as long as the sounds presented to both ears were audible. However, Whilby, Florentine, Wagner, and Marozeau (2006) argued that binaural summation abilities vary greatly across listeners. They suggested that listeners fell into two distinct groups: those who experienced much less binaural summation than listeners with normal hearing and those who experienced much more binaural summation. While some listeners appear to have fairly normal binaural summation, the majority of listeners experience deficits in a number of arenas.

Localization and Lateralization

As a rule, listeners with sensorineural hearing loss experience deficits in their sound localization and lateralization abilities (Akeroyd, 2014). A particular hallmark of these studies is wide variability of performance by listeners with hearing loss. As an example from a comprehensive study that evaluated MAAs in the free field and JNDs for ITDs and ILDs over headphones, Häusler, Colburn, and Marr (1983) measured binaural abilities in 140 listeners using broadband noise stimuli. Regarding the MAA measurements, some listeners with bilateral sensorineural hearing loss had MAAs within the range of normal variability, but other listeners, both those with bilateral hearing loss and those with asymmetrical hearing losses, had abnormally large MAAs. Most of the listeners with bilaterally symmetric hearing losses presented JNDs for ITDs and ILDs within normal limits, although some demonstrated larger ITDs than normal.

Other evaluations of impaired hearing have come to similar conclusions. For example, Koehnke, Culotta, Hawley, and Colburn (1995) found considerable variability across listeners with impaired hearing in their ability to detect ITD and ILDs. Hawkins and Wightman (1980) also measured substantial deficits in some listeners' ability to detect ITDs.

The reasons for poor ITD and ILD perception in listeners with sensorineural hearing loss are still unknown, but may be related to the following factors:

- *Audibility and low sensation level.* Both ITD and ILD discrimination is impaired at low sensation levels for normal-hearing listeners (Dietz, Bernstein, Trahiotis, Ewert, & Hohmann, 2013). Even if sounds are audible, low presentation levels might account for poor performance in listeners with hearing loss on these tasks. The real-world environment also may exacerbate these issues, particularly for the ILD.

  In natural auditory scenes, the head shadow can contribute to the abnormal representation of the ILD. Consider an example in which head shadow renders a sound inaudible in one ear but audible in the other. In this scenario, the representation of the ILD in the auditory system will be larger than that present in the environment, causing distortions to the perception of space. Consider also a listener with small, 5-dB asymmetry in hearing. For example, if his hearing is 5 dB better in the right ear than in the left ear, a sound presented to his left ear will be associated with an ILD that is 10 dB larger than when a sound is presented to his right ear. The auditory system may be unable to compensate for these distortions, leading to disruptions in the perception of space.

  These scenarios, however, do not explain the experimental results of poor ILD perception in listeners with hearing loss, as most studies take great care to control for audibility and ensure that the ear has access to the true acoustic ILD. Thus, poor ILD perception is also a consequence of altered auditory processing. Together, however, it is clear that ensuring appropriate audibility in both ears is critical to provide adequate access to interaural cues for listeners with SNHL. We cannot expect, however, appropriate audibility to fully restore perception of either ILDs or ITDs.

- *Abnormal coding of temporal and intensity information.* Physiological changes have been demonstrated to occur at levels peripheral to the superior olive that alter the way binaural information is processed by that structure. Regarding temporal coding, Ruggero, Rich, and Recio (1992) noted small shifts in the delay of the traveling wave after cochlear death, and Heinz, Swaminathan, Boley, and Kale (2010) have demonstrated that cochlear damage can also distort the across-frequency representation of temporal fine structure in auditory nerve fibers. Such temporal distortions would not need to be large to disrupt the fine temporal synchronization necessary for representation by the MSO. Alterations in the amount of basilar membrane vibration with level (Ruggero & Rich, 1991) also will yield abnormal excitation and inhibition within the LSO.

Although hearing aids can compensate for issues related to audibility, they cannot address abnormal physiological coding. We see evidence that audibility is not the only driving factor of abnormal sound localization in listeners with hearing loss, as hearing aids do not appear to restore sound localization for many listeners. In fact, in some cases, listeners wearing hearing aids make more localization errors than when they are not wearing hearing aids. Note, however, that sound localization with binaural hearing aids is better than with a monaural fitting (Köbler & Rosenhall, 2002).

A listener with a bilateral loss who wears a monaural hearing aid would have an added acoustic asymmetry.

Release from Masking

In general, listeners with hearing loss do not benefit from the binaural masking release abilities to the same degree as listeners with normal hearing. Deficits are present in the:

- *Better-ear advantage.* Like listeners with normal hearing, listeners with hearing loss can benefit from the better-ear effect. However, listeners with bilateral hearing loss will experience deficits simply because their better ear is largely susceptible to masking. Listeners with asymmetrical hearing loss with normal hearing in one ear may also struggle to take advantage of their better ear and will strategically need to move their head or body so that their ear with better thresholds is also the ear with the better SNR. Generally speaking, the better-ear effect will be determined by degree of hearing loss in the better ear, with more hearing loss being associated with more masking and a poorer ability to understand speech in noise. Arsenault and Punch (1999) showed that, on average, listeners with hearing loss did not benefit from the better-ear advantage to the same degree as listeners with normal hearing.

- *Binaural squelch.* The representations of ITD and ILD are important for binaural squelch. Those listeners who experience deficits in the ability to represent ITD and ILD will also experience deficits with binaural squelch. In Arsenault and Punch's (1999) evaluation, listeners with hearing loss experienced only 1.7 dB of advantage due to binaural squelch, in contrast to a 4.9 dB advantage experienced by listeners with normal hearing.

- *Masking level difference.* A number of studies have demonstrated that the masking level difference is reduced in listeners with sensorineural hearing loss (Durlach et al., 1981). The size of the MLD typically decreases as the severity of hearing loss increases, as well as with asymmetric hearing losses. That is, listeners with more severe hearing losses receive less of a binaural release from masking by presenting a signal (but not a noise) in antiphase across the ears. Even small asymmetries across the ears can reduce the size of the MLD. Yet, small differences in hearing levels between the ears cannot fully account for the reductions in the size of the MLD (Hall, Tyler, & Fernandes, 1984; Quaranta & Cervellera, 1974). The poor coding of interaural timing cues in these listeners provides a better explanation for the reduced MLD associated with SNHL.

- *Precedence effect.* Listeners with hearing loss also may experience deficits in the precedence effect and be more susceptible to reverberation. However, studies report wide variability across listeners. Roberts, Besing, and Koehnke (2002) measured *echo thresholds* for click stimuli in listeners with normal hearing and with hearing loss. The echo threshold was defined as the just noticeable delay that determined whether the listeners heard one (the echo stimulus was fused with the leading stimulus) or two clicks. Roberts et al. found large variability across listeners, even when stimuli were presented at the same sensation level for the two groups. Many listeners with hearing loss had higher echo thresholds than those with normal hearing, but not all. As we have seen repeatedly in this text, no correlation was observed between audiometric threshold and echo threshold. Other studies, however, have not found a difference in the precedence effect for listeners with hearing loss (e.g., Roberts & Lister, 2004). Studies which have measured *local-*

ization dominance also have demonstrated large variability across listeners with hearing loss, with some listeners making errors in the perceived origin of a sound source (e.g., Cranford, Andres, Piatz, & Reissig, 1993; Goverts, Houtgast, & van Beek, 2002).

Summary and Implication

It is evident from this review of literature that listeners with sensorineural hearing loss experience substantial deficits in their abilities to take advantage of binaural cues. Listeners with symmetrical hearing loss will experience poor sound localization as well as difficulty in using their binaural hearing to separate target sounds from background sounds. Listeners with asymmetric hearing loss experience even greater difficulties. As a result, the ability of many listeners with hearing loss to utilize their two ears is severely compromised, and they cannot benefit from the multitude of abilities afforded by hearing with two ears. Amplification would not be expected to restore poor sound localization due to abnormal encoding of binaural information, but it could help with the representation of ILDs. Chapter 8 discusses how nonlinear amplification schemes distort the acoustics of sound, further compromising access to binaural cues.

SUMMARY AND TAKE-HOME POINTS

To summarize, having two ears affords us a multitude of auditory abilities. Binaural summation abilities are demonstrated with better detection and discrimination. Two ears also provides information about the location of sound in space, with the duplex theory of sound localization being an important theory describing the mechanisms responsible for sound localization. Two ears provide substan-tial reduction in the effects of masking. The precedence works in concert with binaural unmasking and reduces the impact that echoes have on perception. Listeners with SNHL can have deficits in any or all of these abilities, and substantial variability is present in this population.

The following points are key take-home messages of this chapter:

- Two ears provide binaural summation, or improvements in detection, discrimination, and identification for two ears compared with one.
- Two ears provide the ability to localize sound. The duplex theory of sound localization describes the relationship between acoustic cues and perception, with ITDs driving localization for low-frequency sounds and ILDs driving localization for high-frequency sounds.
- Listening with two ears reduces the effect of masking in the following ways:
  - The better-ear effect—an acoustic effect in which the auditory system can take advantage of the ear with the better SNR.
  - Binaural squelch and the masking level difference—true binaural auditory effects that can improve our perception in noise.
  - The precedence effect—a true binaural auditory effect, effectively suppresses perception of echoes generated in reverberant environments.
- Hearing impairment alters sound localization abilities for many listeners, although there is considerable variability in performance. Some listeners have near-normal sound localization abilities, but many listeners experience deficits. Restoring audibility does not correct these sound localization problems, as the deficits are likely due to changes in neural coding.
- Hearing impairment also degrades the ability to binaurally inhibit background

EXERCISES

1. Discuss the three primary advantages of having two ears and how each of those advantages facilitates listening in everyday environments.

2. Describe why ITDs are only useful for low-frequency sound localization and why ILDs are only useful for high-frequency sound localization.

3. Big Bird and Elmo use different cues for sound localization at different frequencies, and one reason for this is their different head sizes. Big Bird has a head that is 3 times the size of Elmo.
   a. If ILDs are available to Big Bird at frequencies above 900 Hz, at what frequencies would ILDs be available to Elmo? (Be specific here—this answer requires a number.)
   b. Describe why Elmo has ILDs available at different frequencies than Big Bird.
   c. What happens to the ITD processing of Big Bird compared with Elmo?

4. You have a patient with a conductive hearing loss in his left ear. If that conductive hearing loss attenuates sound by 40 dB at all frequencies, calculate his available ILD at 6000 Hz if a sound is presented to his left ear at 40 dB SPL or if that sound is presented at 80 dB SPL. Using your answer, discuss whether his sound localization will be better at the moderate or at the high stimulus level. Use Figure 7–2 to inform your answer.

5. Woodsy the owl has been experiencing difficulty with finding his prey. His vision is already poor (he is an owl after all!) and he really needs his hearing for hunting. ~~s~~ to the "owl"diologist and has his ~~in~~g tested. The owldiologist ~~b~~y has normal ILD ~~qu~~encies, but his ITD ~~n~~ormally high. Discuss ~~d~~ amplification or a ~~hearing~~ aid might help Woodsy.

   What are some other options for Woodsy to localize sounds better? Think outside of the box and what you might be able to do to help with his ITD issue.

6. Maynard has a low-frequency hearing loss, and his wife Betty has a high-frequency hearing loss. Who will be better at localizing sounds with different elevations? Discuss.

7. Describe the difference between the better-ear advantage and binaural squelch.

8. Many people with hearing loss have been shown to have smaller MLDs (masking level differences) than people with normal hearing. What are at least two possible explanations for this finding? Please explain these answers.

9. Listeners with sensorineural hearing loss have greater difficulty communicating in reverberant environments than listeners with normal hearing. Given your knowledge and understanding of the effects of hearing loss on binaural hearing, explain why this might occur.

10. Ellie spends a lot of time at home but her family visits frequently. She has presbycusis (age-related hearing loss) and struggles to hear her family, with particular difficulty localizing the voices of her grandchildren. She has asked that they speak more loudly so that she can more easily figure out where they are. Do you think that this will help her? Discuss.

11. Geoffrey receives a behind-the-ear hearing aid, in which the microphone is located at the top of the pinna. Discuss whether this microphone placement will affect Geoffrey's abilities to localize sounds in elevation and in azimuth.

12. Mr. Scott has asymmetrical hearing loss and requires different amounts of amplification in both of his ears. Discuss whether Mr. Scott has near-normal abilities to localize sounds without his hearing aids and whether his hearing aids are likely to assist him in sound localization.

REFERENCES

Akeroyd, M. A. (2014). An overview of the major phenomena of the localization of sound sources by normal-hearing, hearing-impaired, and aided listeners. *Trends in Hearing, 18,* 1–7.

Algom, D., Rubin, A., & Cohen-Raz, L. (1989). Binaural and temporal integration of the loudness of tones and noises. *Attention, Perception, and Psychophysics, 46*(2), 155–166.

Arsenault, M. D., & Punch, J. L. (1999). Nonsense-syllable recognition in noise using monaural and binaural listening strategies. *Journal of the Acoustical Society of America, 105*(3), 1821–1830.

Bernstein, L. R., & Trahiotis, C. (2010). Accounting quantitatively for sensitivity to envelope–based interaural temporal disparities at high frequencies. *Journal of the Acoustical Society of America, 128*(3), 1224–1234.

Best, V., Mejia, J., Freeston, K., Van Hoesel, R. J., & Dillon, H. (2015). An evaluation of the performance of two binaural beamformers in complex and dynamic multitalker environments. *International Journal of Audiology, 54*(10), 727–735.

Bronkhorst, A. W., & Plomp, R. (1988). The effect of head-induced interaural time and level differences on speech intelligibility in noise. *Journal of the Acoustical Society of America, 83*(4), 1508–1516.

Brownell, W. E., Manis, P. B., & Ritz, L. A. (1979). Ipsilateral inhibitory responses in the cat lateral superior olive. *Brain Research, 177*(1), 189–193.

Carette, E., Van den Bogaert, T., Laureyns, M., & Wouters, J. (2014). Left-right and front-back spatial hearing with multiple directional microphone configurations in modern hearing aids. *Journal of the American Academy of Audiology, 25*(9), 791–803.

Colburn, H. S., & Durlach, N. I. (1978). Models of binaural interaction. In E. Carterette and M. Friedman (Eds.) *Handbook of Perception, 4,* Academic Press: New York, NY 467–518.

Cranford, J. L., Andres, M. A., Piatz, K. K., & Reissig, K. L. (1993). Influences of age and hearing loss on the precedence effect in sound localization. *Journal of Speech, Language, and Hearing Research, 36*(2), 437–441.

Dietz, M., Bernstein, L. R., Trahiotis, C., Ewert, S. D., & Hohmann, V. (2013). The effect of overall level on sensitivity to interaural differences of time and level at high frequencies. *Journal of the Acoustical Society of America, 134*(1), 494–502.

Duquesnoy, A. (1983). The intelligibility of sentences in quiet and in noise in aged listeners. *Journal of the Acoustical Society of America, 74*(4), 1136–1144.

Durlach, N. I., Thompson, C. L., & Colburn, H. S. (1981). Binaural interaction in impaired listeners: A review of past research. *Audiology, 20*(3), 181–211.

Durlach, N. I. & Colburn, H. S. (1978). Binaural Phenomena. In E. Carterette and M. Friedman (Eds.) *Handbook of Perception 4*; Academic Press: New York, NY, 365–466.

Erber, N. P. (1982). Glenondale auditory screening procedure. In *Auditory training* (pp. 47–71). Washington, DC: Alexander Graham Bell Association, .

Feddersen, W. E., Sandel, T. T., Teas, D. C., & Jeffress, L. A. (1957). Localization of high-frequency tones. *Journal of the Acoustical Society of America, 29*(9), 988–991.

Gardner, M. B., & Gardner, R. S. (1973). Problem of localization in the median plane: Effect of pinnae cavity occlusion. *Journal of the Acoustical Society of America, 53*(2), 400–408.

Goverts, S. T., Houtgast, T., & van Beek, H. H. (2002). The precedence effect for lateralization for the mild sensory neural hearing impaired. *Hearing Research, 163*(1), 82–92.

Hall, J. W., & Harvey, A. D. (1985). Diotic loudness summation in normal and impaired hearing. *Journal of Speech and Hearing Research, 28*(3), 445–448.

Hall, J. W., Tyler, R. S., & Fernandes, M. A. (1984). Factors influencing the masking level difference in cochlear hearing-impaired and normal-hearing listeners. *Journal of Speech and Hearing Research, 27*(1), 145–154.

Häusler, R., Colburn, S., & Marr, E. (1983). Sound localization in subjects with impaired hearing: Spatial-discrimination and interaural-discrimination tests. *Acta Oto-Laryngologica, 96*(Suppl. 400), 1–62.

Hawkins, D. B., Prosek, R. A., Walden, B. E., & Montgomery, A. A. (1987). Binaural loudness summation in the hearing impaired. *Journal of Speech and Hearing Research, 30,* 37–43.

Hawkins, D. B., & Wightman, F. L. (1980). Interaural time discrimination ability of listeners with sensorineural hearing loss. *Audiology, 19*(6), 495–507.

Heinz, M. G., Swaminathan, J., Boley, J. D., & Kale, S. (2010). Across-fiber coding of temporal fine-structure: effects of noise-induced hearing loss on auditory-nerve responses. *The neurophysiological bases of auditory perception,* 621–630.

Springer, New York, NY. Henning, B. (1980). Some observations on the lateralization of complex waveforms. *Journal of the Acoustical Society of America, 68*(2), 446–454.

Hirsh, I. J. (1948). The influence of interaural phase on interaural summation and inhibition. *Journal of Acoustical Society of America, 20*(4), 536–544.

Jeffress, L. A. (1948). A place theory of sound location. *Journal of Comparative and Physiological ogy, 41*(1), 35.

Jesteadt, W., & Wier, C. C. (1977). Comparison of monaural and binaural discrimination of intensity and frequency. *Journal of the Acoustical Society of America, 61*(6), 1599–1603.

Kale, S., & Heinz, M. G. (2010). Envelope coding in auditory nerve fibers following noise-induced hearing loss. *Journal of the Association for Research in Otolaryngology, 11*(4), 657–673.

Köbler, S., & Rosenhall, U. (2002). Horizontal localization and speech intelligibility with bilateral and unilateral hearing aid amplification: Localización horizontal y discriminación del lenguaje con adaptación unilateral y bilateral de auxiliares auditivos. *International journal of audiology, 41*(7), 395–400.

Koehnke, J., Culotta, C. P., Hawley, M. L., & Colburn, H. S. (1995). Effects of reference interaural time and intensity differences on binaural performance in listeners with normal and impaired hearing. *Ear and Hearing, 16*(4), 331–353.

Koenig, W. (1950). Subjective effects in binaural hearing. *Journal of the Acoustical Society of America, 22*(1), 61–62.

Licklider, J. C. R. (1948). The influence of interaural phase relations upon the masking of speech by white noise. *Journal of the Acoustical Society of America, 20*(2), 150–159.

Marks, L. E. (1980). Binaural summation of loudness: Noise and two-tone complexes. *Perception and Psychophysics, 27*(6), 489–498.

Mills, A. W. (1958). On the minimum audible angle. *Journal of the Acoustical Society of America, 30*(4), 237–246.

Mills, A. W. (1972). Auditory localization (binaural acoustic field sampling, head movement and echo effect in auditory localization of sound sources position, distance and orientation). *Foundations of Modern Auditory Theory, 2*, 303–348.

Pollack, I. (1948). Monaural and binaural threshold sensitivity for tones and for white noise. *Journal of the Acoustical Society of America, 20*(1), 52–57.

Quaranta, A., & Cervellera, G. (1974). Masking level difference in normal and pathological ears. *Audiology, 13*(5), 428–431.

...berts, R. A., Besing, J., & Koehnke, J. (2002). Effects ...ing loss on echo thresholds. *Ear and Hearing,* ...57.

... I. J. (2004). Effects of age and ...ion and the precedence ...*urnal of Speech, Lan-* ...47(5), 965–978.

... A. (1963). Effect of vary- ...rrelation on the detectabil-

ity of tonal signals. *Journal of the Acoustical Society of America, 35*(12), 1947–1952.

Ruggero, M. A., & Rich, N. C. (1991). Application of a commercially-manufactured Doppler-shift laser velocimeter to the measurement of basilar-membrane vibration. *Hearing Research, 51*(2), 215–230.

Ruggero, M. A., Rich, N. C., & Recio, A.. (1992) Basilar membrane responses to clicks. In Y. Cazals, L. Demany, & K. Horner (Eds.), *Auditory physiology and perception* (pp. 85–91). Oxford, UK: Pergamon Press.

Shaw, W. A., Newman, E. B., & Hirsh, I. J. (1947). The difference between monaural and binaural thresholds. *Journal of the Acoustical Society of America, 19*(4), 734.

Simon, J. R. (1967). Ear preference in a simple reaction-time task. *Journal of Experimental Psychology, 75*(1), 49.

Stevens, S. S. & Newman, E. B. (1936). The localization of actual sources of sound. *American Journal of Psychology, 48*(2), 297–306.

Strutt, J. W. (Lord Rayleigh; 1877). *The theory of sound* (Vol. I). London, UK: Macmillan.

Wallach, H. (1940). The role of head movements and vestibular and visual cues in sound localization. *Journal of Experimental Psychology, 27*(4), 339–368.

Wallach, H., Newman, E. B., & Rosenzweig, M. R. (1949). A precedence effect in sound localization. *Journal of the Acoustical Society of America, 21*(4), 468.

Wenzel, E. M., Arruda, M., Kistler, D. J., & Wightman, F. L. (1993). Localization using nonindividualized head-related transfer functions. *Journal of the Acoustical Society of America, 94*(1), 111–123.

Whilby, S., Florentine, M., Wagner, E., & Marozeau, J. (2006). Monaural and binaural loudness of 5-and 200-ms tones in normal and impaired hearing. *Journal of the Acoustical Society of America, 119*(6), 3931–3939.

Yost, W. A. (1974). Discriminations of interaural phase differences. *Journal of the Acoustical Society of America, 55*(6), 1299–1303.

Yost, W. A., & Dye Jr., R. H. (1988). Discrimination of interaural differences of level as a function of frequency. *Journal of the Acoustical Society of America, 83*(5), 1846–1851.

Zurek, P. M. (1980). The precedence effect and its possible role in the avoidance of interaural ambiguities. *Journal of the Acoustical Society of America, 67*(3), 952–964.

Zwislocki, J., & Feldman, R. S. (1956). Just noticeable differences in dichotic phase. *Journal of the Acoustical Society of America, 28*(5), 860–864.

8

Clinical Implications

LEARNING OBJECTIVES

Upon completion of this chapter, students will be able to:

- Discuss the perceptual consequences of hearing loss and their impact on everyday listening
- Analyze the effects that hearing aid algorithms have on perception
- Apply psychoacoustic principles to evaluation of hearing disorders

INTRODUCTION

The previous chapters of this book have reviewed psychoacoustic characteristics of the auditory system in both the healthy and impaired ear. In many cases, we observed that sensorineural hearing loss leads to deficits in psychoacoustic abilities and that the degree of these deficits can vary considerably for listeners with hearing loss. We also observed that these abilities encompass much more than the audiogram; in fact, in many cases the audiogram does not provide a robust indicator of the degree of deficits experienced by an individual listener.

Given the wide range of variability in perceptual abilities of listeners with hearing loss documented throughout this text, a cogent argument could be made for including additional psychoacoustic tests into an audiological assessment. Yet, even if additional psychoacoustic tests are never included in audiological practice, both audiologists and psychoacousticians who study hearing loss should be aware of the ramifications that perceptual deficits measured psychoacoustically have on everyday listening. The purpose of this chapter is to discuss the consequences of those perceptual deficits and to look at various clinical applications of psychoacoustic experiments. We review hearing aids and their impact on auditory perceptual abilities, as well as how psychoacoustic experiments have impacted components of clinical auditory assessment. This chapter touches on the following topics:

- Everyday consequences of perceptual deficits
- Impact of hearing aid algorithms on perception of sounds
  - Compression

○ Directional microphones and noise reduction
- Influence of psychoacoustics in clinical diagnostics
  ○ Tinnitus
  ○ Retrocochlear assessment
  ○ Non-organic hearing loss
  ○ Auditory processing disorder

CONSEQUENCES OF IMPAIRED PERCEPTION

As we have observed throughout the chapters in this textbook, listeners with hearing loss experience a number of deficits in their auditory perception. Each of these deficits can have a real impact on the ability to communicate in the natural environments. Considering Erber's (1982) hierarchy of perception, deficits at lower levels in the hierarchy (i.e., detection and discrimination) will be propagated to higher levels. Any listener with an elevated threshold or poor discrimination abilities, then, may be expected to experience difficulties in recognition and comprehension. Speech, however, is a rich and highly redundant signal, and a listener can often attend to multiple cues in speech to achieve understanding. Yet, deficits in the representation of any of these cues can lead to poorer performance and increased effort expended to understand speech.

Here, we discuss the implications of perceptual deficits of listeners with sensorineural hearing loss on everyday listening. This section focuses on implications without assuming that listeners are wearing commercial ~ns of amplification that include advanced ~~ designed to improve comfort, ~ and eliminate background ~ we will touch on the .g sound, as the .mpact of modern .n understanding of ⅃ benchmark to assess

where improvements in technology can be made. It is also unfortunate that many listeners with sensorineural hearing loss do not wear hearing aids, and so understanding these deficits is also critical to counseling.

Elevated Thresholds

An obvious correlate of elevated auditory thresholds (poor audibility) is an inability to hear low-level sounds in the environment. Poor audibility can impact the ability to have a conversation, particularly if the conversation is relatively quiet. In these cases, a listener will miss the low-level elements of speech, commonly unvoiced fricatives, but other speech sounds may be rendered inaudible by hearing loss as well. For listeners who do not have flat losses, differences in the threshold across the frequency range of hearing can also cause deficits in perception, particularly for speech cues that require an across-frequency representation. A listener with a sloping, high-frequency hearing loss cannot take advantage of acoustic information in the high-frequency range. If certain formants in speech are rendered inaudible, a listener may confuse speech sounds that contain similar low-frequency formants. In cases of particularly severe hearing loss, listeners may confuse vowel sounds with each other if formants are not audible (Nábělek, 1988). In addition, robust audibility across a wide range of frequencies has been implicated in maintaining an ability to determine which elements of sounds belong together (i.e., *auditory scene analysis*; Bregman, 1990). For example, the ear best utilizes acoustic cues for sound segregation, such as onsets and offsets, when their representation across frequency is full and robust (e.g., Valentine & Lentz, 2012).

To characterize the effects of reduced audibility in speech, the *Speech Intelligibility Index (SII)* (a replacement for the Articulation Index) has also been used. It is accepted as a tool for calculating intelligibility of speech, and can now be used for listeners with normal hearing as well as those with mild-moderate hearing losses (ANSI, S3.5-2017). The SII assumes that different frequency bands contribute different amounts to the ultimate ability to understand speech, and these differences are characterized via frequency importance functions. When a listener has a hearing loss in one of the more important bands, his perception of speech would be affected more than a listener who has a hearing loss in one of the less important bands. Different speech materials have different SII functions, and so one needs to know the testing materials as well as the degree and configuration of hearing loss to predict how much speech will be audible to a listener. The SII is convenient, and using the count-the-dot audiogram, one can quickly calculate and visualize the amount of audible speech information (e.g., Mueller & Killion, 1990).

Clearly without an audible signal, there can be no speech perception, and the remaining supra-threshold deficits are irrelevant. Once audibility is taken into account (e.g., a talker raises his voice or an assistive device is worn), supra-threshold factors begin to impact the perception of sounds in natural scenes, factors which are discussed next.

Loudness Recruitment

Loudness recruitment, the abnormally rapid growth of loudness, can lead to a number of difficulties in everyday communication. For listeners who do not wear hearing aids, talkers often have to raise the level of their voices to be heard by a listener with SNHL. By raising the level of the voice, however, the listener may now have a perception that the speech is too loud. Recall that this phenomenon does not occur because a typical listener with

SNHL experiences abnormally loud sounds, but because the speech is now at a higher level and therefore a higher loudness.

In addition to altering the overall loudness of sounds in the environment, loudness recruitment may lead to deficits in speech perception. Moore and Glasberg (1993) simulated loudness recruitment using a loudness model and measured speech perception ability under different amounts of recruitment. They demonstrated a detrimental impact of loudness recruitment on speech intelligibility, particularly when coupled with simulation of elevated absolute threshold. However, whether loudness recruitment degrades speech perception is not clearly established. For example, Stone, Moore, Alcántara, and Glasberg (1999) demonstrated that compensating for recruitment using hearing aids did not alter speech identification in quiet or noise.

The loss of outer hair cells that causes recruitment also alters the representation of fluctuating sounds and can lead to greater effects of masking by fluctuating maskers. Here, the enhanced representation of those fluctuations compared with normal-hearing counterparts might increase the amount of simultaneous and forward masking (Bacon, Opie, & Montoya, 1998). As a result, recruitment can negatively influence the fluctuating masker benefit.

Reduced Frequency Selectivity

Listeners with hearing loss have been demonstrated to experience poorer frequency selectivity than listeners with normal hearing. Poor frequency selectivity smears the spectral representation of stimuli, and can lead to deficits in perceiving sounds that require a robust representation of the stimulus spectrum (Zeng & Turner; 1990). Baer and Moore (1993), however, simulated reduced frequency selectivity and found that even very poor frequency selectivity (six times worse) had only a very small effect on speech understanding in quiet.

On the other hand, however, Baer and Moore observed very large effects of reduced frequency selectivity for that same speech signal presented in noise. In this case, poor frequency selectivity of the impaired ear increases the susceptibility to masking by other sounds. The poor frequency selectivity of the impaired ear has also been linked to poor abilities to understand speech in noise for people with SNHL (e.g., Dubno, Dirks, & Morgan, 1984). Upward spread of masking can also be problematic, particularly in amplified situations. The low-frequency components of a noise may mask higher frequencies. Such upward spread of masking can also complicate fitting hearing aids for listeners with low-frequency hearing loss, as gain in the low frequencies can lead to upward spread of masking into regions of good hearing.

Poor Temporal Processing

Many listeners with hearing loss do not have large distortions to their ability to follow temporal changes in a sound, when measured using gap and modulation detection. However, deficits are profoundly evident with respect to forward masking and in temporal integration. The longer release of forward masking associated with SNHL has implications for the perception of both speech and music, in quiet and in noisy situations. Consider a highly fluctuating signal that contains information in the high- and low-amplitude epochs. Within this fluctuating stimulus, the high-amplitude components may forward mask the low-amplitude ones. For a speech stimulus, then, we might observe high-energy vowels forward masking the low-energy consonants. Perceiving music might be affected in a similar manner. Deficits in temporal integra-

tion have a variety of consequences as well. One consequence may be that even slowed speech may not provide sufficient benefit to allow listeners to fully integrate information within and across speech segments, because listeners with SNHL are limited in their ability to benefit from increasing the duration of sounds.

Poor Pitch Perception

Deficits in pitch perception lead to a number of problems for listeners with sensorineural hearing loss. For example, diplacusis would be particularly problematic for the perception of pitch in music and can impact the ability of listeners to benefit from two ears if pitch perception differs substantially between the ears.

Because pitch also provides an important cue for the understanding of speech in complex environments, deficits in pitch perception can degrade this ability. Listeners with hearing loss demonstrate difficulty using pitch cues to segregate sounds from a background (Oxenham, 2008). For example, Arehart, King, and McLean-Mudgett (1997) showed that the ability to identify two synthetic vowels with different fundamental frequencies was negatively impacted by hearing loss. The differences were fairly small under quiet conditions but became much larger when the synthetic vowels were presented in a background noise. Summers and Leek (1998) measured direct deficits in f_0 discrimination abilities in listeners with hearing loss and linked these deficits to difficulty discriminating between speech samples presented at different f_0s. Lorenzi, Gilbert, Carn, Garnier, and Moore (2006) and Strelcyk and Dau (2009) noted that deficits in the perception of temporal fine structure were also connected to poor speech perception. On the whole, poor pitch perception has a strong and detrimental effect on the ability to communicate in complex environments.

Pitch perception also facilitates voice identification, intonation perception, and the perception of emotional state. Impairments to pitch perception could undermine one's ability to gather this important information contained in speech. When listeners have difficulty representing the pitch of sounds, we expect a variety of difficulties that are related to communication, and these difficulties are not exclusive to speech understanding.

Poor Binaural Abilities

Poor binaural abilities in listeners with hearing loss have clear implications for the perception of sounds in noisy environments. Binaural release from masking (in terms of the MLD and binaural squelch) is degraded by SNHL. The consequence of these factors is straightforward: Listeners will experience more masking and more deterioration of speech perception in noisy environments. As we know, communicating in noisy environments can be particularly problematic for listeners with hearing loss, and the loss of binaural mechanisms for noise reduction has been implicated in these difficulties (Humes, Kidd, & Lentz, 2013). Listeners can still rely on the better-ear advantage, as it is an acoustic effect, but listeners will not gain great benefits from binaural listening. Deficits in the precedence effect are also associated with greater susceptibility to masking in reverberant environments.

With regard to sound localization, listeners with hearing loss generally have deficits in their ability to represent the ITD and ILD. As a consequence, these listeners will have more difficulty determining where a sound is coming from in the azimuthal plane. While listeners with bilateral, symmetric hearing losses experience difficulty localizing sounds, a unilateral loss can make sound localization almost impossible. Further, due to reductions in audibility and loss of high-frequency hearing, many listeners do not have access to the pinna cues to help them localize sounds along the median plane (e.g., front-back, above-below).

Adding to the problem is that hearing aids, even when they provide linear amplification, distort the natural relationships between ITD and ILD. They do not compensate for the spectral changes imposed by the pinnae, and microphone location can even remove pinnae effects altogether. Most do not amplify sounds above 6 kHz, where pinna cues are most available. As a result, hearing aids do not typically improve sound localization and often make sound localization worse (cf. Akeroyd, 2014).

Summary

These studies on impaired hearing have all, to various extents, attempted to control for the reduced audibility experienced by the listener with hearing loss. That is, when possible, sounds were presented at audible levels or reduced effects of audibility were considered when interpreting the data. The perceptual consequences we have discussed here are generally assumed to be unrelated to reductions in audibility, although in some cases audibility cannot be fully discounted as a driving factor. Because of this, simple amplification would not be expected to improve or compensate for most of these deficits. In fact, the elevated thresholds of the impaired listener are the only deficit that can be compensated for by an amplification device, like a hearing aid.

EFFECTS OF AMPLIFICATION STRATEGIES ON PERCEPTION

Modern hearing aids are an engineering marvel—not only do they amplify sound in a frequency-specific manner, but they include numerous technologies designed to assist the listener in a variety of acoustic environments. As we all know, hearing aids do not work like glasses, which correct for optical deficits in the eye. Hearing loss is not an acoustic deficit; rather, it is a deficit in the sensory representation of acoustic stimuli. Consequently, hearing aids are limited in their ability to compensate for the distortions imposed by the ear. Hearing aids can amplify sound, improve the signal-to-noise ratio through noise reduction or directional microphones, and even include programs to assist with tinnitus tolerance. However, they cannot correct for many of the supra-threshold perceptual deficits experienced by listeners with SNHL.

Regardless, there is no doubt that hearing aids are beneficial to patients with hearing loss. Almost everyone who has a mild or greater hearing loss should wear one, and we might even be able to argue that people with slight hearing losses (thresholds of 16–25 dB HL) could benefit from hearing aids. Hearing aids compensate for the most important auditory deficit, higher auditory thresholds, by providing amplification.

Modern hearing aids primarily address three areas of perceptual deficits experienced by listeners with hearing loss: reduced audibility through amplification, loudness recruitment through compression, and increased susceptibility to noise through directional microphones and noise reduction. This leaves a number of perceptual deficits that are not well addressed by hearing aids: poor frequency resolution, poor temporal processing, and poor pitch perception. Binaural algorithms are becoming increasingly more available in hearing aids, and they may be able to address some of the binaural deficits experienced by listeners with SNHL.

Although hearing aids do not directly address many of the supra-threshold deficits experienced by listeners with hearing loss, technologies available in hearing aids may be able to help with these problems, if they were adequately diagnosed. For example, not all listeners with hearing loss experience the same amount of loudness recruitment, and such information might help an audiologist select among different compression algorithms available. As we have observed throughout the review of psychoacoustic literature, one cannot assume that any given listener has a deficit in a particular perceptual ability without testing it directly. There is a poor correlation with detection thresholds (i.e., the audiogram), and there is wide variability in the type and degree of perceptual deficits across listeners with sensorineural hearing loss. Any listener with hearing loss would be expected to benefit from amplification and improving the signal-to-noise ratio, and while these technologies do not directly address the psychoacoustic deficits experienced by listeners, they can ameliorate some of the negative effects of those deficits by providing a cleaner, better signal. This section reviews how hearing aid algorithms might improve (and also possibly degrade) the representation of information provided to listeners with hearing loss.

Compression

A primary goal of hearing aids is to restore audibility to the impaired ear. Amplification increases the input level of sounds to the ear, with the expectation that the auditory system will then decode the information present in the stimulus (with speech understanding being a primary goal). Listeners with hearing loss also commonly experience frequency-dependent hearing loss, and may have different amplification needs for some frequencies than for others. The reduced dynamic range experienced by listeners with hearing loss makes linear amplification inappropriate, as high input sound levels could become excessively loud and potentially damaging.

How Compression Works

To address these issues, modern hearing aids typically provide multiple channels, and these multiple channels can include different processing schemes. Consequently, most modern hearing aids provide some form of nonlinear amplification, with **wide dynamic range compression** (WDRC) being a very popular amplification scheme. Although WDRC is not the only nonlinear amplification scheme, the benefits and deficits of using this type of algorithm are reasonably illustrative of other nonlinear forms of amplification, and so we only discuss WDRC here. Essentially, a simple form of WDRC works in the following way:

- At low input levels, the hearing aid provides linear amplification. That is, the gain provided by the hearing aid is the same regardless of the input level. For example, the gain provided by the hearing aid might be 20 dB for all low-level stimuli. A 10-dB SPL stimulus would become 30 dB SPL and a 30-dB SPL stimulus would become 50 dB SPL.
- At moderate input levels, the hearing aid provides progressively less amplification. The decibel level above which the algorithm switches from linear to compressive is called the *compression threshold* and can be dependent on frequency. The amount of gain is specified in conjunction with the *compression ratio*, which specifies a reduction of the amount of gain after sound exceeds the compression threshold. For example, a 2:1 compression ratio indicates that for every 2-dB change in the input, only a 1 dB change in output would occur. For example, a 50 dB SPL input sound might be amplified to 70 dB SPL, but a 52 dB SPL input sound would only be amplified to 71 dB SPL.
- At high input levels, stimuli are often not amplified. Hearing aids can also include a maximum output that prevents sounds from being unpleasantly or uncomfortably loud.

Audiologists generally determine the amount of amplification provided by a hearing aid from the audiogram and a prescriptive rule. The amount of gain provided is generally somewhere between one-third and half of the hearing loss. A variety of prescriptive rules are available, but the specific prescriptive rule has been demonstrated to have little effect on speech intelligibility (Humes, 1991).

Compression algorithms provide perceptual benefits in a number of ways. Achieving audibility for speech signals is critically important for speech understanding, and compression algorithms do this in a way that achieves audibility without overly distorting signals at high levels. Nonlinear amplification improves the elevated threshold of a listener and partially restores the distorted perception of loudness for some listeners with sensorineural hearing loss.

Compression algorithms accomplish a great deal in providing comfort for patients and restoring audibility. They have some negative consequences, however, and a patient's specific perceptual deficits might interact with the type of compression parameters used in amplification schemes. Spectral, temporal, and binaural acoustic information is changed by these algorithms. Describing the impact of these algorithms on perception is a large task, as there are many parameters involved in nonlinear hearing aids (including number of channels, compression ratio, etc.). Further, relatively few studies evaluate the effects of compression on psychoacoustic abilities, and so we can only make some logical conclusions about the impact of compression on particular abilities in some cases.

Temporal Distortion

Compression alters the natural fluctuations present in acoustic stimuli. Because low-level sounds are amplified more than high-level sounds, the acoustic waveform of a stimulus will contain fewer fluctuations after being processed by a compression hearing aid. In some cases, the temporal distortion imposed by the hearing aids may correct for some of the temporal distortions associated with hearing impairment. For instance, Glasberg and Moore (1992) demonstrated that a compression algorithm can lead to better gap detection thresholds in listeners with normal hearing.

However, listeners who are required to use temporal cues to identify elements of speech (perhaps due to significant distortions in their spectral representation of sounds) may be negatively impacted by the temporal distortions imposed by WDRC algorithms. Although limited data exist on the topic, Hedrick and Rice (2000) have demonstrated that temporal distortions imposed by these algorithms can disrupt the perception of temporal cues in speech. They evaluated plosive consonants (e.g., /t/ and /b/), which are characterized by a full stoppage of air prior to the noise burst, a temporal cue that is important for their perception, and a cue that is altered by WDRC. Hedrick and Rice demonstrated that stop consonants were more confusable with one another after being processed by WDRC.

Reduced Spectral Contrast

Plomp (1988) proposed that the number of channels would interact with the compression imposed on those channels, with a consequence of smoothing the peaks and valleys in a sound spectrum. He argued that if a different compression channel processed a spectral peak and a spectral valley, the relationship between their output levels would be altered from the original relationship. On the other hand, if the same channel processed the peak and valley, the peak and valley would undergo the same amount of amplification. This would preserve the spectral contrast in the stimulus.

To illustrate the effects of multi-channel compression, consider a vowel, which is char-

acterized by spectral peaks (the formants) and valleys, with a formant at 70 dB SPL and a valley that is at 45 dB SPL. The formant and the valley are processed by different channels but the same compression rule. If we apply a compression algorithm that applies 25 dB of gain below 50 dB SPL and has a 2:1 compression ratio above 50 dB SPL, the valley will be amplified by 25 dB and will have a level of 70 dB SPL at the output of the hearing aid. The peak, on the other hand, will also undergo compression but through a different channel. The peak will only be amplified by 10 dB (as it is in the region of compression), leading to an output of 80 dB SPL. In this way, processing the peak and valley through separate channels will reduce the 25 dB of spectral contrast to 10 dB.

Bor, Souza, and Wright (2008) made acoustic and perceptual measurements and noted that the spectral contrast present in vowels decreased with increasing number of compression channels. Furthermore, perception of the vowels degraded as well. Listeners with hearing loss made more vowel confusions as the number of channels increased. Performance was poorest for 16 channels, and relatively unchanged between 1 and 8 channels. The implications for these results are many, as vowel stimuli are not the only speech sounds that require the presence of spectral contrast. Other sounds, such as fricatives and musical notes produced by different instruments, may also be particularly susceptible to multichannel WDRC algorithms. Yet, note that some studies have not demonstrated a negative relationship between number of channels and speech perception, even in noise (e.g., Yund & Buckles, 1995). Such results suggest that our ability to perceive speech may be very robust even in the presence of acoustic distortion.

Binaural Distortion

Small differences in algorithmic fitting across the ears also can negatively impact a listener's binaural ability. As we observed in Chapter 7, binaural abilities of listeners with hearing loss tend to be substantially poorer than those with normal hearing. Further, because the ears receive different signals for sounds at different locations, one can expect the compression algorithm to be working at a different sound level across the ears. For example, a sound to the left of a person might be 20 dB lower in level when presented to the right ear, particularly the high frequencies present in that sound. If that sound is presented at the level of conversational speech, the hearing aid in the right ear might provide more gain than the left hearing aid. In this way, the representation of ILD presented to the ears would be distorted. Delays imposed by the hearing aid may also impact the ITD representation, causing even more distortions to binaural perception. Truly matched hearing aids may partly solve the binaural discrepancy, and the advent of binaural processing algorithms in hearing aids is likely to restore appropriate binaural acoustic cues. These algorithms have great potential to be beneficial to listeners experiencing binaural deficits associated with hearing aid processing.

Summary

Taken together, there is no doubt that nonlinear algorithms in hearing aids provide benefits to a listener with SNHL. These benefits include, but are not exclusive to, improving the audibility of sounds without exceeding uncomfortable loudness levels and expanding a listener's dynamic range. However, these algorithms include unintended side effects and can distort the cues present in sounds in a variety of different ways. Improvements to hearing aid technology continue to reduce the amount of distortion provided by nonlinear algorithms, and in many cases, the positive effects of wearing a hearing aid far outweigh the negative consequences of the distortion.

Improving the Signal-to-Noise Ratio

Regardless of a listener's perceptual deficit (or even lack of deficits), improving the signal-to-noise ratio is always helpful to a listener. Cleaning up a signal will help with pitch perception and temporal processing, as it allows a listener to apply the auditory mechanisms available without the detrimental effects of masking. Recall that under difficult listening conditions, a 1 dB improvement in the SNR can result in an increase in intelligibility of between 7% and 19%. Due to the deficits associated with sensorineural hearing loss and the large potential benefits of a higher SNR, improving the SNR for listeners with hearing loss has been a focus of modern hearing aids. A variety of techniques are used to improve the SNR, with common ones being directional microphones and noise reduction algorithms.

Directional microphones are more sensitive to sounds coming from a particular direction than to sounds coming from other directions. In the case of a hearing aid, it is generally assumed that the listener's head is pointing in the direction of the sound of interest. In this way, a directional microphone selectively represents sounds to the front of the listener more than sounds to the side or the back of the listener. Assessment of directional microphones includes measurements of speech recognition thresholds (SRTs) in the laboratory, which has demonstrated great success in improving the perception of speech in noise. In some cases improvements in the SNR of over 7 dB have been observed (e.g., Hawkins & Yacullo, 1984; Soede, Berkhout, & Bilsen, 1993), and modern approaches to directionality provide more benefits than have been observed previously (Edwards, 2007).

On the other hand, directional microphones are designed with the purpose of improving the signal-to-noise ratio for the hearing aid wearer, and this technology may have a detrimental effect on the representation of environmental cues, particularly those involved in sound localization. These microphones are often implemented in a monaural manner and do not take into consideration their effects on the ILD. Depending on the type of directional microphone used, sounds directly to the right and to the left of the body can be attenuated. Attenuating sounds to the side of the body could be particularly damaging to the representation of the ILDs that are useful for sound localization. However, the advent of new technologies designed to provide directionality may not have as many negative effects on sound localization as in the past (Best, Mejia, Freeston, Van Hoesel, & Dillon, 2015; Carette, van den Bogaert, Laureyns, & Wouters, 2014). New technologies in which hearing aids can communicate with each other can preserve the binaural cues present in the environment and have great potential to provide spatial hearing for listeners with sensorineural hearing loss.

Noise reduction algorithms also improve the signal-to-noise ratio for the listener. To date, little work has been conducted to evaluate their impact on auditory perceptual abilities. Logically, however, these algorithms have the potential to degrade some of the psychoacoustic cues available in the environment, but to improve others. As with directional microphones, these algorithms improve the SNR, allowing a listener to better use his auditory system to decode a speech signal. However, these algorithms distort binaural cues, particularly the ITD, and thereby degrade sound localization abilities (e.g., van den Bogaert, Doclo, Wouters, & Moonen, 2009). Again, hearing aids that communicate with each other may also be helpful in resolving these situations, and algorithmic advances also promise to improve their distortions.

INFLUENCE OF PSYCHOACOUSTICS ON DIAGNOSTIC AUDIOLOGY

Psychoacoustics has been utterly integral to diagnostic audiology. In addition to the basic audiogram, the audiologist has on hand a variety of psychoacoustic tests that assist with diagnosis. Clearly, the audiogram has deep roots in the field of psychoacoustics, and is critically important for identifying the site of lesion. We have already discussed applications of psychoacoustics in the audiogram, in respect to the techniques and the stimuli used. This section discusses additional applications of psychoacoustics to diagnostic audiology.

Tinnitus

The prevalence of *tinnitus*, the perception of a sound in its absence, in the population is rising, along with a greater number of people presenting with sensorineural hearing loss. For the military, tinnitus is an increasing problem, as it is currently the #1 service-connected disability. Unfortunately, there is no current diagnostic test for tinnitus, and all diagnoses are made on the basis of self-report. Animal and human studies are currently under way that may ultimately lead to diagnostic tests, but to date, diagnoses are made in conjunction with self-report, case history, and characterization of tinnitus. Tinnitus is generally considered to have loudness, quality (i.e., a timbre), and a pitch.

Tinnitus characterization, when conducted, generally assesses the quality first via questionnaire. Next, the assessment consists of loudness balancing and pitch matching. A tinnitus loudness match generally consists of using pure tones and a measurement of the sound level that closely matches the perceived loudness of the tinnitus. In most instances, the sound level in dB HL that best matches the tinnitus loudness is about 5 to 15 dB above the patient's audiometric threshold. There is no relationship between the tinnitus loudness and the annoyance of the tinnitus, and today, tinnitus loudness matches are not considered to be useful to diagnostic audiology.

Obtaining a tinnitus pitch match is similar to loudness balancing, but the frequency that best matches the pitch of the patient's tinnitus is measured. Although tinnitus pitch matching can have very poor test-retest reliability, the frequencies that best match tinnitus frequencies are generally in the range of hearing loss (Henry & Miekle, 2000). Clinical pitch matching uses pure tones, but in the majority of cases, tinnitus cannot easily be described as pure tone. To address the limitations of clinical pitch matching, Noreña, Micheyl, Chéry-Croze, and Collet (2002) and later Roberts, Moffat, Baumann, Ward, and Bosnyak (2008) developed a pitch similarity rating method that was designed to determine whether multiple frequencies were involved in tinnitus. Across over 100 listeners, both studies found that all frequencies in the region of hearing loss were assigned high similarity to the tinnitus pitch. Given the results of these studies, methodologies that converge on a range of frequencies might better characterize the perception of tinnitus. Note that certain tinnitus treatments may require an accurate tinnitus pitch match, which is why pitch matching is sometimes included in a tinnitus assessment.

In modern audiological assessment, the major useful diagnostic component of tinnitus assessment is that of tinnitus quality, although tinnitus quality is rarely measured using psychophysical techniques. Generally, tinnitus is characterized as being noisy, tonal, pulsatile, clicking, or hissing. Noisy, and more particularly, roaring tinnitus is a hallmark of Meniere's disease and can be informative from a diagnostic perspective. Pulsatile tinnitus can be indicative of high blood pressure or a tumor and should be referred for medical evaluation. Not all types of tinnitus are con-

sidered to be life threatening, although they can be debilitating in many cases. Currently, no treatment exists, but some patients benefit substantially from ear-level sound therapies, noise maskers, and forms of cognitive therapy, all which help patients experience less distress from their tinnitus. In some debilitating cases, cochlear implants have successfully treated tinnitus as well.

Retrocochlear Assessment

Before physiological tests and the MRI were developed, audiologists conducted behavioral assessments of *retrocochlear* auditory disorders, or disorders in the auditory system at a level above the cochlea. In many cases, a retrocochlear disorder is caused by a tumor on the auditory nerve or in the brainstem. With the advent of physiological tests such as otoacoustic emissions (a test of cochlear function), immitance testing (a test of middle ear and brainstem function), and auditory brainstem response (ABR; a brainstem evoked potential), behavioral assessment is no longer routinely conducted to determine whether a sensorineural hearing loss is retrocochlear. Importantly, these psychoacoustics tests collectively have reasonably good specificity (ability to identify the healthy ears), but fairly poor sensitivity (ability to accurately identity the presence of a retrocochlear pathology; Turner, Shepard, & Frazer; 1984). Today, an MRI is considered the gold standard of retrocochlear assessment. However, there are patients for whom an MRI is contraindicated, and there are some cases where retrocochlear assessment using behavioral techniques may still be needed.

Alternative Binaural Loudness Balancing (ABLB) Test

The first psychoacoustic test discussed to assess retrocochlear hearing loss is based on the absence of loudness recruitment, a phenomenon associated with loss of outer hair cells. A listener with SNHL is expected to experience loudness recruitment, and this clinical method allows a quick assessment of recruitment, but only for people with unilateral hearing loss. In cases of suspected retrocochlear hearing loss and unilateral hearing loss, the tester can conduct the **ABLB**, the **alternate binaural loudness balancing method**, to determine if the ear with SNHL experiences recruitment or not (Fowler, 1936).

The ABLB is very straightforward—a tone is presented at a specific dB HL to the patient's healthy ear. The audiologist presents a tone at the same frequency to the patient's impaired ear. The tones are always presented sequentially (e.g., alternating). In one approach, the patient hears the reference tone in this good ear and tells the audiologist to increase or decrease the level of the sound in his impaired ear until it is equally loud to the tone in his healthy ear. Another approach is to present the fixed tone to the impaired ear. Whatever

the approach, the audiologist repeats the measurement at another level (usually in 10 or 20 dB steps, depending on the degree of hearing loss). The audiologist then plots a *laddergram*, in which one rung of the ladder plots the dB HL levels in the healthy ear and the other rung of the ladder shows the loudness-matched levels (in dB HL) in the impaired ear. Figure 8–1 illustrates that a laddergram from a patient with recruitment in the right ear will show non-parallel rungs (loudness will grow faster in the impaired ear than in the healthy one; see the right panel of Figure 8–1). An ear that does not exhibit recruitment will show parallel rungs (see the left panel of Figure 8–1). This type of laddergram might be indicative of retrocochlear pathology.

Performance-Intensity Function

Speech testing is also a common component of a standard audiometric assessment. Two types of speech tests are routine: the SRT and word recognition scores measured at a

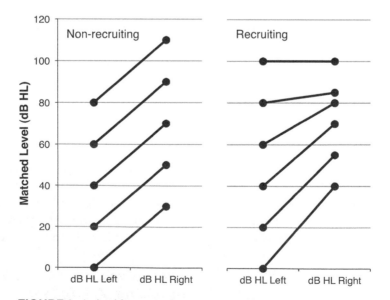

FIGURE 8–1. Laddergrams for a non-recruiting ear (*left panel*) and a recruiting ear (*right panel*) are illustrated.

supra-threshold stimulus level. The SRT has been documented to essentially reflect average audiometric thresholds at 500, 1000, and 2000 Hz, and should be redundant with the audiogram. Word recognition scores, on the other hand, provide an upper limit for a patient's ability to understand speech and are, when possible, measured at audible levels.

Word recognition scores are also fairly predictable based on the audiogram for patients with sensorineural hearing loss of cochlear origin. Yet, a patient with a retrocochlear hearing loss might present with poorer than expected word recognition scores. This finding might be a result of aging, but it may also reflect retrocochlear pathology. Further evidence of retrocochlear pathology can be evident in word recognition measures as a function of the stimulus level. As with the psychometric function, there should be an increasing relationship between presentation level and word recognition scores. In some cases of retrocochlear disorder, however, word recognition decreases with increasing intensity, a phenomenon called *rollover*. Figure 8–2 illustrates a performance-intensity (PI) function, which is a plot relating performance on a speech task (here, word recognition scores in percent correct). The PI function consistent with a cochlear site of lesion is plotted using solid symbols, and the PI function demonstrating rollover is plotted with unfilled symbols. This patient needs referral, as the rollover may indicate a retrocochlear site of lesion. Importantly, large amounts of amplification would be contraindicated for this patient due to his poor word recognition scores at higher stimulus levels.

Non-Organic Hearing Loss

Another common application of psycho-acoustics to diagnostic audiology is the assessment of non-organic hearing loss, commonly called **pseudohypacusis**. Non-organic hearing loss may occur both consciously and uncon-

FIGURE 8–2. Performance-intensity functions for word recognition for a listener with a presumed cochlear site of lesion (*filled circles*) and a presumed retrocochlear site of lesion (*unfilled circles*).

sciously, and non-organic losses manifest themselves in the form of an overly conservative criterion and lead to an overestimate of audiometric thresholds. Determining whether a patient has pseudohypacusis is not always easy and requires an attentive experimenter/audiologist. There are numerous clues to pseudohypacusis, such as:

- *Absence of a shadow curve.* An audiometric shadow curve should be present in patients with true unilateral hearing loss. The shadow curve is a "false" audiometric curve that occurs because a patient hears a sound in a non-test ear due to bone conduction from the sound presented in a test ear. The amount of sound "crossover" is roughly 0 to 10 dB for bone conduction and 40 to 80 dB for air conduction. A patient with a true, and large, unilateral hearing loss should present with a shadow curve during audiometric testing. The absence of a shadow curve when there should be one is clear evidence of a non-organic hearing loss.
- *Disagreement among test results.* For patients with all types of hearing loss, the SRT is expected to be a close approximation of the audiogram, within ±5 dB. Any SRT that is better than expected based on the audiogram provides a sign to non-organic hearing loss. Word recognition scores also provide clues, and scores that are better than predicted by the audiogram also suggest nonorganic hearing loss.
- *No false positives.* Patients following appropriate instructions are expected to provide some false positives during threshold testing. The complete absence of false positives can be indicative of false hearing loss.

Once the pseudohypacusis is suspected, obtaining an accurate audiogram can be relatively difficult. Obtaining the correct audiogram is easier for a patient feigning a unilateral hearing loss, but it is not impossible to do

so for bilateral hearing loss. Here, we discuss some of the strategies employed in audiology and how they are connected to psychoacoustic principles.

For patients with bilateral pseudohypacusis, the audiologist must make modifications to the audiometric procedures in order to determine true absolute thresholds. The procedures in place were specifically designed in order to encourage patients to provide a neutral or liberal criterion. However, in the cases of pseudohypacusis, these practices have not achieved that goal. To obtain a more accurate audiologic threshold, the audiologist essentially applies the principles of Signal Detection Theory to encourage the patient to adopt a more neutral or liberal criterion. Consequently, the first step in audiometric testing for patients with suspected pseudohypacusis is to re-instruct the patient. This allows patients to be aware that you are suspicious of their thresholds and gives them the opportunity to readjust their criterion (whether it is consciously or unconsciously overly conservative). In many cases, re-instruction is sufficient to obtain a true audiogram. During the audiometric threshold search, the audiologist may need to adjust the step size used in testing (often it is lowered to 2 dB), increase the variability in presentation intervals, or estimate the thresholds using descending trials to ensure that the threshold is commensurate with that obtained using ascending trials. Ultimately, these practices effectively make it difficult for the patient to maintain an overly conservative criterion.

For unilateral hearing losses, the audiologist can apply the **Stenger** test, which is based on the principles of lateralization. The test relies on the psychoacoustic principle that a listener will lateralize a binaurally presented sound to the ear with the louder sound. When applying the Stenger test, the audiologist presents stimuli to both ears: The sound in the better ear is presented 10 dB above audiometric threshold (10 dB SL). The sound in the poorer (presumed pseudohypacusic) ear is presented at 10 dB below the measured (but presumed false) threshold. The patient who is not feigning hearing loss will respond to this stimulus because the binaural sound will lateralize to his better ear, and he will hear it. In contrast, the patient with pseudohypacusis will not respond to this stimulus because the sound will lateralize to the feigned ear (because it is above his true audiometric threshold). This result provides evidence of pseudohypacusis because the tester knows that he can hear the sound in the healthy ear.

Once the Stenger test has identified the presence of pseudohypacusis, the principle of ***contralateral interference*** can be used in an attempt to obtain true thresholds in the feigned ear. When applying this technique, the tester presents a stimulus at 10 dB SL in the better ear, and the sound level in the poorer starts at 0 dB HL and increases in 5 or 10 dB steps until the patient stops responding. This level is the contralateral interference level. The actual threshold is then inferred as being about 15 to 20 dB lower than the contralateral interference level.

Auditory Processing Disorder

The notion of ***(central) auditory processing disorder*** (APD) is controversial, in particular as there is no consensus that a single-locus disorder of auditory processing exists (Moore, Ferguson, Edmonson-Jones, Ratib, & Riley, 2010). To the extent that APD is a disorder separate from one involving speech areas or cognitive processing, it is defined as a disorder in the central auditory pathway that is distinct from peripheral and cognitive pathologies. Symptomology includes no peripheral pathology but difficulty listening in a variety of envi-

ronments. A key diagnostic criterion of APD is difficulty in processing non-speech sounds (Moore, 2006).

When selecting tests that might reflect central auditory abilities, tests should assess central auditory abilities, and use peripheral or cognitive tests to rule out pathologies in those domains. Psychoacoustic tests that have been strongly linked to cochlear function and pathology, such as recruitment or masking, are not diagnostically helpful in isolation. Additionally, tests that require substantial cognitive components also should not be used in isolation. However, these tests are important for APD diagnosis, as they are needed to rule out the presence of the peripheral and cognitive pathologies. The core, informative APD tests are those that implicate central auditory processing, such as *temporal processing* tests and tests of *binaural hearing*. Other tests involving sequential *masking* effects (forward and backward) and some speech tests can be used in conjunction with the psychophysical assessments in an attempt to provide differential diagnosis.

Summary

Clearly psychoacoustics has had a strong impact on diagnostic audiology. Even today, a variety of tests are conducted that rely on the principles of psychoacoustics from masking to the diagnosis of APD and the assessment of tinnitus. Although we rarely use behavioral tests to identify retrocochlear disorders, there are cases where such tests are warranted, and an adept audiologist should be aware of the possibilities. There may come a time when additional psychoacoustic tests are adopted in the clinic to assess temporal, spectral, or binaural abilities in listeners. As we move toward precision medicine, it seems that using diagnoses of individual-specific disorders to influence treatment decisions may not be that far away.

SUMMARY AND TAKE-HOME POINTS

On the whole, psychoacoustics is connected to audiological assessment and treatment in many ways: from providing information that would be useful for counseling patients when they might experience problems listening to the diagnostic tests used regularly within the field. Impairments to perceptual abilities can be expected to lead to impairments in speech perception in natural environments, and psychoacoustics has informed our understanding of the nature of communication difficulties experienced by listeners with sensorineural hearing loss. Further, audiology has its roots in psychoacoustics, and the foundation of psychoacoustics remains an integral component of any diagnostic audiometric assessment. One might expect that the future would lead to the development of additional psychoacoustic tools for audiometric assessment as the field moves toward individualized medicine.

The following points are key take-home messages of this chapter:

• Deficits in auditory perceptual abilities have a direct consequence for perception of sounds in natural environments. Audibility is the greatest factor in communication difficulties for listeners with hearing loss. However, supra-threshold deficits all contribute to poor auditory perception.

• Specific deficits can be difficult to compensate for using modern hearing aid technology, and in many cases, hearing aid algorithms distort the cues available to a listener with SNHL. Despite the distortion provided by these algorithms, hearing aids provide benefits to speech understanding. This result has been documented over and over and over.

• Audiological assessment relies on psychoacoustic tools which are used to measure the audiogram, including tinnitus assessment, retrocochlear assessment, pseudohypacusis, and auditory processing disorder. Time will tell if more psychoacoustic assessments will be included in clinical testing in the future.

EXERCISES

1. Assume a situation in which a listener with sensorineural hearing loss receives linear amplification that ensures audibility but does not exceed uncomfortable levels. Discuss the effects of linear amplification (in this case, simply making the sound audible) on the following:
   a. masking of pure tones
   b. loudness perception
   c. temporal processing
   d. ILD processing
   e. ITD processing
   f. Pitch perception
2. Explain why technologies that could improve perceptual abilities would not benefit a listener with sensorineural hearing loss unless they also received amplification.
3. Discuss why low-frequency amplification will exacerbate upward spread of masking experienced by a listener with SNHL.
4. Consider the following situation: A patient presents with pseudohypacusis, and you, the audiologist, are attempting to obtain an accurate threshold. Nothing in the standard audiometric procedure seems to work. Given what you have learned in other chapters of this book, provide a methodological suggestion that might allow you to avoid problems with a conservative criterion. Discuss your reasoning.
5. Kendra has a monaural hearing loss and wears a hearing aid in her impaired ear that amplifies sound by 20 dB across all frequencies. Her hearing aid has an average time delay of about 4 ms, and the delay is greater at low frequencies than

high. Considering the topics discussed in this class, how might these perceptual abilities be affected by this hearing aid:

a. Absolute threshold in her impaired ear
b. Speech understanding in her impaired ear
c. Sound localization based on the ITD
d. Sound localization based on the ILD
e. Binaural release from masking

REFERENCES

Akeroyd, M. A. (2014). An overview of the major phenomena of the localization of sound sources by normal-hearing, hearing-impaired, and aided listeners. *Trends in Hearing, 18*, 1–7.

NSI/ASA S3.5-1997. (R2017). American National Standard methods for calculation of the speech intelligibility index. New York, NY: American National-Standards Institute.

Arehart, K. H., King, C. A., & McLean-Mudgett, K. S. (1997). Role of fundamental frequency differences in the perceptual separation of competing vowel sounds by listeners with normal hearing and listeners with hearing loss. *Journal of Speech, Language, and Hearing Research, 40*(6), 1434–1444.

Bacon, S. P., Opie, J. M., & Montoya, D. Y. (1998). The effects of hearing loss and noise masking on the masking release for speech in temporally complex backgrounds. *Journal of Speech, Language, and Hearing Research, 41*(3), 549–563.

Baer, T., & Moore, B. C. (1993). Effects of spectral smearing on the intelligibility of sentences in noise. *Journal of the Acoustical Society of America, 94*(3), 1229–1241.

Best, V., Mejia, J., Freeston, K., Van Hoesel, R. J., & Dillon, H. (2015). An evaluation of the performance of two binaural beamformers in complex and dynamic multitalker environments. *International Journal of Audiology, 54*(10), 727–735.

Bor, S., Souza, P., & Wright, R. (2008). Multichannel compression: Effects of reduced spectral contrast on vowel identification. *Journal of Speech, Language, and Hearing Research, 51*(5), 1315–1327.

Bregman, A. S. (1990). *Auditory scene analysis* (Vol. 10). Cambridge, MA: MIT Press.

Carette, E., van den Bogaert, T., Laureyns, M., & Wouters, J. (2014). Left-right and front-back spatial hearing with multiple directional microphone configurations in modern hearing aids. *Journal of the American Academy of Audiology, 25*(9), 791–803.

Dubno, J. R., Dirks, D. D., & Morgan, D. E. (1984). Effects of age and mild hearing loss on speech recognition in noise. *Journal of the Acoustical Society of America, 76*(1), 87–96.

Edwards, B. (2007). The future of hearing aid technology. *Trends in Amplification, 11*(1), 31–45.

Erber, N. P. (1982). Glenondale auditory screening procedure. In *Auditory training* (pp. 47–71). Washington, DC: Alexander Graham Bell Association.

Fowler, E. P. (1936). A method for the early detection of otosclerosis: A study of sounds well above threshold. *Archives of Otolaryngology, 24*(6), 731–741.

Glasberg, B. R., & Moore, B. C. (1992). Effects of envelope fluctuations on gap detection. *Hearing Research, 64*(1), 81–92.

Hawkins, D. B., & Yacullo, W. S. (1984). Signal-to-noise ratio advantage of binaural hearing aids and directional microphones under different levels of reverberation. *Journal of Speech and Hearing Disorders, 49*(3), 278–286.

Hawkins Jr., J. E., & Stevens, S. S. (1950). The masking of pure tones and of speech by white noise. *Journal of the Acoustical Society of America, 22*(1), 6–13.

Hedrick, M. S., & Rice, T. (2000). Effect of a single-channel-wide dynamic range compression circuit on perception of stop consonant place of articulation. *Journal of Speech, Language, and Hearing Research, 43*(5), 1174–1184.

Henry, J. A., & Meikle, M. B. (2000). Psychoacoustic measures of tinnitus. *Journal of the American Academy of Audiology, 11*(3), 138–155.

Humes, L. E. (1991). Understanding the speech-understanding problems of the hearing impaired. *Journal of the American Academy of Audiology, 2*(2), 59–69.

Humes, L. E., Kidd, G. R., & Lentz, J. J. (2013). Auditory and cognitive factors underlying individual differences in aided speech-understanding among older adults. *Frontiers in Systems Neuroscience, 7*(55), 1–16.

Humes, L. E., & Roberts, L. (1990). Speech-recognition difficulties of the hearing-impaired elderly: The contributions of audibility. *Journal of Speech, Language, and Hearing Research, 33*(4), 726–735.

Lentz, J. J., Leek, M. R., & Molis, M. R. (2004). The effect of onset asynchrony on profile analysis by normal-hearing and hearing-impaired listeners. *Journal of the Acoustical Society of America, 116*(4), 2289–2297.

Lorenzi, C., Gilbert, G., Carn, H., Garnier, S., & Moore, B. C. (2006). Speech perception problems of the hearing impaired reflect inability to use temporal fine structure. *Proceedings of the National Academy of Sciences, 103*(49), 18866–18869.

Moore, B. C., & Glasberg, B. R. (1993). Simulation of the effects of loudness recruitment and threshold elevation on the intelligibility of speech in quiet and in a background of speech. *Journal of the Acoustical Society of America, 94*(4), 2050–2062.

Moore, D. R. (2006). Auditory processing disorder (APD): Definition, diagnosis, neural basis, and intervention. *Audiological Medicine, 4*(1), 4–11.

Moore, D. R., Ferguson, M. A., Edmondson-Jones, A. M., Ratib, S., & Riley, A. (2010). Nature of auditory processing disorder in children. *Pediatrics, 126*(2), e382–e390.

Mueller, H. G., & Killion, M. C. (1990). An easy method for calculating the articulation index. *Hearing Journal, 43*(9), 14–17.

Nábělek, A. K. (1988). Identification of vowels in quiet, noise, and reverberation: Relationships with age and hearing loss. *Journal of the Acoustical Society of America, 84*(2), 476–484.

Noreña, A., Micheyl, C., Chéry-Croze, S., & Collet, L. (2002). Psychoacoustic characterization of the tinnitus spectrum: Implications for the underlying mechanisms of tinnitus. *Audiology and Neurotology, 7*(6), 358–369.

Oxenham, A. J. (2008). Pitch perception and auditory stream segregation: Implications for hearing loss and cochlear implants. *Trends in Amplification, 12*(4), 316–331.

Plomp, R. (1988). The negative effect of amplitude compression in multichannel hearing aids in the light of the modulation-transfer function. *Journal of the Acoustical Society of America, 83*(6), 2322–2327.

Roberts, L. E., Moffat, G., Baumann, M., Ward, L. M., & Bosnyak, D. J. (2008). Residual inhibition functions overlap tinnitus spectra and the region of auditory threshold shift. *Journal of the Association for Research in Otolaryngology, 9*(4), 417–435.

Soede, W., Berkhout, A. J., & Bilsen, F. A. (1993). Development of a directional hearing instrument based on array technology. *Journal of the Acoustical Society of America, 94*(2), 785–798.

Stone, M.A., Moore, B. C. J., Alcántara, J. I., & Glasberg, B. R. (1999). Comparison of different forms of compression using wearable digital hearing aids, *Journal of the Acoustical Society of America, 106*(6), 3603–3619.

Strelcyk, O., & Dau, T. (2009). Relations between frequency selectivity, temporal fine-structure processing, and speech reception in impaired hearing. *Journal of the Acoustical Society of America, 125*(5), 3328–3345.

Summers, V., & Leek, M. R. (1998). F0 processing and the separation of competing speech signals by listeners with normal hearing and with hearing loss. *Journal of Speech, Language, and Hearing Research, 41*(6), 1294–1306.

Turner, R. G., Shepard, N. T., & Frazer, G. J. (1984). Clinical performance of audiological and related diagnostic tests. *Ear and Hearing, 5*(4), 187–194.

Valentine, S., & Lentz, J. J. (2012). The influence of reduced audible bandwidth on asynchronous double-vowel identification. *Journal of Speech, Language, and Hearing Research, 55*(6), 1750–1764.

van den Bogaert, T., Doclo, S., Wouters, J., & Moonen, M. (2009). Speech enhancement with multichannel Wiener filter techniques in multimicrophone binaural hearing aids. *Journal of the Acoustical Society of America, 125*(1), 360–371.

Yund, E. W., & Buckles, K. M. (1995). Multichannel compression hearing aids: Effect of number of channels on speech discrimination in noise. *Journal of the Acoustical Society of America, 97*(2), 1206-1223.

Zeng, F. G., & Turner, C. W. (1990). Recognition of voiceless fricatives by normal and hearing-impaired subjects. *Journal of Speech, Language, and Hearing Research, 33*(3), 440–449.

Glossary

A

absolute threshold—the minimum detectable level of a sound in the absence of external noise.

alternate binaural loudness balancing method (ABLB)—an audiological method based on loudness matching between the ears. It is used to identify whether a listener with unilateral hearing loss experiences recruitment in the ear with poorer thresholds.

amplitude—the size of a stimulus.

amplitude modulation detection—an experimental paradigm in which a listener is asked to detect the presence of modulation on a sound. It measures the amplitude modulation detection threshold.

audiogram—a plot of absolute threshold in dB HL versus frequency.

auditory filters—a psychophysical model that describes the filtering process of the ear.

auditory processing disorder (APD)—a condition that affects the way the brain processes auditory information.

auditory scene analysis—the process by which the auditory system organizes sound into meaningful elements.

autocorrelation—a process that determines the periodicities present in a stimulus.

B

bandwidth—the range of frequencies passed by a filter or contained within a stimulus.

better-ear advantage—an effect in which interactions between the head and a sound field cause one ear to have a better signal-to-noise ratio than the other.

binaural masking level difference (BMLD or MLD)—an improvement in signal detection from binaural effects. It is characterized by a reduction in the masked threshold for a binaural signal presented with binaural noise when the signal (but not the masker) is presented out-of-phase at one of the ears.

binaural squelch—the ability to supplement the better-ear advantage with binaural hearing and take advantage of the ear with the poorer signal-to-noise ratio.

binaural summation—improvements in auditory abilities from having two ears.

binaural unmasking—the ability of two ears to reduce the effects of masking noise.

C

carrier—*see* temporal fine structure.

categorical loudness scaling—a procedure used to measure the loudness of sounds using categories ranging from very soft to uncomfortably loud.

center frequency—the frequency at the center of a filter's or a stimulus' frequency range.

complex tones—sounds that consist of multiple tones.

compressive nonlinearity—the range of sound levels at which basilar membrane vibration grows more slowly than the input signal.

cone of confusion—a 3D conical surface extending out of each ear that represents the same ITD on the surface.

critical band—a measure of the effective bandwidth of the filtering provided by the ear. It is the range of frequencies within which one tone interferes with the perception of another.

critical duration—the duration beyond which thresholds no longer increase with increasing duration.

cut-off frequencies—the highest or lowest frequencies before a filter attenuates sound.

D

dichotic—presenting different signals to both ears.

difference limen—*see* the just noticeable difference.

diotic—presenting identical signals to both ears.

dip listening—the ability to take advantage of temporal waveform valleys which have a high signal-to-noise ratio to improve performance.

diplacusis—the perception of hearing the same tone at a different pitch in each ear.

duplex theory of sound localization—the theory that proposes two acoustic cues for sound localization: intensity differences across the ears for high frequencies and time differences across the ears for low frequencies.

dynamic range of hearing—the range of sound levels between absolute threshold and the threshold of discomfort or pain.

E

effective masking level (EML)—the dB HL value to which threshold is shifted in the presence of a noise at that dB EML.

energy detector—a model of temporal integration which posits that the ear integrates the intensity over time up to the critical duration.

envelope—slow stimulus fluctuations in the waveform.

equal-loudness contour—a measure of sound pressure levels across frequency for which a listener perceives equal loudness.

excitation pattern—a psychoacoustic representation of the stimulus spectrum after auditory filtering.

existence region—frequency region over which the pitch does not change when harmonics are removed.

F

filter—a device that modifies sound.

fluctuating masker benefit—an improvement in masked threshold provided by a fluctuating (modulated) stimulus.

forward masking—a process in which masking occurs when a masker precedes a stimulus in time.

Fourier analysis—a process by which complex sounds can be decomposed into sine waves.

frequency—the number of cycles a sound completes in a second.

frequency discrimination—an experimental paradigm that measures the ability to determine whether one sound has different frequency from another. It measures the JND for frequency.

frequency selectivity—the ability of the auditory system to represent one frequency as independent of another.

frequency specific—containing few frequencies.

fundamental frequency—the lowest frequency of a complex tone. Other tones within the stimulus occur at integer multiples of the fundamental frequency.

G

gap detection—an experimental paradigm in which a listener is asked to determine whether a brief temporal gap is present in a sound. It measures the gap detection threshold.

H

harmonic sounds—complex tones containing frequencies that are related to each other by integer multiples.

harmonic template models—models that posit that the fundamental frequency of a sound is coded on the basilar membrane and can be derived from the location of the peaks of the traveling wave distributed along the length of the cochlea.

head-related transfer function (HRTF)—a three-dimensional function that codes for the spectral and phase changes that occur when sounds are presented at different locations with respect to the body.

head shadow—a reduction in intensity at the ear distant from the source.

hyperacusis—increased sensitivity to sounds.

I

increment detection—*see* intensity discrimination.

intensity discrimination—an experimental paradigm that measures the ability to determine whether one sound is more intense than another. It measures the JND for intensity.

interaural level difference—the level difference (in dB) between the two ears.

interaural time difference—the time difference between two ears.

J

just noticeable difference (JND)—the smallest difference on some dimension between two sounds that is detectable or discriminable.

L

level per cycle (LPC)—the amount of power in dB SPL within a sound contained within a 1-Hz band.

localization—the ability to locate the position of a sound in space.

loudness—the attribute of auditory sensation by which sounds can be ordered on a scale ranging from soft to loud.

loudness balancing—a procedure in which level of a sound is adjusted so that its loudness matches that of a reference sound.

loudness discomfort level—the level of sound in dB at which sound is uncomfortably loud.

loudness growth function—a function that relates the loudness of sounds to intensity.

loudness level—level of an equally loud 1000-Hz tone in dB SPL for a test sound, measured in phons.

loudness recruitment—an abnormally rapid growth of loudness. Common in listeners with SNHL.

M

magnitude estimation—a procedure in which a listener estimates the relationship between the loudness of one sound compared with another at a different intensity.

masker—a stimulus that raises the threshold of another stimulus.

masking—the process by which the presence of one sound interferes with the perception of another.

masking pattern—the amount of masking in dB for a single masker plotted as a function of the frequency of the signal being masked.

mel—the perceptual unit of pitch. One thousand mels is defined as the pitch associated with a 1000-Hz tone.

method of adjustment—a method to estimate threshold in which the listener adjusts the level of a stimulus to find threshold.

method of constant stimuli—a method which presents stimuli at randomly selected levels and measures the percent detections (or discriminations).

method of limits—One of the three classical psychoacoustic procedures used to estimate threshold. The experimenter presents stimuli at a level below (or above) the threshold and increases (or decreases) the stimulus level until it is perceivable (or rendered inaudible) to the listener.

minimum audible field (MAF) curve—a free-field, binaural measurement of the minimum detectable sound pressure level as a function of frequency.

minimum audible pressure (MAP) curve—a monaural measurement made over headphones of the minimum detectable sound pressure level as a function of frequency.

modulator—*see* envelope.

monotic—presenting a stimulus to a single ear.

multiple looks hypothesis—a model of temporal integration which states that increasing the duration of the stimulus provides more opportunities to detect the stimulus.

N

near miss to Weber's law—the JND for intensity, when expressed as a proportion of the intensity of the stimulus, decreases with increasing intensity across the audible range for tones.

noise—any unwanted sound. *See also* white noise.

notched-noise method—a technique used to estimate the size and shape of the auditory filter using a noise stimulus with a spectral notch.

O

observation interval—the interval of time during which a listener is expecting a stimulus.

P

partial recruitment—*see* underrecruitment.

peak amplitude—the maximum amplitude value achieved by a sound.

performance-intensity (PI) function—a function relating performance on a speech recognition task to the intensity of the stimulus.

period—the time a sound takes to complete a single cycle.

phase locking—a characteristic of auditory nerve fibers in which they tend to fire at a particular phase of a low-frequency stimulus.

phon—the unit of loudness level equal in number to the decibel level of a 1000-Hz tone.

pitch of the missing fundamental—*see* residue pitch.

pitch strength—a characterization of the salience of the pitch of sounds, ranges from strong to weak.

place code—a spectral representation for pitch. The frequency of a sound is coded in terms of the place of stimulation in the auditory pathway.

power spectrum model of masking—a theory stating that masking is determined by the power at the output of a single auditory filter.

precedence effect—a binaural effect that describes the fusion of sound and its echo. Sound localization is based on the acoustic cues associated with the sound that arrives first at the ears.

profile analysis—an experimental paradigm which measures the ability to discriminate between sounds with different power spectra.

pseudohypacusis—false or feigned hearing loss.

psychometric function—a function relating the percentage of sound detections or discriminations to a signal strength parameter.

psychophysical tuning curve (PTC)—*see* tuning curve (psychological).

psychophysics—the study of the relationship between the physical stimuli and their perception.

R

rate-level function—a function relating a neuron's output firing rate to input stimulus level.

reaction time—the time it takes for a listener to react to a stimulus.

release from forward masking—as a signal and forward masker become more separated in time, the masker has less of an effect on the signal detection threshold.

residue pitch—pitch of a complex sound when the component associated with the fundamental frequency is removed.

response interval—the interval of time during which a listener is expected to respond to a stimulus.

response proclivity—how the listener responds to the stimuli and associated biases.

S

scaling—see magnitude estimation.

sensitivity—the strength of the capacity to perceive a stimulus or a change in a stimulus.

sensorineural hearing loss—hearing loss associated with cochlear damage.

signal—a stimulus being detected.

signal detection theory—a framework to quantify the ability to discern between a signal and noise.

simultaneous masking—a paradigm in which maskers and signals are presented at the same time.

softness imperception—a theory which claims that the loudness of sounds at and near threshold may be higher for listeners with SNHL than for those with normal hearing.

sone—a unit of subjective loudness equal to the loudness of a 1000-Hz tone presented at 40 dB SPL.

sound level—a general term describing the magnitude or amplitude of a sound.

spectral loudness summation—a phenomenon in which the loudness level of a broadband sound is greater than a narrowband sound with the same total power.

spectral splatter—refers to an unintended increase in the range of frequencies present in a stimulus, usually caused by a rapid stimulus onset or offset.

spectrum—a plot of amplitude versus frequency.

spectrum level—the amount of power in dB SPL contained within a 1-Hz band.

Speech Intelligibility Index (SII)—a measure that represents the intelligibility of speech under a variety of listening conditions.

speech recognition threshold (SRT)—the level in dB HL at which words can be identified 50% of the time.

staircase method—an adaptive method in which the signal levels are determined by a listener's previous responses.

Stenger test—a test based on the principle of lateralization to identify the presence of pseudohypacusis.

Stevens' power law—a characterization of how loudness changes with intensity. Empirically, loudness grows in proportion to stimulus intensity raised to the power of 0.3.

T

temporal code—a mechanism in which the pitch of a stimulus is based on the temporal patterns of neural impulses evoked by that stimulus.

temporal fine structure—rapid stimulus fluctuations in the waveform.

temporal integration—the ability of the ear to accumulate information over time to improve detection threshold.

temporal masking—*see* forward masking.

temporal modulation transfer function (TMTF) —a plot relating amplitude modulation detection threshold to the modulation rate.

temporal processing—the general ability of the ear to represent stimulus changes over time.

temporal resolution—the ability to represent changes in the envelope of sound.

temporal summation—*see* temporal integration.

time-frequency tradeoff—an acoustic principle in which short-duration sounds must have a spectrum with a wide bandwidth.

tinnitus—the perception of a sound in its absence.

tonotopic organization—Different areas or cell populations of the brain respond to different frequencies. It begins at the basilar membrane and is maintained throughout the auditory pathways.

total power—the amount of power contained across all frequencies in a sound.

transfer function—a function that characterizes a system's frequency-gain characteristics.

traveling wave—a wave of basilar membrane vibration that travels through the basilar membrane until it reaches its place of maximum vibration.

trial—a sequence of the observation interval(s) plus the response interval.

tuning curve (physiological)—a plot relating the threshold sound level required to elicit a neural or basilar membrane response.

tuning curve (psychological)—a plot showing the level of a sound stimulus required to mask a fixed low-level signal.

two-tone suppression—a process in which one tone suppresses the neural activity produced by a second tone.

U

uncomfortable loudness level (UCL or ULL)—the level of sound in dB at which sound becomes uncomfortably loud.

underrecruitment—a phenomenon in which the loudness of sounds, even at high levels, does not approach the loudness measured in listeners with normal hearing.

upward spread of masking—a phenomenon in which low-frequency sounds mask high-frequency sounds more than the reverse.

V

volley theory—A theory first proposed by Wever and Bray that individual fibers could be synchronized to a waveform, even if they did not fire on every cycle. A group of fibers could then code for the frequency of sound via their pooled response.

W

waveform—a plot of instantaneous amplitude versus time.

wavelength—the distance sound travels in a single cycle.

Weber fraction—the mathematical characterization of Weber's law: $\Delta S/S = k$, where S is the size of a stimulus and k is a constant.

Weber's law—the just noticeable change in a stimulus is a constant ratio (or percentage) of the original stimulus.

white noise—a broad bandwidth stimulus that has a relatively flat power spectrum and randomly distributed instantaneous amplitude in the waveform.

wide dynamic range compression (WDRC)—a nonlinear hearing aid algorithm that makes low-level sounds audible and high-level sounds more comfortable.

Index

A

ABLB (Alternative binaural loudness balancing test), 213–214
ABR (Auditory brainstem response), 213
Absolute threshold, 2, 14, 41, 219
  auditory sensitivity and, 13
  defined, 7
  effect of frequency, 53
  Hughson–Westlake procedure and, 36
  quantifying hearing loss and, 31
  unmasked/masked condition and, 52
Acoustical Society of America, 6
Acoustics
  amplitude modulation, 120–121
  filters and, 48–50
  gap detection, 113
  harmonic complex tones, 142–145
  horizontal plane, localization in, 175–180
  noise and, 46–48
  pure tones, 14–15
Adaptive procedures
  based on, 41
  Hughson–Westlake procedure, 33–36
  measuring threshold and, 33
  staircase, 35–38
APD (Auditory processing disorder), 217
Afferent
  fibers, 23
  neurons, 23
Alternative binaural loudness balancing (ABLB) test, 213–214
American National Standards Institute (ANSI)
  ANSI S3.4-2007, 92
  ANSI S3.5-2017, 7, 205
  ANSI S3.6-2010, 10
  ANSI S1.1-2013, 141
American Speech-Language-Hearing Association (ASHA), 18
  audiometric assessment standards, 131
Amplification
  by pinna and meatus, 26
  effects on perception, 207–212

hearing aids and, 208
Amplitude
  coding, 23–25
  defined, 14
  modulation
    acoustics, 120–121
    detection, 120, 121–124
Anechoic chamber, 186
  HRTF (Head-related transfer functions) and, 189
ANSI S3.4-2007, 92
ANSI S3.5-2017, 7, 205
ANSI S3.6-2010, 10
ANSI S1.1-2013, 141
Articulation Index, 7, 204–205
ASA-51, 10
  See also ANSI
ASHA (American Speech-Language-Hearing Association), 18
  audiometric assessment standards, 131
Audibility, low sensation level and, 197
Audiogram, 30
Audiology perception, measurements of, 4
Audiometer
  Western Electric Model 1-A, 6
  Western Electric, Model 2-A, 8
Auditory assessment, 7–11
Auditory brainstem response (ABR), 213
Auditory filters
  broadening of, 69–70
  excitation pattern, 61–64
  thresholds and, 59–61
Auditory nerve, 23–25
  dB SPL and, 147
  fibers, 23–25
    dynamic range and, 87
    high stimulus levels and, 87
  phase locking and, 149
  response, 82–83
  spontaneous rates, 24–25
  thresholds and, 59–61
Auditory perception, levels of, 14
Auditory processing disorder (APD), 217

Auditory processing disorder *(continued)*
central (CAPD), 217
Auditory scene analysis, 204
Auditory sensitivity, 38
absolute threshold and, 13
Auditory threshold
assessment of, tone duration in, 18–19
elevated, 204–205
Autocorrelation, 152

B

Balancing, loudness, 88–89
Band-pass filter, 49
Band-reject filter, 49
Bandwidth, 16, 47
fluctuations and, 118
gap detection and, 115–118
masker, 73
of a filter, 50
of noise, 48, 56, 74
loudness and, 92
total power, 48
Basilar membrane, 22
stimulus level and, 81–82
Beasley survey, 9
Beasley, Willis, 9
Bell, Alexander Graham, 5
Bell Labs, 5–6, 10, 11
Best frequency, 51
Better-ear
advantage, 191, 198
effect, 191
Bias
response
defined, 38
psychophysical measurements and, 41
Binaural
hearing loss and, 207
cues, hearing aids and, 212
distortion, 210–211
hearing, 173
aids, 197
defined, 174
hearing loss and, 196–199
physiology of, 174–175
tests, 213–214, 217
masking level difference (BMLD), 192–194
frequency and, 192–193

processing algorithms, 211
squelch, 191, 198
summation, 196
unmasking, 174, 190–196
in free field, 191–192
precedence effect, 194–196
BMLD (Binaural masking level difference), 192–194
frequency and, 192–193
Bunch, Cordia, 6

C

CAPD (Central auditory processing disorder), 217
Carrier, defined, 110
Categorical loudness scaling, 88, 104
Center frequency, 47, 51
Central auditory processing disorder (CAPD), 217
Chroma, pitch, 154
Cochlea, 20, 21–22
Cochlear
implant, 154
nucleus, 180–181
Coding, amplitude, 23–25
Cognitive therapy, tinnitus and, 213
Coincidence detector, MSO (Medial superior olive) and, 181
Complex
pitch
sounds, 160–164
temporal code for, 162–163
tones, 142–145
Comprehension
defined, 14
impaired perception and, 204
Compression, 208–209
algorithms, 209
ratio, 209
temporal distortion and, 209–210
threshold, 209
Compressive
function, 81–82
nonlinear, 93
hearing loss and, 134
Cone of confusion, 180
Conservative criterion, 218
non-organic hearing loss and, 216

SDT (Signal detection theory), 38, 39–41
Contralateral interference, 217
Correct rejection. *See* True negative
Criterion
    bias, 38
    SDT (Signal detection theory), 38–41
Critical
    band
        defined, 58
        masking and, 56–57
    duration, 128
Cross-hearing, 73
Cross-modality scaling, 88
Cut-off frequencies, 47–50

D

Decibel difference, JND (Just noticeable
        difference) and, 98
Decibels, 19–20
    calculating, 81
    dB A, 5, 90–91
    dB EML, effective masking level, 73
    dB HL, 5
        ABLB (Alternative binaural loudness
            balancing test) and, 214
        effective masking level, 73
        loudness discomfort level, 102–103
        using, 28–31
    dB SPL, 5, 19, 47, 91–93, 98
        auditory nerve fiber and, 147
        calculating, 20
        compression and, 209
        intensity and, 155
        loudness in sones versus, 102
    intensity and, 80–81
    plotting thresholds in, 7
Delay line, MSO (Medial superior olive) and, 181
Detection
    auditory, 14
    gap, 111
    increment, 96
    modulation, 121–124
Difference limen, 2, 96
Dip listening, 68
Diplacusis, 167
Directional microphones, 208
    described, 211
    SNHL (Sensorineural hearing loss) and, 211

Discrimination
    auditory, 14
    f_0, 163–164
    frequency, 156–158
    ILD, 188–189
    intensity, 96–101
    ITD/IPD, 186–188
Distortion
    binaural, 210–211
    temporal, 209–210
Duplex theory of sound localization, 4, 176–177,
        180, 184
Duration
    critical, 127–129
    effects, 16–19
    note, 109
Dynamic range, 7
    auditory nerve fibers and, 87
    of hearing, 7

E

Ear canal, 20
Ear-level sound therapies, tinnitus and, 213
Early onset, otitis media, 42
Early-stage otosclerosis, 30
Echo
    fusion, 195
    suppression, 195
    threshold, 198
        defined, 198
Effective masking level (EML), 73
Effectiveness, masker, 73
Elements of Psychophysics, 2
Elevated auditory thresholds, 204–205
EML (Effective masking level), 73
Energetic masking, 45
Envelope
    defined, 110
    white noise, 112
Equal loudness, 88–89
    contours, 80, 89
Equivalent rectangular bandwidth (ERB), 93
ERB (Equivalent rectangular bandwidth), 93
Excitation
    calculated, 62
    pattern, 62–65
        auditory filter, 61–64
        stimulus filtering by, 93

Existence region, 161
External ear
    hearing loss and, 26
    resonant property change and, 28

F

F_0 discrimination, 163–164
    frequency and, 168
Falling phonometer, 4–5
False
    alarm, 39
    negative, 39
    positive, 39, 216
Familiarization, 34, 41
FDL (Frequency difference limen)
    higher intensities and, 158
    frequency effects and, 156
Fechner, Gustav, 2
Filtering, white noise, 118
Filters
    acoustics and, 48–50
    auditory
        broadening of, 69–70
        excitation pattern, 61–64
        thresholds and, 59–61
    band-pass, 49
    band-reject, 49
    described, 48–49
    high-pass, 49
    low-pass, 49
Fine structure, temporal, 110
Fletcher, Harvey, 6
Fluctuating
    maskers
        benefit, 68, 120
        masking by, 72
    sounds
        gap detection and, 118–119
        masking, 67–69
        temporal resolution and, 132–133
F_0DL (Fundamental frequency difference limen), 163
Force per unit area, 15
    defined, 81
Forced-choice paradigm, 36, 40
Formants, smoothed representation of, 62–63
Forward masking, 65, 124–126

    release from, 125
    temporal masking and, 135–136
Fourier analysis, 3, 15, 145
Fowler, Edmund Prince, 7
Frequency
    best, 51
    center, 51
        masking patterns and, 55
    cut-off, 47, 122
    discrimination, 156
    effects
        gap detection and, 115–118
        masking, 53
        pitch and, 153–154
    gain functions, 20
    loudness and, 88–92
    pitch and, 153–154, 155
    reduced selectivity of, 205–206
    resolution, hearing aids and, 208
    sound pressure level and, 25
    selectivity, 49
        intensity affected by, 56
        masking, 54
Frequency difference limen (FDL), 156
    higher intensities and, 158
    frequency effects and, 156
Frequency-specific sounds, 14
Fundamental frequency, 143
Fundamental frequency difference limen (F_0DL), 163
Fusion, 195

G

Gain
    in hearing aids, 209
    otosclerosis and, 28
    outer and middle ear, 20–22
Gap detection, 111–120
    acoustics, 113
    background, 111
    paradigm, 111–113
    psychological factors, fluctuating sounds, 118–119
    psychophysical findings, 114–118
        bandwidth, 115–118
        level effects, 114–115
    stimulus

bandwidth and, 119
  fluctuation and, 120
  level and, 119
uses of, 111
GCF (Greatest common frequency), 144
Glorig, Aram, 9–10
Greatest common frequency (GCF), 144

H

Harmonic
  resolved, 62
  sounds, 142
    acoustic characteristics of, 143
  tones, 142
  template models of pitch, 146
  unresolved, 164
Harmonics, low-frequency, 62
Head movements, cone of confusion and, 180
Head-related transfer functions (HRTF), 189–190
  anechoic chamber and, 189
Head shadow, 177
Hearing
  binaural, 173
  dynamic range of, 7, 87
  monaural, 173
  threshold of, 25–31
    measuring, 31–38
Hearing aids
  binaural, 38
  binaural cues and, 212
    effects on, 207
  compression and, 208–209
  goal of, 208
  loudness recruitment and, 205
  matched, 211
  physiological coding and, 197
  reduced frequency selectivity and, 205
Hearing loss
  described, 208
  effects of, 27–31
    on temporal processing, 131–138
  forward masking and, 135
  frequency selectivity and, 69–71
  non-organic, 215–216
  sensorineural
    masking and, 69–72
    physiological factors, 69–71

tinnitus pitch and, 213
Helmholtz, Hermann von, 3
Helmholtz resonator, 3, 4
Helmholtz's theory, of pitch, 3, 160
Hertz, 15
High blood pressure, tinnitus and, 213
High frequency, pitch and, 155
High spontaneous, rate fibers, 24, 25
High stimulus levels, auditory nerve fibers and, 87
High-pass filter, 49
Horizontal plane, 173
  binaural cues and, 176
  sound localization in, 175, 180, 182
HRTF (Head-related transfer functions), 189–190
  anechoic chamber and, 189
Hughson–Westlake procedure, measuring threshold and, 33–35
Hyperacusis, 95
  measuring, 104–105

I

ILD (Interaural level difference), 176, 177–178
  binaural distortion and, 211
  discrimination, 188–189
Immitance testing, 213
Impaired perception, consequences of, 204–207
Impedance
  matching, 20
  of air, 81
Implant, cochlear, 154
Increment detection, 96
Incus, 20
Informational masking, 45
Inhibitory connections, 180, 181
Inner ear, 21–23
Input-output functions (I-O)
  basil membrane and, 81, 86
  loudness growth functions and, 103
Intensity, 79
  decibels and, 80–81
  discrimination, 80, 96–101
    Weber's law and, 97–100
  frequency selectivity, affected by, 56–57
  loudness and, 84–88
  pitch, 154–155
  pressure, 81

Interaural level difference (ILD), 176, 177–178
  binaural distortion and, 211
  discrimination, 188–189
Interaural phase difference (IPD), 179
Interaural time difference (ITD), 177,
    178–180
  discrimination, 186–188
  noise reducing algorithms and, 212
Interference, contralateral, 217
International Organization of Standardization.
    See ISO
I-O (Input-output functions)
  basil membrane and, 81, 86
  loudness growth functions and, 103
IPD (Interaural phase difference), 179
  discrimination, 186–188
Ipsilateral cochlear nucleus, 180
ISO 226-2003, 90
ISO-64, 10
ITD (Interaural time difference), 177, 178–180
  discrimination, 186–188
  noise reducing algorithms and, 212

J

JND (Just noticeable difference), 2, 96
  decibel difference and, 98
  Weber fraction and, 98
Just detectable modulation depth, 121–122
Just noticeable difference (JND), 2, 96
  decibel difference and, 98
  Weber fraction and, 98

L

Lateral superior olive (LSO), 180–182
Lateralization, 185–190, 196–197
  defined, 173
  duplex theory of sound, 176
Late-stage otosclerosis, 30
LDL (Loudness discomfort level), 102
Level per cycle (LPC), 47
LFN (Low fluctuation noise), 118–119
Liberal criterion
  non-organic hearing loss and, 216
  SDT (Signal detection theory), 38–41
Line spectrum, 16
Listening, 26

importance of pitch perception in, 165–167
Localization, 175, 196–198
  cone of confusion and, 180
  defined, 173
  dominance, 198–199
  duplex theory of sound, 176–177
  elevation, 185
  hearing loss effects, 196–197
  horizontal plane, 175–180
Long duration sounds, 16
Lord Rayleigh, 4, 176–177
Loudness
  balancing, 88–89
  calculating, 92–93
  defined, 6
  frequency and, 88–92
  growth, 80
    basilar membrane and, 103
    function, 84
  intensity and, 84–88
  magnitude production and, 88
  measuring, 83–84, 104–105
    scaling, 84
  patterns, stimulus filtering by, 93
  phons and, 89
  reaction time as measure of, 93–95
  recruitment, 101–104, 205
    hearing aids and, 208
  sensorineural hearing loss and, 101–105
  sound pressure level and, 86, 89
  summation, 80, 91–92
Loudness discomfort level (LDL), 102
Low
  fluctuation noise (LFN), 118–119
  frequency harmonics, 62
  frequency, pitch and, 155
  pass filter, 49
  spontaneous rate fibers, 24
LPC (Level per cycle), 47
LSO (Lateral superior olive), 180–182

M

MAA (Minimum audible angle), 183–184
MAF (Minimum audible field), 25
  connecting physiology to, 27
  hearing loss and, 27–31
Magnitude

estimation technique, 84
production, 153
   cross-modality scaling and, 88
   loudness and, 88
Malleus, 20
MAP (Minimum audible pressure), 25
   connecting physiology to, 27
   hearing loss and, 27–31
MAP/MAF, connecting physiology to, 27
Masker
   bandwidth, 73
   effectiveness, 73
Masking, 52–56
   by fluctuating maskers, 72
   clinical implications of, 72–74
   critical band, 56–57
   defined, 45, 52
   fluctuating sounds, 67–69
   forward, 65, 124–126
      release from, 125
   frequency
      effects, 53
      selectivity, 54
   level difference, 198
   noise and, wide bands, 52–54
   patterns, 54–55
   release from, 198–199
   sensorineural hearing loss and, 69–72
   simultaneous, 52, 65
   temporal and, 124–126
   thresholds
      by frequency, 54–56
      power spectrum model of, 57–59
   upward spread of, 55–56
Maximum audibility, 7
Meatus, amplification by, 26
Medial superior olive (MSO), 180–182
Median plane, sound localization in, 185
Mel scale, 153
   criticism of, 154
Membrane
   basilar, 22
      stimulus level and, 81–82
   tympanic, 20, 22
Meniere's disease, 213
Method of adjustment, 2
   psychometric function and, 33
Method of constant stimuli, 3

psychometric function and, 32
Method of limits, 2
   psychometric function and, 33
Microphones
   directional, 208
      described, 211
      SNHL (Sensorineural hearing loss) and,
         211–212
Middle ear, 20–21.
   stimulus filtering by, 93
Minimum audibility, 7
Minimum audible angle (MAA), 183–184
Minimum audible field (MAF), 25
   connecting physiology to, 27
   hearing loss and, 27–31
Minimum audible pressure (MAP), 25
   connecting physiology to, 27
   hearing loss and, 27–31
Missing fundamental, pitch of, 160
MLD. *See* BMLD (Binaural masking level
      difference)
Models of pitch perception, 152, 164
   evaluating, 168
   theories of, 4
Modified Hughson–Westlake procedure,
      measuring threshold and, 33–35
Modulation, 68
   detection, 99, 111, 121–124
      amplitude, 120–121
Modulator, defined, 110
Monaural hearing, 173
Moore, Brian C. J., 92
MSO (Medial superior olive), 180–182
Multiple looks hypothesis, 129

N

Narrow band noise
   described, 47
Narrow band noise
   gap detection and, 112
   white noise and, 50, 118
Near miss to Weber's law, 99–101
Nerve, auditory, 23–25
Nerve response, auditory, 82–83
Neuron, threshold, 24
Neutral criterion, 218
   SDT (Signal detection theory), 38, 39–41

New York, world fair, 10
Noise
    acoustics and, 46–48
    defined, 46
    estimating thresholds and
        filters and, 48–50
        psychological factors, 46–48, 50–51
    maskers, tinnitus and, 213
    masking and, wide bands, 52–54
    reduction algorithms, 211, 212
    thresholds and
        masking fluctuating sounds, 67–69
        psychophysical tuning curves/suppression,
            65–67
Nonlinear algorithms, 211
Non-organic hearing loss, 215–216
Notched-noise method, 59
Note duration, 109
Nulls, frequency of, 17

O

Observation interval, 158
    defined, 31
    undefined, 34
    yes/no test and, 31
Off-frequency, auditory filters, 100
Ohm, Georg, 3
Ossicular chain, 20
Otitis media, 21
    early onset of, 42
Otoacoustic emissions, 100, 213
    test, 213
Otosclerosis, 21, 28
    early-stage, 30
    late-stage, 30
Outer ear, 20–21, 27
Outer hair cells, 69
    basilar membrane and, 82
    hearing loss and, 103
Output waveforms, 152

P

Partial recruitment, 103
Pascal, Blaise, 15
Pascals, 15
Peak

amplitude, 15, 16
    rms pressure and, 19
    pressure, 16
Percent of normal hearing, 8
Perception, 182–184
    amplification strategies effects, 207–212
    consequences of impaired, 204–207
    investigation of, 1–3
    measurements of, 4
    of pitch, importance of, 165–167
Performance-intensity (PI) function, 214–215
Phase locking
    defined, 147
    frequency effects, 149
Phons, loudness and, 89
PI (Performance-intensity function), 214–215
Pinna, 20
    amplification by, 26
Pitch
    chroma, 154
    coding, pure tones and, 158–160
    complex sounds and, 142
    defined, 141
    frequency and, 153–154
    intensity, 154–155
    models of, 152
    of complex sounds, 160–164
    of pure tones, 152–158
    of the missing fundamental, 160
    perception, 141
        codes for, 142
        hearing aids and, 208
        importance of, 165–167
        poor, 206–207
        SNHL (Sensorineural hearing loss) and,
            167–169
    pure tones, 142
        frequency discrimination, 156–158
        compared with, 164
    theories of, 145–152
        place code, 145–147
        psychophysical representations of, 150–152
        temporal code, 147–150
    white noise, 63
    strength, 154
Place code
    evidence supporting, 159
    pitch perception and, 145–147

versus temporal code, 159–160
Power spectrum model, masking thresholds and, 57–59
Precedence effect, 198
  binaural unmasking, 194–196
  described, 194
  echo suppression, 195
  fusion, 195
  localization dominance, 195
Profile analysis, 64–65
Pseudohypacusis, 215–216
Psychoacoustics, 121–124
  beginning of, 2–3
  influence of, 212–217
  origins of, 3–5
Psychometric function, 31–33, 94, 215
  method of
    adjustment and, 33
    constant stimuli and, 32
    limits and, 33
Psychophysical measurements
  adjustment, 33
  classical, 32
  constant stimuli, 32
  limits, 33
  response bias and, 41
Psychophysical turning curves (PTC),
    suppression and, 65–69
Psychophysics, beginning of, 1–3
PTC (Psychophysical turning curves),
    suppression and, 65–69
Pulsatile tinnitus, 213
Pure tones, 14–19
  coding the pitch, 158–160
  frequency effects on, 153–154
  gap detection and, 112
  pitch and, 142
    frequency discrimination, 156–158
  pitch compared with, 164

R

Rate-level function, 24
Rayleigh, Lord, 4, 176–177
Rayleigh's duplex theory, 183
Reaction time
  as a measure of loudness, 93–95
  sound pressure level and, 95

Recognition
  auditory, 14
  impaired perception and, 204
Reference threshold levels SPL (RETSPL),
    29–30, 73
Reissner's membrane, 22
Residue pitch, 160
  code for, 162
Resolved
  harmonics, 62
  interval, 31
Response bias
  defined, 38
  psychophysical measurements and, 41
Response proclivity, 38
Retrocochlear assessment, 213
Rms pressure, peak amplitude and, 19

S

San Francisco, world fair, 10
Scaling
  categorical loudness, 88, 95, 104
  cross-modality, 88, 95, 104
    magnitude production and, 88
  measuring loudness and, 84
Schouten, J.F., 4
Schouten's residue theory, 4
SDT (Signal detection theory), 38–41
Seebeck, August, 3
Sensation
  area, 7
  level, 30, 136
    low, audibility and, 197
Sensations of Tone, 3
Sensitivity, auditory, 38
Sensorineural hearing loss (SNHL)
  hearing aids and, 208
  loudness and, 101–105
  masking and, 69–72
  physiological factors, 69–71
  pitch perception and, 167–169
  temporal integration and, 136–138
  temporal resolution in, 132
    fluctuating sounds and, 133–135
    steady sounds and, 132–133
Shadow curve, absence of, 216
Signal detection theory (SDT), 38–41

Signal detection theory (SDT) *(continued)*
    application of, 40–41
Signal-to-noise ratio (SNR)
    improving, 211–212
    noise reducing algorithms and, 212
SII (Speech Intelligibility Index), 7, 204–205
Simultaneous masking, 52, 65
Sine wave. *See* Pure tones
SNHL (Sensorineural hearing loss)
    hearing aids and, 208
    loudness and, 69–72
    masking and, 69–72
    pitch perception and, 167–169
    physiological factors, 69–72
    temporal integration and, 136–138
    temporal resolution in, 132
        fluctuating sounds and, 133–135
        steady sounds and, 132–133
SNR (Signal-to-noise ratio)
    improving, 211–212
    noise reducing algorithms and, 212
SOC (Superior olivary complex), 180
Softness imperception, 102
Sone
    defined, 84
    measuring, 85
Sound
    reflections of, 26
    level, 81
    localization
        in horizontal plane, 180–182
        in median plane, 185
    pendulum, 4–5
    pressure, in pascals, 15
    pressure level, 5, 19–20, 81, 84, 136
        bandwidth and, 92
        frequency and, 25
        loudness and, 86, 89
        reaction time and, 95
        vibration and, 82
Sounds
    harmonic, 142
        acoustic characteristics of, 143
    hearing aids and, 208
    identifying, 2
    pitch and, 142
    virtual representations of, 189
Specific loudness pattern, 93
Spectral

contrast, reduced, 210
loudness summation, 91
profiles, 64
shape discrimination. *See* Profile analysis
splatter, 16–18
    calculating, 17
    gap detection and, 113
Spectrum, 15–16
    level, 47
Speech and Hearing, 6
Speech and Hearing in Communication, 6
Speech Intelligibility Index (SII), 7, 204–205
Speech recognition threshold (SRT), 175
    hearing loss and, 216
Spike rate, neuron threshold and, 24
Spontaneous firing rate, 24
Squelch, binaural, 191, 198
SRT (Speech recognition threshold), 175, 216
Staircase adaptive procedure, 35–38
Stapes, 20
    footplate of, 22
Starting signal level, measuring threshold and, 37
Stenger test, 216–217
Step size, measuring threshold and, 37
Stevens, Stanley S., 152
Stevens' power law, 84–86
Stimulus
    bandwidth, 115
        gap detection and, 113, 119
        TMTF and, 123–124
    fluctuation, gap detection and, 120
    frequency, TMTF and, 123
    intensity, cochlea and, 81
    level
        gap detection and, 119
        physiological representation of, 81–83
        TMTF and, 123
Strutt, James William, 4
Superior olivary complex (SOC), 180
Suppression
    psychophysical turning curves (PTC) and, 65–69
    two-tone, 65–67

T

Telephone, advent of, 5–7
Temporal
    acuity, 110

forward masking and, 135–136
integration, 110
masking, 110, 124–126
resolution, 110
Temporal code
evidence supporting, 159
for complex pitch perception, 162–163
pitch perception and, 147–150
versus place code, 159–160
Temporal distortion, 209–210
Temporal fine structure, 110
Temporal integration, 127–131
audiology applications of, 130–131
critical duration, 127–129
defined, 127
mechanisms of, 129–130
energy detection, 129
multiple looks hypothesis, 129–130
SNHL (Sensorineural hearing loss) and,
136–138
temporal processing and, 206
Temporal modulation transfer function (TMTF),
122–123
listeners and, 133
Temporal ordering, 117
Temporal processing
comparison of measures, 126–127
defined, 109
effects of, on hearing loss, 131–138
hearing aids and, 208
level effects, 114–115
perceptual aspects of, 111
poor, 206
tests, 217
Temporal resolution
amplitude modulation detection, 120
gap detection, 111
in sensorineural hearing loss (SNHL), 132
fluctuating sounds and, 133–135
steady sounds and, 132–133
Temporal summation. *See* Temporal
integration
The Theory of Sound Localization, 4, 176–177,
180, 184
Thresholds
absolute, 2, 41
unmasked/masked condition and, 52
auditory filter and, 59–61
critical band, 56–57

elevated, 204–205
feeling, 7
hearing, 25–31
measuring, 31–38
masking
by frequency, 54–56
power spectrum model of, 57–59
measurement, adaptive procedures and, 33
measuring
starting signal level, 37
step size, 37
when to end, 37
neuron, 24
noise and, 45–75
masking fluctuating sounds, 67–69
psychological factors, 50–51
psychophysical tuning curves/suppression,
65–67
temporal ordering and, 117
Time constant, 129
Time-frequency tradeoff, 16, 18, 113
Tinnitus, 208, 212–213
TMTF (Temporal modulation transfer function),
122–123
hearing-impaired listeners and, 133
Tones
harmonic, 142
complex, 142–145
pure, *see* pure tone
Tonotopic organization, 22
Total power, 47
Transfer function, 49
Traveling wave, 22–23
True negative, 39
True positive, 39
Tumors, tinnitus and, 213
Tuning curve, 49, 50
physiological factors and, 50
psychophysical, 65–67
Two-alternative forced choice, two-interval, 36
Two-interval, two-alternative forced choice, 36
Two-tone suppression, 65–67
Tympanic membrane, 20, 22

U

UCL (Uncomfortable loudness level), 102
ULL. *See* UCL (Uncomfortable loudness level)
Uncomfortable loudness level (UCL), 102

Undefined observation interval, 34
Underrecruitment, 103
University of Iowa, 6
Unmasking
    binaural, 174, 190–196
        in free field, 191–192
        precedence effect, 194–196
Upward spread of masking, 206
U.S. Public Health Service, 9

V

Velocity, basilar membrane, 82
Virtual sound representations, 189
Volley theory, 147
von Helmholtz, Hermann, 3

W

Waveforms, 14–15
    output, 152
Wavelength, 176
WDRC (Wide dynamic range compression), 209
Weber, Ernst Henrich, 2
Weber fraction, 97
    JND (Just noticeable difference) and, 98

Weber's law, 2, 96–97
    intensity discrimination and, 97–100
    near miss and, 99–101
Wegel, R.L., 6
Western Electric, 5
    audiometer Model
        1-A, 6
        2-A, 8
When to end, measuring threshold and, 37
White noise, 112–114, 116
    described, 47
    filtering, 118
    long duration sounds and, 16
    long-term, 47
    narrow band noise and, 50, 118
    pitch perception and, 163
    pure tones and, 59
Wide dynamic range compression (WDRC),
    209
Wisconsin State Fair, 9
World fair, 1939, 10
Wundt, Wilhelm, 4

Y

Yes/no test, 31